New

W9-BYQ-402

Health

7

Editorial Advisory Board

The Career Information Center includes:

- Agribusiness, Environment, and Natural Resources / 1
- Communications and the Arts / 2
- Computers, Business, and Office / 3
- Construction / 4
- Consumer, Homemaking, and Personal Services / 5
- Engineering, Science, Technology, and Social Science / 6
- Health / 7
- Hospitality and Recreation / 8
- Manufacturing / 9
- Marketing and Distribution / 10
- Public and Community Services / 11
- Transportation / 12
- Employment Trends and Master Index / 13

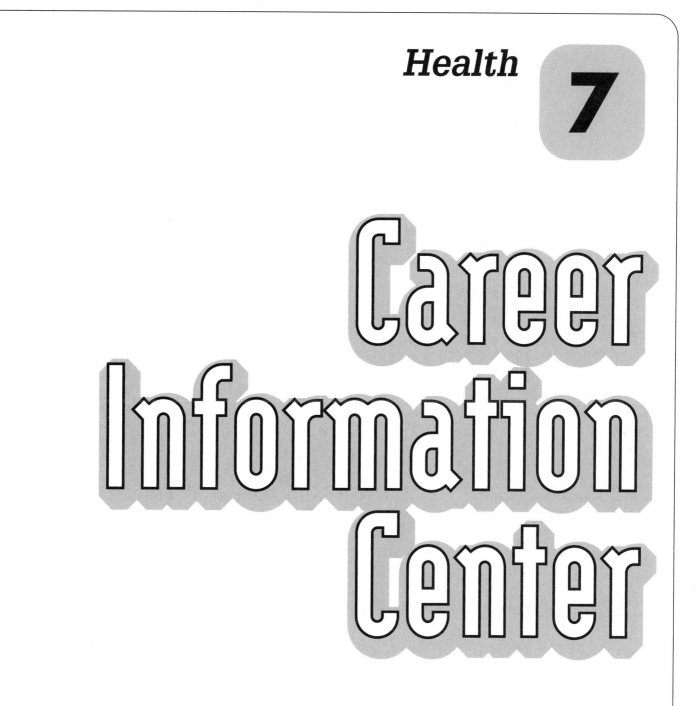

Health

7

Career Information Center

Ninth Edition

MACMILLAN REFERENCE USA
An imprint of Thomson Gale, a part of The Thomson Corporation

Detroit • New York • San Francisco • New Haven, Conn. • Waterville, Maine • London

THOMSON

★

GALE

Career Information Center, Ninth Edition

Paula Kepos, Series Editor

Project Editor
Mary Rose Bonk

Editorial
Jennifer Greve

Imaging
Lezlie Light, Daniel Newell, Christine O'Bryan

Permissions
Kelly A. Quin, Tim Sisler, Andrew Specht

Manufacturing
Rhonda Dover

For permission to use material from this product, submit your request via Web at http://www.gale-edit.com/permissions, or you may download our Permissions Request form and submit your request by fax or mail to:

Permissions
Thomson Gale
27500 Drake Rd.
Farmington Hills, MI 48331-3535
Permissions Hotline:
248-699-8006 or 800-877-4253 ext. 8006
Fax: 248-699-8074 or 800-762-4058

Since this page cannot legibly accommodate all copyright notices, the acknowledgments constitute an extension of the copyright notice.

While every effort has been made to ensure the reliability of the information presented in this publication, Thomson Gale does not guarantee the accuracy of the data contained herein. Thomson Gale accepts no payment for listing; and inclusion in the publication of any organization, agency, institution, publication, service, or individual does not imply endorsement of the editors or publisher. Errors brought to the attention of the publisher and verified to the satisfaction of the publisher will be corrected in future editions.

ISBN 0-02-866047-1 (set)
ISBN 0-02-866048-X (v.1)
ISBN 0-02-866049-8 (v.2)
ISBN 0-02-866050-1 (v.3)
ISBN 0-02-866051-X (v.4)
ISBN 0-02-866052-8 (v.5)
ISBN 0-02-866053-6 (v.6)
ISBN 0-02-866054-4 (v.7)
ISBN 0-02-866055-2 (v.8)
ISBN 0-02-866056-0 (v.9)
ISBN 0-02-866057-9 (v.10)
ISBN 0-02-866058-7 (v.11)
ISBN 0-02-866059-5 (v.12)
ISBN 0-02-866060-9 (v.13)
ISSN 1082-703X

This title is also available as an e-book.
ISBN 0-02-866099-4
Contact your Thomson Gale representative for ordering information.

Printed in the United States of America
10 9 8 7 6 5 4 3 2 1

Contents

Job Summary Chart

Job	Salary	Education/ Training	Employment Outlook	Page
Job Profiles—No Specialized Training				
Admitting Interviewer	Median—$11.94 per hour	High school	Good	33
⭐ **Dental Assistant**	Median—$13.62 per hour	High school plus training	Excellent	34
Dialysis Technician	$25,682 to $32,413 per year	High school	Very good	36
⭐ **Home Health Aide**	Median—$8.81 per hour	Varies—see profile	Excellent	37
Laboratory Animal Care Worker	Median—$7.86 per hour	High school	Very good	39
⭐ **Nursing Aide and Orderly**	Average—$10.09 per hour	High school	Very good	40
Optometric Assistant	$12,000 to $30,000 per year	High school	Excellent	42
Psychiatric Aide	Median—$11.19 per hour	High school plus training	Fair	44
Substance Abuse Counselor	Median—$32,960 per year	High school	Very good	45
Ward Clerk	$24,320 to $28,167 per year	High school	Good	47
Job Profiles—Some Specialized Training/Experience				
AIDS Counselor	Median—$34,820 per year	Varies—see profile	Varies—see profile	49
Ambulance Driver	Median—$24,722 per year	License plus training	Excellent	51
Biomedical Equipment Technician	Median—$17.90 per hour	High school plus training	Good	53
Cardiac Monitor Technician	Median—$26,513 per year	High school plus training	Poor	55
Cardiology Technologist	Median—$38,690 per year	High school plus training	Excellent	56
Clinical Laboratory Technician	Median—$30,840 per year	High school plus training	Excellent	58
⭐ **Dental Hygienist**	Median—$28.05 per hour	2-year college; license	Excellent	60
Dental Laboratory Technician	Median—$14.93 per hour	High school plus training	Fair	62
Dental and Medical Secretary	Median—$26,540 per year	High school plus training	Good	64
Dispensing Optician	Median—$27,950 per year	High school plus training	Good	66
Electroneurodiagnostic Technologist	Median—$44,621 per year	High school plus training	Fair	68
⭐ **Emergency Medical Technician/ Paramedic**	Median—$25,310 per year	High school plus training	Excellent	70
Environmental Health Specialist	$37,300 to $57,551 per year	Varies—see profile	Good	72
⭐ **Licensed Practical Nurse**	Median—$33,970 per year	High school plus training; license	Good	74
Medical Assistant	Median—$24,610 per year	High school plus training	Excellent	76
⭐ **Medical Records and Health Information Technician**	Median—$25,590 per year	2-year college	Very good	78

⭐ High-growth job

Job	Salary	Education/ Training	Employment Outlook	Page
Nuclear Medicine Technologist	Median—$56,450 per year	Varies—see profile	Fair	80
⭐ **Occupational Therapist Assistant**	Median—$38,430 per year	Varies—see profile	Very good	82
Ophthalmic Laboratory Technician	Median—$11.40 per hour	High school plus training	Fair	83
Pharmaceutical Sales Representative	Median—$60,130 per year	2- or 4-year college plus training	Good	84
⭐ **Physical Therapist Assistant**	Median—$37,890 per year	2-year college	Very good	86
Radiologic Technologist	Median—$43,350 per year	2- or 4-year college plus training	Good	88
Respiratory Therapist	Median—$43,140 per year	2- or 4-year college	Very good	90
Surgical Technologist	Median—$34,010 per year	2-year college or voc/tech school	Very good	92

Job Profiles—Advanced Training/Experience

Job	Salary	Education/ Training	Employment Outlook	Page
Acupuncturist	Median—$50,000 per year	Some college plus training	Good	94
Anesthesiologist	Median—$321,686 per year	Advanced degree plus training	Very good	95
Audiologist	Median—$51,470 per year	Advanced degree	Good	98
Cardiac Perfusionist	Median—$96,144 per year	College plus training	Excellent	100
⭐ **Chiropractor**	Median—$69,910 per year	Advanced degree; license	Good	101
Clinical Laboratory Technologist	Average—$45,730 per year	College plus training	Excellent	103
⭐ **Dentist**	Median—$129,920 per year	Advanced degree	Good	105
Dermatologist	Median—$193,870 per year	Advanced degree plus training	Excellent	107
Epidemiologist	Median—$54,800 per year	Advanced degree	Good	108
Geriatric Social Worker	Median—$40,080 per year	Varies—see profile	Excellent	109
Geriatrician	Median—$166,420 per year	Advanced degree plus training	Excellent	111
Health Educator	Median—$52,639 per year	Advanced degree	Very good	113
Medical and Health Services Manager	Median—$67,430 per year	Advanced degree	Good	114
Medical Illustrator	Median—$59,000 per year	Advanced degree	Good	117
Medical Physicist	Median—$124,532 per year	Advanced degree	Good	119
⭐ **Occupational Therapist**	Median—$54,660 per year	Advanced degree	Excellent	121
Ophthalmologist	Median—$199,423 per year	Advanced degree plus training	Very good	122
Optometrist	Median—$88,410 per year	College plus training	Good	124
Orthoptist	Average—$45,000 to $50,000 per year	College plus training	Excellent	126
Orthotist and Prosthetist	Median—$59,540 per year	College degree	Good	128
Osteopathic Physician	Median—$156,010 per year	Advanced degree plus training	Very good	129
Pharmacist	Median—$84,900 per year	Advanced degree	Very good	131
Pharmacologist	Average—$91,407 to $118,828 per year	Advanced degree	Very good	133

⭐ **High-growth job**

Job	Salary	Education/ Training	Employment Outlook	Page
★ **Physical Therapist**	Median—$60,180 per year	Advanced degree	Very good	134
Physician	Varies—see profile	Advanced degree plus training	Good	136
★ **Physician Assistant**	Median—$69,410 per year	Varies—see profile	Excellent	139
Podiatrist	Median—$94,400 per year	Advanced degree	Good	140
Psychiatrist	Median—$180,000 per year	Advanced degree plus training	Very good	142
Psychologist	Median—$54,950 per year	Advanced degree	Good	143
Recreational Therapist	Median—$32,900 per year	College plus training	Fair	145
★ **Registered Nurse** ✈	Median—$52,330 per year	Varies—see profile	Excellent	147
Speech-Language Pathologist	Median—$52,410 per year	Advanced degree	Good	150
Surgeon	Median—$282,504 per year	Advanced degree plus training	Very good	152

★ **High-growth job**

Foreword

The ninth edition of the *Career Information Center* mirrors the ongoing changes in the job market caused by new technological and economic developments. These developments continue to change what Americans do in the workplace and how they do it. People have a critical need for up-to-date information to help them make career decisions.

The *Career Information Center* is an individualized resource for people of all ages and at all stages of career development. It has been recognized as an excellent reference for librarians, counselors, educators, and other providers of job information. It is ideally suited for use in libraries, career resource centers, and guidance offices, as well as in adult education centers and other facilities where people seek information about job opportunities, careers, and their own potential in the workforce.

This ninth edition updates many of the features that made the earlier editions so useful.

- A Job Summary Chart, a quick reference guide, appears in the front section of each volume to help readers get the basic facts and compare the jobs described in the volume. High-growth jobs are highlighted and identified with a star.

- Each volume of the *Career Information Center* begins with an overview of the job market in that field. These "Looking Into..." sections have been completely revised and updated. They also include new graphs, charts, and boxes providing information such as industry snapshots and the fastest-growing and top-dollar jobs in the field. The "Global View" feature tells how the new global economy is affecting jobs in the field.

- Each volume has a section called "Getting Into...," which contains useful information on entering the particular field. It offers self-evaluation tips and decision-making help, and it relates possible job choices to individual interests, abilities, and work characteristics. There is also practical information on job hunting, using the Internet and classified ads, preparing resumes, and handling interviews. "Getting Into..." also includes a section on employee rights.

- Each volume has a listing of all job profiles in the series and the volumes in which they appear, making access to profiles in other volumes easy.

- *Career Information Center* contains 694 job profiles. Each profile describes work characteristics, education and training requirements, getting the job, advancement and employment outlook, working conditions, and earnings and benefits.

- Job summaries, provided for each job profile, highlight the education or training required, salary range, and employment outlook.

- Volume 13 has been revised to reflect career concerns of the new century and employment trends through the year 2014. This volume includes updated articles on benefits, employment law, health in the workplace, job search strategies, job training, job opportunities at home, and identifying opportunities for retraining.

- More than 530 photographs provide a visual glimpse of life on the job. Photos have been selected to give the reader a sense of what it feels like to be in a specific field or job.

- Updated bibliographies in each volume include recommended readings and Web sites in specific job areas. Additional titles for the vocational counselor are included in Volume 13.

- Each volume also contains a comprehensive directory of accredited occupational education and vocational training facilities listed by occupational area and grouped by state. Directory materials are generated from the IPEDS (Integrated Postsecondary Education Data System) database of the U.S. Department of Education.

The *Career Information Center* recognizes the importance not only of job selection, but also of job holding, coping, and applying life skills. No other career information publication deals with work attitudes so comprehensively.

Using the Career Information Center

The *Career Information Center* is designed to meet the needs of many people—students, people just entering or reentering the job market, those dissatisfied with present jobs, those without jobs—anyone of any age who is not sure what to do for a living. The *Career Information Center* is for people who want help in making career choices. It combines the comprehensiveness of an encyclopedia with the format and readability of a magazine. Many professionals, including counselors, librarians, and teachers, will find it a useful guidance and reference tool.

The *Career Information Center* is organized by occupational interest area rather than in alphabetical order. Jobs that have something in common are grouped together. In that way people who do not know exactly what job they want can read about a number of related jobs. The *Career Information Center* classifies jobs that have something in common into clusters. The classification system is adapted from the cluster organization used by the U.S. Department of Labor. Each of the first twelve volumes of the *Career Information Center* explores one of twelve occupational clusters.

To use the *Career Information Center*, first select the volume that treats the occupational area that interests you most. Because there are many ways to group occupations, you may not find a particular job in the volume in which you look for it. In that case, check the central listing of all the profiles, which is located in the front of Volumes 1 through 12. This listing provides the names of all profiles and the volume number in which they appear. Volume 13 also includes a comprehensive index of all the jobs covered in the first twelve volumes.

After selecting a volume or volumes, investigate the sections that you feel would be most helpful. It isn't necessary to read these volumes from cover to cover. They are arranged so that you can go directly to the specific information you want. Here is a description of the sections included in each volume.

- **Job Summary Chart**—This chart presents in tabular form the basic data from all profiles in the volume: salary, education and training, employment outlook, and the page on which you can find the job profile. Jobs with a high growth potential are highlighted and starred.

- **Looking Into...**—This overview of the occupational cluster describes the opportunities, characteristics, and trends in that particular field.

- **Getting Into...**—This how-to guide can help you decide what jobs may be most satisfying to you and what strategies you can use to get the right job. You will learn, for example, how to write an effective resume, how to complete an application form, what to expect in an interview, how to use networking, and what to do if someone has discriminated against you.

- **Job Summary**—These summaries, located at the beginning of each profile, highlight the most important facts about the job: education and training, salary, and employment outlook.

Education and Training indicates whether the job requires no education, high school, college, advanced degree, vocational/technical school, license, or training.

Salary Range provides median or average salaries that may vary significantly from region to region.

Employment Outlook is based on several factors, including the Bureau of Labor Statistics' projections through the year 2014. The ratings are defined as follows: *poor* means there is a projected employment decrease of any amount; *fair* means there is a projected employment increase of 0 to 8 percent; *good* means there is a projected employment increase of 9 to 17 percent; *very good* means there is a projected employment increase of 18 to 26 percent; and *excellent* means there is a projected employment increase of 27 percent or more. The outlook is then determined by looking at the ratings and other employment factors. For example, a job with excellent projected employment growth in which many more people are entering the field than there are jobs available will have an outlook that is good rather than excellent.

For all categories, the phrase *Varies—see profile* means the reader must consult the profile for the information, which is too extensive to include in the Job Summary.

- **Job Profiles**—The job profiles are divided into three categories based on the level of training required to get the job. Each profile explores the following topics: description of the job being profiled, the education and training requirements, ways to get the job, advancement possibilities and employment outlook, the working conditions, the earnings and benefits, and places to go for more information.

Job Profiles—No Specialized Training includes jobs that require no education or previous work experience beyond high school.

Job Profiles—Some Specialized Training/Experience includes jobs that require one, two, or three years of vocational training or college, or work experience beyond high school.

Job Profiles—Advanced Training/Experience includes jobs that require a bachelor's degree or advanced degree from a college or university and/or equivalent work experience in that field.

- **Resources—General Career Information** includes a selected bibliography of the most recent books and Web sites on general career information, including how-to books on such topics as resume writing and preparing for tests. In addition, there is a special guide to readings for the career counselor in Volume 13.

- **Resources**—Each volume also contains a bibliography of books and Web sites for specific fields covered in that volume.

- **Directory of Institutions Offering Career Training**—This listing, organized first by career area, then by state, includes the schools that offer occupational training beyond high school. For jobs requiring a bachelor's degree or an advanced degree, check a library for college catalogs and appropriate directories.

- **Index**—This index, which is located at the end of each volume, lists every job mentioned in that volume. It serves not only to cross-reference all the jobs in the volume but also to show related jobs in the field. For example, under the entry OCEANOG-RAPHER, you will find chemical oceanographer, marine biologist, and marine geophysicist.

- **Volume 13, Employment Trends and Master Index**—This volume includes several features that will help both the job seeker and the career counselor. A useful guide provides the *DOT (Dictionary of Occupational Titles)* number of most of the job profiles in the *Career Information Center*. There is also a special section on career information for Canada. The updated and revised "Employment Trends" section contains articles on health in the workplace; search strategies for finding your first job; employment trends for women, minorities, immigrants, older workers, and the physically challenged; employment demographics; benefit programs; training; employment opportunities at home; employment law; and identifying opportunities for retraining. The articles provide job seekers and career professionals with an overview of current employment issues, career opportunities, and outlooks. Finally, there is a master index to all the jobs included in all 13 volumes.

The *Career Information Center* is exactly what it says it is—a center of the most useful and pertinent information you need to explore and choose from the wide range of job and career possibilities. The *Career Information Center* provides you with a solid foundation of information for getting a satisfying job or rewarding career.

Comprehensive Job Profile List

The following list includes job profiles and corresponding volume numbers.

Accountant, Management, 3
Accountant, Public, 3
Actor, 2
Actuary, 3
Acupuncturist, 7
Administrative Assistant, 3
Admitting Interviewer, 7
Adult Education Worker, 11
Advertising Account Executive, 10
Advertising Copywriter, 2
Advertising Manager, 10
Aerospace Engineer, 6
Aerospace Engineering and Operations
   Technician, 6
Aerospace Industry, 9
Agricultural Engineer, 1
Agricultural Inspector, 1
Agricultural Technician, 1
Agronomist, 1
AIDS Counselor, 7
Air Pollution Control Technician, 1
Air Traffic Controller, 12
Air-Conditioning Engineer, 6
Air-Conditioning, Heating, and
   Refrigeration Mechanic and Installer,
   4
Aircraft Dispatcher, 12
Aircraft Mechanic, 12
Airline Baggage and Freight Handler, 12
Airline Flight Attendant, 12
Airline Reservations Agent, 12
Airline Ticket Agent, 12
Airplane Pilot, 12
Airport Manager, 12
Airport Utility Worker, 12
Alternative Fuels Vehicle Technician, 6
Aluminum and Copper Industries, 9
Ambulance Driver, 7
Amusement and Recreation Attendant, 8
Anatomist, 6
Anesthesiologist, 7
Animal Caretaker, 8
Animal Scientist, 1
Animal Trainer, 1
Announcer, 2
Anthropologist, 6
Apparel Industry, 9
Apparel Workers, 9
Appliance Service Worker, 5
Appraiser, 5
Architect, 4
Architectural Drafter, 4
Architectural Model Maker, 4
Armed Services Career, 11
Art Director, 2
Artificial Intelligence Specialist, 6
Artist, 2
Assembler and Fabricator, 9

Astronomer, 6
Athletic Coach, 8
Athletic Trainer, 8
Auctioneer, 10
Audiologist, 7
Auditor, 3
Auto Body Repairer, 12
Auto Parts Counter Worker, 10
Auto Sales Worker, 10
Automobile Driving Instructor, 12
Automotive Exhaust Emissions
   Technician, 12
Automotive Industry, 9
Automotive Mechanic, 12
Avionics Technician, 12

Baker, 1
Bank Clerk, 3
Bank Officer and Manager, 3
Bank Teller, 3
Barber and Hairstylist, 5
Bartender, 8
Bicycle Mechanic, 12
Billing Clerk, 3
Biochemist, 6
Biological Technician, 6
Biologist, 6
Biomedical Engineer, 6
Biomedical Equipment Technician, 7
Boilermaker, 9
Bookbinder, 2
Bookkeeper, 3
Border Patrol Agent, 11
Botanist, 6
Bricklayer, 4
Bridge and Lock Tender, 12
Broadcast News Analyst, 2
Broadcast Technician, 2
Brokerage Clerk, 3
Building Custodian, 11
Building Inspector, 4
Bulldozer, Grader, or Paving Machine
   Operator, 4
Business Family and Consumer Scientist,
   5
Business Machine Operator, 3

Cable Television and
   Telecommunications Technician, 6
Cable Television Engineer, 6
Cafeteria Attendant, 8
Camera Operator, 2
Candy Manufacturing Worker, 1
Car Rental or Leasing Agent, 12
Car Wash Worker, 12
Cardiac Monitor Technician, 7
Cardiac Perfusionist, 7
Cardiology Technologist, 7

Carpenter, 4
Cartographer, 1
Cartoonist and Animator, 2
Cashier, 10
Caterer, 8
Ceiling Tile Installer, 4
Cement Mason, 4
Ceramic Engineer, 6
Ceramics Industry, 9
Chauffeur, 5
Cheese Industry Worker, 1
Chemical Engineer, 6
Chemical Technician, 6
Chemist, 6
Child Care Worker, Private, 5
Chiropractor, 7
Choreographer, 2
City Manager, 11
Civil Engineer, 4
Civil Engineering Technician, 4
Claims Adjuster, 3
Claims Examiner, 3
Clinical Laboratory Technician, 7
Clinical Laboratory Technologist, 7
College Student Personnel Worker, 11
College/University Administrator, 3
Companion, 5
Comparison Shopper, 10
Compensation and Benefits Analyst, 3
Composer, 2
Computer and Information Systems
   Manager, 3
Computer and Office Machine Repairer,
   3
Computer Consultant, 3
Computer Control Operator, 9
Computer Control Programmer, 9
Computer Database Administrator, 3
Computer Network Technician, 3
Computer Operator, 3
Computer Programmer, 3
Computer Security Specialist, 3
Computer Software Documentation
   Writer, 3
Computer Software Engineer, 3
Computer Support Specialist, 3
Computer Systems Analyst, 3
Conservation Scientist, 1
Construction Electrician, 4
Construction Equipment Dealer, 4
Construction Equipment Mechanic, 4
Construction Laborer, 4
Construction Millwright, 4
Construction Supervisor, 4
Consumer Advocate, 5
Consumer Credit Counselor, 5
Controller, 3
Cook and Chef, 8

Looking Into Health

To be healthy, wealthy, and wise, as the old saying puts it, is the goal of nearly everyone. Perhaps it's no accident that health comes first, for getting and staying well is the basis for enjoying everything else life has to offer. Health care workers in the United States have the privilege of providing Americans with the most valued kind of care, that which preserves and prolongs their very lives. Because people will continue to be born, get sick or injured, and die, health care workers will always be in great demand and held in high esteem.

Every day millions of Americans turn to trained care providers for their medical needs. In private medical offices around the nation, physicians—assisted by nurses and aides—treat minor injuries such as sprained ankles and illnesses such as strep throat and childhood mumps, test patients to diagnose their ailments, and screen people for potential problems. They examine pregnant women and provide prenatal care. They also perform checkups for children and adults. For children and individuals at high risk for certain diseases, they administer immunizations.

In hospitals, a greater variety of health care professionals perform a wider variety of tasks. Medical professionals help individuals who have immediate, severe, or longer-term needs. Emergency room physicians examine and treat people with immediate life-threatening illnesses or those who suffer from severe bleeding or injuries. Internists diagnose and treat medical problems and prescribe medications that pharmacists prepare. Surgeons, with the help of anesthesiologists, nurses, and others, perform surgical operations.

As the demand for health care services rises, some of the fastest-growing occupations will be in allied health. (© Steve Prezant/Corbis.)

1

Every day, technicians in hospitals take X-rays and perform lab analyses and other diagnostic tests. Hospital nurses check the vital signs of patients, administer medications, and maintain charts on patient progress. Orderlies, nursing aides, and others tend to the physical needs of patients, bathe them, and deliver their meals. Dietitians, social workers, and physical, occupational, and other therapists help patients prepare for release from the hospital. Behind the scenes, supervisors, managers, accountants, maintenance workers, admitting interviewers, medical records and health information technicians, and other staff members keep the hospital running smoothly.

On the road, ambulance drivers rush paramedics and emergency medical technicians to people injured in car accidents, caught in fires, and endangered by other emergencies. These medical workers provide immediate first aid, set fractures, and keep injured or ill people safe until they get to the hospital. In private homes, outpatient treatment centers, and residential health care facilities, nurses, aides, and doctors tend to elderly people and people with chronic medical problems, providing more of the services traditionally delivered in hospitals.

Keeping Americans healthy requires millions of workers and billions of dollars—and the numbers keep growing. In 2004 the health care industry in the United States employed about 13.5 million trained workers. By 2014 health care and social assistance—including private hospitals, nursing homes and residential care facilities, and family services—is expected to add 3.6 million jobs over the 2004 level. Registered nurses (RNs) make up the largest health care occupation, numbering well over two million. Yet these numbers will need to grow if Americans are to keep enjoying some of the world's best health care. It is expected that nursing will see a 30.5 percent growth in the number of RNs between 2004 and 2014. Other jobs in the health care field that will grow at an even higher percentage rate than RNs between 2004 and 2014 include chiropractors, physician's assistants, dental hygienists, home health aides, physical therapist assistants and aides, dental assistants, and medical assistants. A current shortage of health care workers means faster-than-average job growth for workers who like helping people to get and stay well.

FROM MAGIC TO MODERN MEDICINE

In ancient times, people knew little about what caused disease or how the human body worked. They concluded that evil spirits or angry gods caused illness. Some of their cures—boring holes in the skull to let out evil spirits, for example—did more harm than good. Nevertheless, ancient people made some important medical discoveries. More than four thousand years ago, people in ancient Egypt were already using castor oil to purge the digestive system and tannic acid to treat burns. An Egyptian text written around 2500 B.C. describes how to use compression to stop bleeding.

The man considered to be the founder of modern medicine was a Greek physician named Hippocrates, who lived in the 5th century B.C. Hippocrates and his followers wrote about seventy books describing a new philosophy of medicine, based not on folklore or magic but on careful observation of patients and detailed records of their symptoms. With this information, physicians could draw accurate conclusions about what caused disease and how it could be treated. This procedure—collecting data and using the data to draw conclusions—is the basis of what we call the "scientific method."

Hippocrates made two other lasting contributions to medical science. His observations led him to conclude that disease is often the result of diet, climate, occupation, or other environmental factors. Hippocrates also established a standard of conduct for physicians, which still guides the medical profession today. These standards are summarized in the *Hippocratic Oath*, which most new physicians take in one form or another. Depending on where they earn their medical degrees, some physicians take another oath or pledge instead of one of the forms of the *Hippocratic Oath*. One of those oaths is the *World Medical Association Declaration of Geneva Physician's Oath*, which was adopted in 1948. It includes this vow: "I will practice my profession with conscience and dignity; the health of my patient will be my first consideration."

The Search for Causes

Ideas like those of Hippocrates did not have a widespread effect on medicine until the Renaissance in the sixteenth century. The Renaissance was a period of intense intellectual awakening and scientific inquiry in all fields, including medicine. The first accurate anatomy text was published in 1543, about the same time that serious research began into the cause of infectious diseases. A century later, the first precise description of blood circulation appeared, along with an explanation of how the lungs work.

Until then, no one had developed compelling evidence to show how disease spread. In the mid-nineteenth century, a series of experiments by Louis Pasteur showed that microorganisms called bacteria can invade the body and cause infection and dis-

Global View: Health

As in other career fields, opportunities for health care are expanding with the growth of the global economy and the Internet. Doctors are finding work abroad as well as in the United States. Medical students may seek training in a foreign nation. Even patients are going global, using the Internet to research everything from doctors to advances in medical treatments.

The ease of international communications has prompted several American firms to open health care facilities in foreign nations. Such operations have opened in Eastern Europe and the former Soviet Union, where traditional state-run health care systems are unable to care for the region's aging population. Other U.S.-based medical facilities soon may appear on foreign soil, as the World Trade Organization plans to open public health care systems around the world to private investment and competition.

With many nations (including the United States) experiencing a shortage of trained health care professionals, demand for an education in medicine is high. Some U.S. medical schools state that ten to twenty candidates apply for every opening, and some nursing schools report a three-year waiting period for acceptance. As a result, many students are seeking training at accredited medical schools in other nations. Programs span the globe, from the West Indies to Israel, and include training in a wide range of medical fields. Many of these schools are approved for U.S. federal financial aid.

The Internet has made it easier for students to find foreign medical schools. Many of these schools process application forms over the Internet and provide online guidance regarding financial aid. Some school Web sites enable prospective students to "chat" with current students, graduates, and professors to learn about the school.

The Internet has also created a new health care field. Health information Web sites, such as WebMD (www.WebMD.com), are among the sites most often visited by the general public. They allow consumers far greater access to health care information than ever before—from news and warnings on drugs and updates on clinical trials, to in-depth studies of diseases and conditions. Hospitals, insurance companies, and nonprofit organizations, such as the American Heart Association, sponsor many of these sites. Thousands of health care professionals, including physicians and nurses, act as writers and consultants to the Web sites.

---

ease. More important, Pasteur discovered how to prevent this bacterial invasion through immunization. Robert Koch, considered a cofounder with Pasteur of the science of bacteriology, identified the specific bacteria that cause tuberculosis and cholera.

The pace of medical progress quickened in the nineteenth and twentieth centuries. In the 1840s, the use of ether as an anesthetic made possible many surgical operations that were previously too painful for patients to bear. Wilhelm Roentgen's discovery of X-rays in 1895, and Marie Curie's pioneering research, revolutionized the diagnostic process. Alexander Fleming's 1928 discovery of penicillin, the first antibiotic, was also a landmark achievement. For the first time a drug could kill disease-causing organisms inside the body of a person who was already ill.

Medical Science and Public Health

By the beginning of the twentieth century, medical science provided convincing evidence for what Hippocrates had suspected: Disease is often caused by an unsafe environment. This knowledge led officials to begin massive programs to improve public health. They drained swamps to eliminate disease-carrying insects, sanitized drinking water supplies, and quarantined people with infectious diseases. They also began programs of education and vaccination, which led to the virtual eradication of diseases such as cholera, typhus, typhoid fever, and yellow fever in the United States.

Today public health agencies continue their work to keep the public safe and well informed. The United States Center for Disease Control and Prevention (CDC), the World Health Organization (WHO), and other agencies continue to research new ways to prevent the spread of infectious diseases, promote health, and prolong life.

The CDC's mission is to track diseases in the United States and help control them. Statisticians and lab workers at the agency pay close attention to epidemics, their spread, and their prevention. The role of the WHO is to oversee the public health of all member nations of the United Nations. The WHO helps governments to promote family planning and

Top-Dollar Jobs in Health

These are high-paying jobs described in this volume. The figures represent typical salaries or earnings for experienced workers.

$150,000–$325,000	• Anesthesiologist
	• Dermatologist
	• Geriatrician
	• Ophthalmologist
	• Osteopathic Physician (General Practice)
	• Physician (General Practice)
	• Psychiatrist
	• Surgeon
$75,000–$149,999	• Cardiac Perfusionist
	• Dentist
	• Medical Physicist
	• Optometrist
	• Pharmacist
	• Pharmacologist
	• Podiatrist

provide their citizens with access to primary health care. It also watches population patterns and funds public health research and development. The WHO employs researchers, primary health care providers, and others who focus on education, food and water supply, sanitation, immunization, and the prevention and control of disease.

Public health agencies also serve as educators, warning people of health hazards such as those posed by smoking, alcohol and drug abuse, occupational hazards, and environmental pollution. Outbreaks of the E. coli bacterium, found in tainted food, are often reported on the national news. The fight against the deadly AIDS epidemic continues to be a key focus of public health agencies around the world. One of 2005's major health stories was the threat of the spread of bird flu. Epidemiologists worried that this bird virus, which can be spread from birds to humans, could be spread from human to human. If that were possible, a highly deadly worldwide pandemic could result.

THE TECHNOLOGY REVOLUTION

Technology has revolutionized the practice of medicine throughout the 20th century and into the twenty-first century. The first three high-tech diagnostic tools—X-ray machines, electroencephalographs (EEGs), and electrocardiographs (EKGs or ECGs)—were all developed early in the twentieth century. X-ray machines aim X-ray beams at patients' bodies. Since X-rays are better absorbed by bone and other dense structures than by soft tissue such as the lungs, their beams cast shadows of varying intensity. These shadows can be captured on X-ray film. Trained physicians and X-ray technicians can read this film to detect bone fractures and locate unexplained shadows that may be cast by tumors, infections, or foreign objects. EEGs and EKGs use electrical impulses to diagnose physical problems. By placing electrodes on a patient's scalp or chest, medical personnel can study the patterns generated by electrical impulses within the body. Certain distinct, abnormal patterns of electrical activity are signs of epilepsy, stroke, or brain tumors. These patterns may also indicate disorders in the heart muscle. Advanced EKG technology, in conjunction with imaging technology such as ultrasound and nuclear-imaging equipment, works with imaging computer software to construct a three-dimensional model of the heart, showing problem areas.

Computers and the Medical Profession

In recent decades computer technology has continued to have a tremendous effect on medicine. Computerized axial tomography (CAT) scanners, first used in the 1970s, process X-rays into computerized three-dimensional images of slices of the body, giving physicians even greater detailed information about tumors, cysts, and other tissue abnormalities within the body. Magnetic resonance imaging (MRI) scanners use a powerful magnet and radio waves to make computerized two- or three-dimensional images of the inside of the body, which helps physicians diagnose disorders as well.

Positron-emission tomography (PET) scanners are a more recent visualizing technology. PET scanners can show the level of cell activity in certain parts of the body. These diagnostic tools are used primarily to detect cancer cells, which generally grow more quickly than normal cells. PET scans are also used to gather information about patients' heart disease, dementia, or seizures.

Another new technology—magnetoencephalography (MEG)—permits physicians to characterize electrical activity within the brain by mapping associated magnetic fields, providing even greater detail on brain activity than EEGs can provide. With these high-tech computer-aided tools, and others, physicians are learning more about the body—both its functions and its malfunctions.

Computer technology also helps physicians, technicians, and nurses manage the vast amount of medical information and patient data they need to make diagnoses and decide on treatment plans. Some computer programs permit physicians to input the medical history of a patient along with information on the patient's current symptoms. The program then compares this information to databases of general medical and pharmaceutical information. After analyzing the symptoms, the program suggests several possible diagnoses, ranks their probability, and lists the tests, treatments, and drug therapies appropriate for each one. Of course, computer technology cannot replace the role of the physician, but it can save physicians and patients time and money.

Computers can also aid in patient therapy. Besides helping medical personnel design artificial bones and limbs, prosthesis software gives orthopedic surgeons the ability to customize artificial limbs to match patients' individual needs. In the future, prostheses will likely be available that contain computers embedded in them. Nerve signals from the patient's brain will "tell" the prosthesis how to move. Prototypes of this technology were being studied in 2005.

Computer-assisted training also is a major part of medical school education. Research developed from detailed CAT scans of cadavers, for example, has resulted in detailed computer-based anatomy texts, which give medical students the ability to use computers to study their subjects in color, from any angle, and with enhanced detail. Interactive diagnostic programs provide students with experience that cannot be found in ordinary textbooks. The programs allow students to practice observing and diagnosing medical problems. Computers are also playing a growing role in patient care, with some physicians using personal digital assistants to prescribe medication and check for drug interactions and others using portable computers to review and enter information into computerized patient records. Computers also help nursing staff and records technicians keep patient records up to date and accessible at a keystroke.

THE PEOPLE DOING THE WORK

All the technology available today is useless without trained, educated health care workers. Inside the hospitals, in doctors' offices, and elsewhere, experts with a wide variety of skills provide medical care. Within the broad categories of doctors, nurses, and technicians are scores of specialized occupations.

Physicians

Physicians today make up slightly over three percent of the health care workforce. Until World War I, almost all doctors were general practitioners who treated anyone who came to them, young and old alike. These professionals delivered babies, set broken bones, prescribed medicines and other treatments for disease, and comforted the dying.

As medicine became more complex, medical doctors became more specialized. In 2003 roughly 60 percent of all physicians and surgeons in the United States were specialists. The majority practice near major medical centers in and around large cities. Cardiologists treat heart patients; nephrologists treat individuals with kidney problems; geriatricians work with the elderly; hematologists deal with diseases of the blood; and dermatologists treat skin diseases and skin problems. Occupational medicine physicians study problems caused by the workplace, such as noise-induced hearing loss, multiple chemical sensitivity, and repetitive stress injury. Today there are specialists in every field, including gynecology, ophthalmology, urology, neurology, otolaryngology, psychiatry, and dozens of others.

Although the long-standing trend has been toward specialization, an increasing portion of medical students are preparing for a career in general practice (often called family practice). Family physicians often run private practices. They treat minor and chronic ailments; teach disease prevention, nutrition, and good health care; and screen for potential problems. This trend toward family practice has been spurred in part by federal student loan programs designed to help students who agree to work

Although the long-standing trend has been toward specialization in medicine, increasing numbers of medical students are preparing for careers in general practice. (© Terry Wild Studio. Reproduced by permission.)

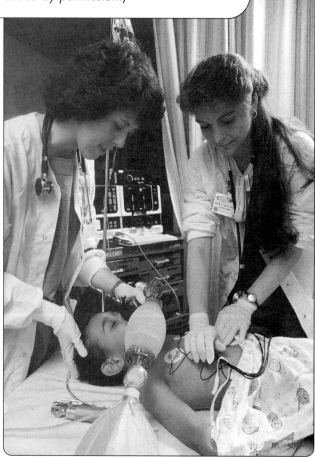

in urban and rural areas facing a shortage of primary caregivers. Although family practice has traditionally been a lower-paying field than most specialties, the current trend is toward equalization of salaries among family practitioners and specialists.

Not all doctors are M.D.s (doctors of medicine). D.O.s (doctors of osteopathy), for example, receive much the same education and training as M.D.s and employ many standard medical techniques. However, osteopaths approach medicine with a different philosophy. They take a holistic approach to medicine, looking for a connection between diet, lifestyle, and environmental factors in diagnosis and treatment. Osteopaths generally focus on the effect of the musculoskeletal system on illness and disorders and often use physical manipulation, rather than medicine or surgery, to diagnose and treat problems.

Some health care practitioners have advanced degrees and licenses but are neither M.D.s nor D.O.s. These include chiropractors, who concentrate on skeletal and muscular wellness and treat pain and problems of alignment by manipulating the bones and muscles; optometrists, who prescribe corrective lenses for sight or eye muscle problems and, in most states, perform other tasks connected with eye health; and psychologists, who treat mental problems such as bipolar disorder and depression.

Nurses and Nurse Practitioners

According to some estimates, the current supply of physicians and surgeons (about 567,000 in 2004) exceeds the demand throughout much of the country, although many urban and rural areas still suffer a shortage. In stark contrast, nurses, pharmacists, and technicians have been in short supply for the past several decades, and the demand will continue to grow in the next few decades. On top of this is an increased demand for nurses in home and outpatient services.

One reason for the increased demand is that as people live longer, they need more nursing care. Also, the level of training required to operate high-tech monitoring and treatment equipment has led many hospitals and other health care facilities to require that nurses have advanced training. Like people in other medical professions, many nurses now specialize, getting additional training beyond a four-year degree or diploma. In hospitals and clinics, some nurses work in a particular area of care, such as cardiology, pediatrics, or psychiatry. Others become nurse anesthetists, nurse clinicians, or nurse educators. Nurse-midwives, who are qualified to provide gynecological care and obstetric care, are able to deliver babies when no medical complications exist.

Nurse practitioners are registered nurses with advanced training. Some practice alongside physicians; others work independently. Nurse practitioners perform many of the same tasks as physicians. Frequently they examine and treat patients in settings where physicians are not available.

Allied Health Professionals

Changes in technology and escalating health care costs combined with an increased demand for health care have all led to an increased need for workers who can provide medical services. Virtually every health care occupation, including physicians, can expect above-average growth between 2004 and 2014. This includes home care aides, medical assistants, audiologists, dental assistants, and pharmacy technicians.

Medical assistants work in hospitals and doctors' offices, performing both clinical and administrative work. Physical therapists, occupational therapists, respiratory therapists, recreational therapists, speech pathologists, and other therapists help patients regain or improve their physical skills. Therapy assistants and aides work with therapists and prepare patients for therapy. Medical social workers help patients and health care providers to navigate the complex health care system to find necessary services and the means to pay for them.

Athletic trainers and sports therapists work with athletes and others to keep them physically fit and less prone to injury. Dietitians and nutritionists, working both inside and outside hospitals, help individuals learn how what they eat can affect their health. Physician assistants, like nurse practitioners, have some of the training of medical doctors and may examine patients alongside doctors. Physician assistants and nurse practitioners may perform laboratory tests, make preliminary diagnoses, and work without physician supervision depending on state regulations.

As health care becomes even more dependent on technology, the demand for medical technicians continues to rise. Three of the fastest-growing occupations are physician assistants, medical assistants, dental hygienists, and home care aides.

Alternative Medicine Professionals

Although many alternative medicine treatments are considered unorthodox, or even worthless, by the medical establishment, an increasing number of people are turning to these methods. In addition, more and more doctors trained in conventional medicine are incorporating these alternatives into their practices to treat certain disorders, such as chronic pain. Some health insurers, in exchange for slightly higher monthly payments, cover the costs of certain alternative treatments, such as visits to a chiropractor or acupuncturist. Sometimes unconventional treatments test the limits of legality. By January 2006 over a dozen states allowed some provision for the medical use of marijuana.

Some health care practitioners specialize in one area of alternative medicine. For example, herbologists use herbs and other plants to heal and prevent disease. Homeopaths work under the theory that giving an individual a minute amount of a substance that causes a disease can cure or prevent that disease. Acupuncturists insert thin needles into certain parts of the body to ease pain and cure problems. Acupressurists use pressure and touch to help relieve patients' physical problems. These and other alternative healing methods date back centuries.

The art of healing is as old as humankind, and while the marvels of modern medicine have transformed the world, some people consider medicinal drugs, invasive tests, and surgery unnatural. They might begin their search for treatment with a holistic health practitioner, who emphasizes "natural" remedies and lifestyle changes. Chinese medicine, dating back five thousand years, is also gaining new adherents. But responsible alternative health providers usually recommend modern medical attention when an injury or illness warrants it.

BEYOND THE MEDICAL OFFICE AND HOSPITAL

Not all health care is delivered in medical offices or hospitals. Hospitals today have diversified their services to include hospital-run convalescent units, outpatient clinics, rehabilitation centers, and treatment centers for patients suffering from substance abuse.

Ambulatory surgical centers, also known as "surgicenters," and free-standing emergency centers, or "urgicenters," play an important role in giving individuals greater access to medical care. Low-risk minor surgical procedures such as hernia repairs, tissue biopsies, and some forms of cosmetic surgery are performed in surgicenters. These centers can keep their costs low because they do not need sophisticated backup equipment or provisions for long hospital stays.

Urgicenters (called urgent care centers in many areas) operate much like hospital emergency rooms. They are often open seven days a week, twelve to twenty-four hours a day. Doctors, physician assistants, and nurse practitioners at urgicenters treat minor problems such as broken bones, sprained ankles, sore throats, stomachaches, and cuts that require stitches. A visit to an urgicenter is usually more ex-

The demand for home-based health care, especially for the elderly, is increasing rapidly. One of the reasons for that is that patients are being released from hospitals more quickly than they used to be in order to reduce costs. (© LWA-Dann Tardif/Corbis.)

pensive than a visit to a doctor's office but less costly than a visit to a hospital emergency room.

While these centers often prevent the need to enter a hospital, home-based health care is becoming an alternative to staying in the hospital longer than necessary. Home-based care helps hospitals work to keep costs down by shortening patients' hospital stays. More patients are now sent home while still requiring full-time or frequent medical care. Thousands of agencies in this country offer home health care services for the elderly, people who are recovering after surgery, and people who are chronically ill. Some of these agencies are hospital-based, whereas others are affiliated with community health centers or religious groups. Skilled home health service agencies provide nursing, physical and occupational therapy, and speech therapy. Some agencies also provide support services such as personal care, light housekeeping, meal preparation, and transportation, which enable people to continue living independently despite their health limitations. A great number of elderly people now live on their own, with only occasional care from home health care aides who can help with chores or physical care.

Individuals who cannot live on their own without frequent medical or nursing care often move into nursing homes, rehabilitation centers, assisted-living centers or other long-term care facilities. Here they have twenty-four-hour access to nurses and aides and ready access to physicians.

Hospices, which can be either part of residential health care facilities or home-based, are for terminal patients who need palliative care—treatment for pain or other symptoms that makes them as comfortable as possible during the last months or weeks of their lives.

The range of health care delivery options will grow even more diverse in the future, as health care delivery becomes more complex and providers look for new ways to hold down costs. The good news for health care workers is that the development of new health care delivery systems will mean more jobs. From an employment perspective, the health care industry will likely be a center of growth throughout the twenty-first century.

HEALTH CARE RESEARCH AND EDUCATION

A major area of health care is research and education. The current trends in federal funding are to increase spending on research in health services and

Industry Snapshots

HEALTH CARE

The future of health care will continue to be driven by the debate over how to control costs. Regardless of the decisions made, the field will remain one of the strongest growth industries throughout the early twenty-first century. The increasing prominence of cost-effective alternative delivery care systems, such as home-based health care, as well as technological advances requiring specialized training, will create many jobs.

HOSPITALS AND HEALTH MAINTENANCE ORGANIZATIONS

The growing cost of health insurance means that more and more individuals and employers have turned to alternative health care plans such as health maintenance organizations (HMOs) and preferred provider organizations (PPOs). Competition among hospitals and HMOs has led to widespread restructuring, with large hospital chains and HMOs coming out on top.

DOCTORS

Most physicians—nearly 60 percent of all physicians in the United States in 2004—were specialists. However, many physicians have returned and are returning to family or general practice. Employment of physicians and surgeons is projected to grow faster than average for all occupations through the year 2014 due to continued expansion of health care industries. As the number of insured people covered by HMOs has increased, more and more doctors are now working as salaried employees for group medical practices, clinics, or health care networks.

NURSES

The rapid growth of home health care and the high demand for nurse practitioners have made the shortage of nurses even more acute. As the largest health care occupation, registered nurses held about 2.4 million jobs in 2004 in the United States, and the number is expected to increase to over 2.9 million by 2012. The greatest opportunities will be for those nurses trained in high-tech medical specialties.

ALLIED HEALTH WORKERS

This field includes some of the fastest-growing occupations in health care, particularly home health aides, medical assistants, physician assistants, physical therapist assistants, dental hygienists, dental assistants, personal and home care aides, physical therapists, physical therapist aides, occupational therapist assistants, medical scientists, and occupational therapists. As health care becomes even more technology-intensive, health workers with technical and computer training will continue to be in demand.

---

health care policy issues (such as cost effectiveness studies) while maintaining or decreasing funding for scientific and medical research.

Health care researchers are constantly working to invent new technologies and improve existing technologies. Researchers and inventors continue to look for technology that will help individuals overcome or compensate for disabilities. Medical researchers, epidemiologists, and pathologists study diseases and seek cures and preventive measures. Geneticists study genes to determine how they may be used to predict or even prevent problems in patients. The Human Genome Project, launched in 1990 by the U.S. Department of Energy and the National Institutes of Health, finished mapping the approximately twenty-five thousand genes in human DNA in 2003. The hope is that this breakthrough will lead to new treatments of disease based on the identification and replacement of a patient's defective genes.

Biotechnology is one of the most exciting and promising new fields in health care research. The biotechnology revolution began in the late 1970s when small start-up companies, mainly in the San Francisco Bay area, developed a new generation of drugs made from genetically engineered copies of human molecules. By using living systems, such as those of bacteria, to produce human proteins, these companies created medicines that were more precise and predictable—with fewer side effects—than animal-derived versions.

The technologies currently used to diagnose illness are also being used to discover more about the human body and mind. PET scanners, for example, are used to discover how we learn and retain language. They are also an integral part of the study of the causes of hyperactivity disorders. EEG brain wave studies are used to learn more about depression and other mental problems. Other technologies are being developed that promise to diagnose heart and brain problems before they become acute.

Research into health care policy also is extremely active today. Health economists, for example, advise hospital administrators and public health officials on the financing of health services. Health economists are playing a role in developing reform measures for health care funding.

Health educators go to schools, public health clinics, and workplaces to teach people how to care for their own health. They teach about nutrition, exercise, alcoholism, smoking cessation, stress reduction, and ways to avoid sexually transmitted diseases. They also maintain libraries, serve as information resources for the public, and write articles for popular journals about health care.

PAYING FOR HEALTH CARE

While health care technologies and techniques continue to develop, the provision of health care has become increasingly expensive. From the point of view of many Americans, the cost of health care has reached a crisis level. Yet the nation is at odds about how to solve this problem and how health care should be paid for. Some are calling for major reform of the American health care system, but change in this area has traditionally been very slow to come. One of the major issues in the 2004 U.S. presidential election was a prescription drug benefit for the elderly on Medicare and the poor on Medicaid. Such a plan went into effect in January 2006, but not everyone agreed that it was beneficial. Many

Summer Jobs in Health

HEALTH CARE

Summer internships are available in hospitals and health care agencies. Summer jobs are available for medical and dental assistants, nursing aides and orderlies, therapy assistants, and laboratory assistants. Contact:
- doctors' and dentists' offices
- hospitals and clinics
- nursing homes
- health care agencies
- summer camps for the disabled

Sources of Information
American Hospital Association
One North Franklin
Chicago, IL 60606-3421
www.aha.org

National Association of Community Health Centers
7200 Wisconsin Ave., Ste. 210
Bethesda, MD 20814
www.nachc.com

RELATED SERVICES

Summer jobs are available in hospitals and nursing homes for catering and housekeeping workers. Clerical workers are needed in hospital admissions and records departments and in doctors' offices. Home health care workers can assist housebound patients. Contact:
- hospitals
- nursing homes
- employment agencies
- social service agencies

Sources of Information
American Health Care Association
1201 L St., NW
Washington, DC 20005
www.ahca.org

National Association of Health Unit Coordinators
1947 Madron Rd.
Rockford, IL 61107
www.nahuc.org

MEDICAL RESEARCH

Summer internships are available in universities, research institutes, and hospitals. Summer jobs include research assistant, laboratory assistant, and animal care worker. Clerical workers are also needed during summer vacations. Contact:
- research institutions
- hospitals
- medical supply companies
- pharmaceutical companies
- government research agencies

Sources of Information
American Federation for Medical Research
900 Cummings Center, Ste. 221-U
Beverly, MA 01915
www.afmr.org

Association of Clinical Research Professionals
500 Montgomery St., Ste. 800
Alexandria, VA 22314
www.acrpnet.org

argued that the plan was complicated and difficult to understand, and that in some cases, benefits were worse than under the former plan. The benefit helped seniors with only part of the cost of prescription drugs.

The Increasing Cost of Health Care

Today the nation's skilled corps of health care professionals, supported by an army of scientists and a sophisticated array of diagnostic and treatment tools, provide an unprecedented level of health care. However, the cost of this care is unprecedented as well. In January 2006 the Centers for Medicare and Medicaid Services released a report stating that the United States spent $1.87 trillion in health care in 2004. Consumers paid an average of $6,280 for health care in 2004. Although health care spending rose 7.9 percent from 2003 to 2004, this increase is less than the increase of 8.2 percent from 2002 to 2003. Nonetheless, health care spending doubled from 1994 to 2004. Although the rate of increase is slowing somewhat, it continues to outpace inflation, and by 2014 total health spending is projected to constitute an 18.7 percent share of the national economy.

Several factors account for the rapid growth of health care costs over the past several decades. First and foremost, Americans are now living longer. Over the years, medical advances have reduced the number of people who die young from diseases such as polio and tuberculosis. Americans take better care of themselves through increased workplace safety and better preventive care, although the obesity epidemic is putting more people at risk for diabetes, heart disease, and other obesity-related ailments. Nonetheless, medical science has developed drugs and other therapies to help people lower their cholesterol and live healthier lives in spite of health-compromising lifestyle factors such as obesity. Longer life expectancy, combined with a lowered birth rate, has driven the median age of the population upward.

The number of expensive treatment and diagnostic options has also increased. Major organ transplants, coronary bypass surgery, and long-term kidney dialysis—all extremely costly procedures—have become commonplace. Technological innovations permit low-birthweight babies and individuals with serious physical impairments (such as accident victims) to survive, although at significant expense. Equipment costs, development costs, and usage costs can be extremely high. Some technologies, such as PET scanners, can cost millions of dollars and are expensive to maintain. Developing, testing, and receiving approval for new drugs can also prove very costly.

Another factor driving up the cost of health care is malpractice suits against doctors and other medical professionals. Physicians today pay tens of thousands of dollars each year in malpractice insurance premiums.

Insurance: The Traditional Payment Method

Americans' health care is typically paid for by medical insurance, which is supplied wholly or in part by their employers. Under traditional indemnity insurance, patients receive medical treatment from the providers of their choice and send the bills to the insurance companies for payment. Under this system, individuals have no incentive to shop around for bargains, and providers have no incentive to limit costs.

This situation has changed in recent years. As the cost of health care increases, the cost of health care insurance also rises, causing employers to cut back on insurance coverage or to limit the options available to employees. Data released by the U.S. Census Bureau in August 2005 showed that 16.7 percent of the American population—45.8 million people—had no health care coverage. The number has been rising each year in recent years. The uninsured face staggering medical bills when they become sick or injured.

Since the mid-1960s, the federal government has been paying medical costs for two groups that do not generally have employers—the elderly and the poor—through its Medicare and Medicaid plans. These plans help to make sure that everyone has access to health care. Nevertheless, increasing numbers of people have little or no health insurance and are at risk of not getting the care they need in a timely and comprehensive way.

Cost-Saving Initiatives

In recent years the nation's health care providers have been under increasing pressure to curb spiraling costs. Hospitals that are part of chains owned by for-profit corporations have also been under pressure to increase profits.

As a result, health care providers, economists, and regulators continue to look for more cost-effective ways to deliver and pay for health care. Political leaders, insurance companies, and providers are working together to find a solution to the dilemma of rising costs. One approach is to reduce costs through new delivery systems, such as outpatient (or ambulatory) surgery centers. In these facilities, patients have surgery performed but go home that same day. In October 2004 the American Society of Anesthesiologists reported that ambulatory surgery currently accounts for almost 80 percent of all surgical procedures performed in the United States

(*ASA Newsletter*, vol. 68, no. 10). Another approach is to use less expensive providers, such as nurse practitioners, instead of doctors, whenever feasible.

Other innovations are directed at how health care is paid for. One innovation was the development of diagnostic related groups (DRGs). DRGs were first implemented by the U.S. government in its Medicare system. Under the older system, hospitals had treated Medicare patients and then billed the government. The longer patients stayed in the hospital and the more procedures they underwent, the more the hospital could charge. Under this system, the hospital had no incentive to minimize costs.

The DRG plan, initiated by Congress in 1983, put health economists to work to predetermine how much a hospital should expect to spend for each of nearly five hundred categories of illnesses. The government established fees for each illness, based on the average cost of treating it, taking into account the length of a typical hospital stay, the number of diagnostic tests, and the cost of surgery and other procedures. Under this system, hospitals may charge the government only the DRG rate and no more. If the hospital's actual cost of treating a Medicare patient exceeds the set DRG rate, then the hospital loses money. On the other hand, hospitals that find ways to cut the cost of treatment are allowed to keep the overpayment amount. Unfortunately, this system sometimes results in abuses such as a patient not being kept in the hospital long enough to get well, or receiving a diagnosis more serious than is actually warranted.

Many private insurers have adopted a similar payment system. Because nearly all medical care in this country is paid for by private insurance or the government, this trend has significant implications. Specifically, it means that the control of health care is shifting from health care providers to insurance companies and others who pay for the health care. In fact, many health care providers must first obtain approval from an insurer before proceeding with a medical treatment.

More Innovations

Whereas the government took the lead in establishing the DRG system, private insurers and providers organized two managed health care plans in their effort to help curtail rising costs. Health maintenance organizations (HMOs) offer medical coverage in a way that is fundamentally different from standard private medical insurance. An HMO is a group of health care providers—including doctors, nurses, and other health care specialists—located at one or more of the facilities affiliated with an HMO. People join an HMO by paying a fixed monthly fee. When members become ill or need checkups, they visit physicians associated with the HMO, usually at little or no cost to the member. When necessary, HMO physicians refer patients to outside specialists and hospitals. However, some people feel that this requirement for a referral is too restrictive, and there has been legal and political controversy over the question of whether patients should have the right to sue their HMO if they are denied adequate care. Many employers will pay some or all of the costs for employees who join an HMO because the monthly fees are usually lower than comparable coverage under conventional medical insurance. Under an HMO system, the emphasis is on preventive care. Individuals are encouraged to visit doctors and other providers before their problems become severe.

A variation of the health maintenance organization is the preferred provider organization (PPO). A PPO is a network of physicians designated by a particular insurance company to provide medical service. The insurance company offers incentives to its subscribers for choosing a preferred provider. For example, if a patient visits a preferred provider, the insurance company may pay 80 percent of the charges, whereas it may pay only 50 percent of the bill if the patient visits a doctor who is not a member of its designated PPO network.

National Health Care Coverage Debate

Even with these new developments, the cost of health care continues to rise and access remains limited. Many political and business leaders believe that the time is ripe for a comprehensive reform of the health care system. Proposals vary, but one of the most frequently suggested alternatives to the current system is an organized delivery system based on managed competition. The idea originated with the Department of Defense in the 1960s and became dominant in discussions of health care reform in the 1980s and 1990s. By 2005, small companies were able to access managed competition through two companies: CaliforniaChoice (only in California) and BENU (in Oregon, Washington State, and the Washington, D.C., area). The way these plans work is that employers get one monthly bill no matter what plans their employees choose. This arrangement allows employers to contribute a specified amount. The result is that their health care costs stay fixed from year to year.

HEALTH CARE AND YOUR FUTURE

This volume describes occupations in a career field that is exciting, stimulating, and rewarding. By carefully examining each occupation and honestly evaluating your talents and interests, you can decide if one is right for you. As you look into the health field, remember two key trends.

First, the health care industry as a whole will continue to grow rapidly in the twenty-first century, creating a wealth of new and diverse opportunities and jobs. For example, as new technologies develop, opportunities for medical technicians will continue to increase. As new treatment techniques are developed, the need for physical therapists, medical assistants, and other aides and assistants will also increase. Few other industries will offer as many opportunities for employment and advancement.

Second, health care providers will find themselves in an increasingly competitive environment in the future. The pressure to keep costs under control may force unprofitable hospitals to close down. Those in overstaffed professions will face stiff competition for jobs and slower salary growth. Nurses will see their roles change as they take over more responsibilities from doctors and relinquish some of their traditional duties to aides and other patient care workers. Wise job seekers will monitor these changes and evaluate their impact on employment.

ood jobs do not magically appear. Anyone who has been in the job market knows that landing the right job takes planning, preparation, perseverance, and patience. This is true whether you are looking for your first job, reentering the job market, trying to get a new job, or planning a mid-career change. This essay is designed to guide you through the process of finding a job, from helping you define your career objectives to suggesting ways to prepare yourself for interviews. Use the advice and checklists below to help identify the kind of work that fits your personality, skills, and interests. Then learn how to locate job openings that match your criteria. Finally, use these tips to help you create a resume and prepare for the interview that helps you land the job that's right for you.

PLANNING YOUR CAREER

What are your unique skills? What kind of workplace appeals to you? What do you find most rewarding in your daily life? Answering these questions can help you identify a career path that will enrich your life, financially and otherwise. Most people enjoy doing a job well. There is an inner satisfaction that comes from taking on a challenge and accomplishing something worthwhile. Whether you are just starting out in the working world or you are at the midpoint of a career, it is worth taking some time to consider whether or not you are in the right kind of work—or looking for the right kind of job. If you are unhappy or dissatisfied in your daily work and are just trying to do enough to get by, you may not be in the right job or the right field. The following ideas can help you match your skills and interests with the kind of work you will find most rewarding.

Evaluate Yourself

Before you make any career decisions, think about subjects or topics that interest you and tasks you do well. This can help you pinpoint the kind of work you would be happy doing. One way to go about this is to compile a self-inventory chart. Such a chart will be helpful as you decide which jobs you want to consider. Including details about your work history and educational background will also make the chart useful to you as you compile your resume, write cover letters, complete job application forms, and prepare for job interviews.

Begin your self-inventory chart by listing all the jobs you have ever had, including summer employment, part-time jobs, volunteer work, and any freelance or short-term assignments you have done. Include the dates of employment, the names and addresses of supervisors, and the amount of money you earned. Then compile a similar list of your hobbies and other activities, including any special experiences you have had, such as travel. Next, do the same for your educational history, listing schools attended, major courses of study, grades, special honors or awards, courses you particularly enjoyed, and extracurricular activities.

At this point, you may see a career pattern emerging: perhaps your list is already suggesting a direction for your career search. If the picture still lacks detail or focus, expand your self-inventory chart by compiling a list of standard workplace aptitudes, and rate yourself *above average*, *average*, or *below average* for each one. Some skill categories to include in your list are administrative, analytic, athletic, clerical, language, leadership, managerial, manual, mathematical, mechanical, sales, and verbal abilities. Also rate your willingness to accept responsibility and your ability to get along with people. In combination with your educational background, work history, and list of personal interests, this information should help you understand why some kinds of work appeal to you and others do not.

Evaluate Workplace Characteristics

Another tool to help you find a rewarding job is the "Work Characteristics Checklist" below. Some of these characteristics will be attractive to you. Some will not. Perhaps you will discover that having a workplace with flexible hours, for example, is more important to you than being able to work outdoors. Or maybe you will find that these are both very significant issues in your quality of life.

This checklist can be useful as a guide as you compile your own list of what is important to you in a job or workplace. Do not expect a job to meet all your requirements, however. Focusing on the job characteristics that are most important to you will help you identify the type of work you would find

Work Characteristics Checklist

Do you want a job in which you can

- work outdoors?
- be physically active?
- work with your hands?
- be challenged mentally?
- work with machines?
- work independently?
- work on a team?
- follow clear instructions?
- earn a lot of money?
- have a chance for rapid advancement?
- have good benefits?
- travel in your work?
- work close to home?
- work regular hours?
- have a flexible schedule?
- have a variety of tasks?
- have supervisory responsibilities?
- express your own ideas?
- be a decision maker?

most rewarding. It will also be helpful when it is time to decide whether or not to apply for jobs you discover during the search process.

Evaluate Career Options

Now that you've evaluated your personal skills, aptitudes, interests, and experience, and you've identified the kinds of workplace characteristics that are important to you, do you feel confident that you know what kinds of jobs you'd be good at? If not, you may wish to consult an experienced career counselor or take advantage of online resources that can help you find a good career field match.

Most high schools, vocational schools, and colleges provide vocational testing and career counseling guidance for students and alumni. Some local offices of the state employment services affiliated with the federal employment service offer free counseling. Commercial career centers also offer guidance services.

There are many tools available to test your interests and aptitudes for the purpose of career counseling. The personal profile that emerges from a skills inventory can be matched with potential career fields to show you what kinds of jobs might be good matches for your interests. These assessment tools will also show you what kind of training is necessary to qualify for jobs in these career fields. You may find programs like this online that you can try for yourself. For a more comprehensive approach, you may prefer to look into aptitude tests that are administered and interpreted by a career counselor.

Most major cities have professional career consultants and career counseling firms. You should make sure to check their reputations before paying for their services. A list of counseling services in your area is available from the American Counseling Association in Alexandria, Virginia (http://www.counseling.org).

You can also search the Internet for many services that career counselors provide. Some sites have online counselors who can help you with a variety of tasks, such as obtaining information on jobs, careers, and training. They may be able to provide information on available services, including housing assistance, day care facilities, and transportation. A list of career planning resources, including Web sites, is available at the end of this volume.

EVALUATE SPECIFIC JOBS

After you have considered what you do well and what you enjoy doing, and identified some career options that provide a good match with your interests and abilities, you're ready to focus on the specific types of jobs that may be available to you. First, make a note of all the jobs in this volume that interest you. Then examine the education and training required for these jobs. Decide whether you qualify or would be able to gain the qualifications.

If possible, talk with people who have the kinds of jobs you are considering. Firsthand information can be invaluable. Also look through the appropriate trade and professional journals listed at the end of this essay and check the section at the end of the volume called "Resources" for books and Web sites that contain more detailed information about the jobs. In addition, counselors usually are helpful. For more detailed information, you can contact the trade and professional associations listed at the end of each occupational profile.

Once you have found out all you can about a particular type of job, compare the features of the job with your work characteristics checklist. See how many characteristics of the job match your work preferences. By completing these steps for all the jobs that appeal to you, you should be able to come up with a list of jobs that match your interests and abilities.

FINDING JOB OPPORTUNITIES

Once you've decided what kind of job suits you, the next step is to look for available positions. Obviously, the more openings you can find, the better your chance of landing a job. People usually apply

Job Finder's Checklist

The following list of job-hunting tips may seem obvious, but getting all the bits and pieces in order beforehand helps when you're looking for a job.

Resume Find out whether you will need a resume. If so, bring your resume up to date or prepare a new one. Assemble a supply of neatly printed copies and have an electronic version ready to e-mail to prospective employers.

References Line up your references. Ask permission of the people whose names you would like to use. Write down their addresses, phone numbers, and job titles.

Contacts Put the word out to everyone you know that you are looking for a job.

Job market Find out where the jobs are. Make a list of possible employers in your field of interest.

Research Do a little homework ahead of time—it can make a big difference in the long run. Find out as much as you can about a job, the field, and the company before you apply. A knowledgeable job applicant makes a good impression.

Organization Keep a file on your job-hunting campaign with names and dates of employers contacted, ads answered, results, and follow-up.

Appearance Make sure that the clothes you plan to wear to an interview are neat and clean. You may need to dress more formally than you would on the job, particularly if you are visiting a personnel office or meeting with a manager. Keep in mind that people will form an opinion of you based on their first impressions.

---

for many job openings before they find the right employment match.

There are many ways to find out about or apply for job openings. Some of these job-hunting techniques are explained on the pages that follow, along with information about how to follow up on job leads.

Applying in Person

For some jobs, especially part-time or entry-level jobs, you may be able to find employment by visiting the company or companies for which you would like to work. This works best when a company is expanding or jobs are plentiful for other reasons, or when a "help wanted" sign is posted at the company. Applying in person can sharpen your interviewing techniques and give you a chance to see a variety of workplaces. This direct approach is best for hourly labor or service jobs; when applying for other types of work, it is not the method to use unless you are directed to do so. Applicants for professional or supervisory jobs should always send a letter and resume to the company.

Phone and Letter Campaigns

To conduct a phone campaign, use the business listings of your telephone directory to build a list of companies for which you might like to work. Call their personnel departments and find out whether they

have any openings. This technique is not useful in all situations, and it has its drawbacks: you may not be able to make a strong impression by phone, and you will not have a written record of your contacts.

Letter writing campaigns can be very effective if the letters are well thought out and carefully prepared. Your letters should always be typed. Handwritten letters and photocopied letters convey a lack of interest or motivation.

You may be able to compile a good list of company addresses in your field of interest by reading the trade and professional publications listed at the end of this essay. Many of the periodicals publish directories or directory issues. Other sources you can use to compile lists of companies are the trade unions and professional organizations listed at the end of each job profile in this volume. The reference librarian at your local library can also help you find appropriate directories.

You can also e-mail letters to human resource departments of many companies. Be sure to follow all the same guidelines as you would for traditional letter correspondence.

Whether they are paper or electronic, your letters should be addressed to the personnel or human resources department of the organization. If possible, send the letter to a specific person. If you don't know who the correct person is, try to find the name of the personnel director through the directories in the library. You can also call on the phone and say, "I'm writing to ask about employment at your company. To whom should I address my letter?" If you can't find a name, use a standard salutation. It's a good idea to enclose a resume (described later in this essay) with the letter to give the employer a brief description of your educational and work experience.

Keep a list of all the people you write to, along with the date each letter was mailed, or keep a photocopy of each letter. Then you can follow up by writing a brief note or calling people who do not reply within about three weeks.

Job Databases Online

The World Wide Web can be an excellent resource for job hunters. The Internet currently has thousands of career-related sites where you can read about job openings or post your resume in a database for a possible match with available jobs. Some sites, such as The Monster Board (http://www.monster.com), help you build a resume and post it online as well as allow you to search through a massive database of help-wanted listings. Others employ a search engine to find jobs that match your background, then post your resume online for employers. The Web site called CareerBuilder (http://www.careerbuilder.com) uses an interactive personal search program that lets you select job criteria such as location, title, and salary; you are then notified by e-mail when a matching position is posted in the database.

Many companies post job openings in their human resource Web pages. You can usually access these lists by visiting the Web site of a company and clicking on a link called "jobs," "careers," or "employment opportunities." If you find a job that interests you during your online search, whether it's posted at a company's own Web site or on a general listing of jobs, follow the directions given for applying for the position. Some online ads will provide the contact information you need to send your resume and cover letter directly to the employer, either by e-mail or by traditional mail, but other ads direct job hunters to apply directly through a link at the job description.

Many career-related Web sites can be found on the Internet. This hypothetical site (for illustration purposes only) allows job-seekers to search for a position by location and by job description.

Job hunters can often find job listings through the Web sites of the professional associations in their career fields. State government Web sites may also provide links to job listings—or to non-government sites that list available jobs.

Help-Wanted Ads

Many people find out about job openings by reading the "help-wanted" sections of newspapers, trade journals, and professional magazines. Employers and employment agencies often, though not always, use these classified ad sections to publicize available jobs.

Classified ads use unique terms to convey basic information. You will find some common abbreviations in the chart in this essay titled "Reading the Classifieds." You can usually decode the abbreviations by using common sense, but if something puzzles you, call the newspaper and ask for a translation. Classified ads usually list the qualifications that are required for a particular job and explain how to contact the employer.

As you find openings that interest you, answer each ad using the method requested. Record the date of your contact, and if you don't hear from the employer within two or three weeks, place another

call or send a polite note asking whether the job is still open. Don't forget to include your phone number and address in your initial contact.

Some help-wanted ads are "blind ads." These ads give contact information for replying but provide no name, phone number, or address that would identify the company. Employers and employment agencies may place these ads to avoid having to reply to all of the job applicants or being contacted directly by job-seekers.

Situation-Wanted Ads

Another way to get the attention of potential employers is with a situation-wanted ad. You can place one of these in the classified section of your local newspaper or of a trade journal in your field of interest. Many personnel offices and employment agencies scan these columns when they're looking for new employees. The situation-wanted ad is usually most effective for people who have advanced education, training, or experience, or who are in fields where their unique skills are in great demand.

A situation-wanted ad should be brief, clear, and to the point. Its main purpose is to interest the employer enough so you are contacted for an inter-

Reading the Classifieds

HELP WANTED

BIOMEDICAL TECHNICIAN
Suburban hospital is seeking 2 perm f/t biomed techs to supervise medical equipment, maintenance program. For further information call 000-0000.
Pine Springs Hospital
Equal Opportunity Employer.

DENTAL ASSISTANT—Fee neg. Chair side & desk work. Exp. pfd. but not nec. Zenith Personnel, 555 Riverview, 000-0000.

LPN—Position avail. all shifts. Must have 1 yr. exp. and successful completion of formal medication course. Call Joan Philips, 000-0000. Orange County Hospital. Equal Opportunity Employer.

MEDICAL LAB. TECH.
Must have cert. Min. 3 yrs. exp., prefer emerg. lab. exp. Sal. commensurate w/exp. Ask for John, 000-0000.

MEDICAL SECRETARY F/P Avail. immed. 2 yrs. medical sec. training or equivalent exp. Gd. typ., office skls. WP exp. helpful. Top hosp., sal., gd. bnfts. MEDICAL PLACEMENTS (agency), 000-0000 ext. 24.

ORDERLY
Good oppty for person with 2-3 yrs. exp. & good refs. H.S. grad prfd. Call 000-0000. Equal Opportunity Employer.

PHYSICAL THERAPIST PROGRESSIVE
Rehabilitation center is now accepting applications for registered physical therapists. Responsibilities incl. developmental therapy technique. Avail. Nov. 1. Call for appt. 000-0000.

RESPIRATORY THERAPIST
Afternoon shift. Immediate opening for person with AA degree in respiratory therapy & 6 months experience. Prefer registered therapist. Excellent benefits. Send resume to OAK PARK HOSPITAL. Equal Opportunity Employer.

CLASSIFIED ABBREVIATIONS

appt.	appointment
bkgd.	background
cert.	certification, certificate
co.	company
col.	college
emerg.	emergency
eves.	evenings
exp.	experience
fee neg.	fee negotiable (fee can be worked out with employer)
f/p., f/pd.	fee paid (agency fee paid by employer)
f/t	full time
gd. bnfts.	good benefits
hosp.	hospital
K	thousand
M	thousand
mgr.	manager
min.	minimum
nec.	necessary
neg.	negotiable
oppty.	opportunity
perm.	permanent
pfd.	preferred
p/t	part time
sal.	salary
sec., secy.	secretary
techs.	technicians
temp.	temporary
typ.	typist, typing
w/	with
WP	word processing

SITUATION WANTED

DENTAL HYGIENE—Student seeking summer job. 000-0000 Eves.

DENTIST
Trained in American university. Endo & Perio oriented. Seeks to join group practice in downtown area. Call 000-0000.

LPN—12 yrs. exp., hosp. trained. F/t or p/t. Excellent refs. 000-0000.

MEDICAL ASSISTANT—Excellent skills & experience, 000-0000.

MEDICAL RECORD TECHNICIAN
Organized, exp. tech seeks challenging oppty. HS grad w/3 yrs exp county hosp. Knowledge of computer systems. Call 000-0000.

MEDICAL SECY—Excellent skills & experience, 000-0000.

NURSE
Student seeks position in Dr.'s office or home. Also have volunteer and office exp. Call 000-0000.

NURSE'S AIDE seeks f/t temp work. Able to work eves. Hosp. & home nursing exp. Good refs. Call 000-0000.

OPTICIAN
Exp. dispensing & shopwork. Superior customer contact, seeks position 3 days a week. Would consider Saturday work, 000-0000.

PHARMACIST
Exp. hosp. dept. supervisor, state registered. Seek hosp. position conducting training programs, upgrading personnel, 000-0000.

RADIOLOGIC TECHNOLOGIST
Career-minded indiv. Grad. AMA approved program w/2 yrs exp. Avail immed, willing to work any shift. Call 000-0000.

view. It should tell exactly what kind of job you want, why you qualify, and whether you are available for full-time or part-time work. Use the same abbreviations that employers use in classified ads.

If you are already employed and do not want it known that you are looking for a new position, you can run a blind ad. A blind ad protects your privacy by listing a box number at the publication to which all replies can be sent. They are then forwarded to you. You do not need to give your name, address, or phone number in the ad.

Networking

A very important source of information about job openings is networking. This means talking with friends and acquaintances about your area of interest. If any of them have friends or relatives in the field, ask if they would be willing to speak with you. There's nothing wrong with telling anyone who will listen that you are looking for a job—family, friends, counselors, and former employers. This will multiply your sources of information many times over.

You can use the Internet to make contacts, too. You can meet people with similar interests in news groups, which are organized by topic. Then you can correspond individually via e-mail. Many fields have professional organizations that maintain Web sites. These can help you keep current on news affecting your field, including employment opportunities.

Sometimes a contact knows about a job vacancy before it is advertised. You may have an advantage, then, when you get in touch with the employer. Don't, however, use the contact's name without permission. Don't assume that a contact will go out on a limb by recommending you, either. Once you have received the inside information, rely on your own ability to get the job.

Notes on Networking

Let people know you're looking. Tell friends, acquaintances, teachers, business associates, former employers—anyone who might know of job openings in your field.

Read newspapers and professional and trade journals. Look for news of developments in your field and for names of people and companies you might contact.

Use the World Wide Web. Make contacts through news groups, or find information on Web sites for professional organizations in your field.

Join professional or trade associations. Contacts you make at meetings could provide valuable job leads. Association newsletters generally carry useful information about people and developments in the field.

Attend classes or seminars. You will meet other people in your field at job-training classes and professional development seminars.

Participate in local support groups. You can gain information about people and places to contact through support groups such as those listed by *The Riley Guide*, available online at http://www.rileyguide.com/support.html, as well as through alumni associations.

Be on the lookout. Always be prepared to make the most of any opportunity that comes along. Talk with anyone who can provide useful information about your field.

Placement Services

Most vocational schools, high schools, and colleges have a placement or career service that maintains a list of job openings and schedules visits from companies. If you are a student or recent graduate, you should check there for job leads. Many employers look first in technical or trade schools and colleges for qualified applicants for certain jobs. Recruiters often visit colleges to look for people to fill technical and scientific positions. These recruiters usually represent large companies. Visit your placement office regularly to check the job listings, and watch for scheduled visits by company recruiters.

State Employment Services

Another source of information about job openings is the local office of the state employment service. Many employers automatically list job openings at the local office. Whether you're looking for a job in private industry or with the state, these offices, which are affiliated with the federal employment service, are worth visiting, online or in person, if there are offices locally.

State employment service offices are public agencies that do not charge for their services. They can direct you to special programs run by the government in conjunction with private industry. These programs, such as the Work Incentive Program for families on welfare, are designed to meet special needs. Some, but not all, of these offices offer vocational aptitude and interest tests and can refer interested people to vocational training centers. The state employment service can be a valuable first stop in your search for work, especially if there are special circumstances in your background. For example, if you did not finish high school, if you have had any difficulties with the law, or if you are living in a difficult home environment, your state employment service office is equipped to help you.

Private Employment Agencies

State employment services, though free, are usually very busy. If you are looking for more personal service and want a qualified employment counselor to help you find a job, you might want to approach a private employment agency.

Private employment agencies will help you get a job if they think they can place you. Most of them get paid only if they're successful in finding you a job, so you need to show them that you are a good prospect. These agencies will help you prepare a resume if you need one, and they will contact employers they think might be interested in you.

Private employment agencies are in the business of bringing together people who are looking for jobs and companies that are looking for workers. For some positions, usually mid- and higher-level jobs, the employment agency's fee is paid by the employer. In such cases, the job seeker pays no fee. In other cases, you may be required to pay the fee, which is usually a percentage of your annual salary. Paying a fee can be a worthwhile investment if it leads to a rewarding career.

Some agencies may also ask for a small registration fee whether or not you get a job through them. Some agencies may demand that you pay even if you find one of the jobs they are trying to fill through your other contacts. Be sure to read and understand the fine print of any contract you're expected to sign, and ask for a copy to take home. Since the quality of these agencies varies, check to see if an agency is a certified member of a state or national association.

Some employment agencies, called staffing services, operate in a different way. They are usually paid by employers to screen and refer good candidates for job openings. They earn money when they refer a candidate who is hired by the employer. The employee pays no fee. Staffing firms, however, only spend time on candidates they think they may be able to place.

Private employment agencies are usually helping many people at one time. They may not have the time to contact you every time they find a job opening. Therefore, you may need to phone them at reasonable intervals after you have registered.

Civil Service

In your search for work, don't forget that the civil service—federal, state, and local—may have many jobs in your field. You may contact the state employment office or apply directly to the appropriate state or federal agency. The armed services also train and employ civilians in many fields. Don't neglect these avenues for finding jobs. Civil service positions usually require you to take a civil service examination. Books are available to help you prepare for these exams, and your local civil service office can also provide information.

Unions

In certain fields, unions can be useful sources of information. If you are a member of a union in your field of interest, you may be able to find out about jobs in the union periodical or through people at the union local. If you do not belong to a union, you may contact a union in the field you are interested in for information about available employment services. You will find addresses for some unions in the job profiles in this book.

Temporary Employment

A good way to get a feel for the job market—what's available and what certain jobs are like—is to work in a temporary job. There are both private and state agencies that can help place people in short-term jobs. Some jobs are seasonal, and extra workers may be needed in the summer or at another busy time.

Temporary employment can increase your job skills, your knowledge of a particular field, and your chances of hearing of permanent positions. In today's tight labor market, many companies are using the services of temporary workers in increasing numbers. In fact, temporary agencies may sign multimillion-dollar contracts to provide businesses with a range of temporary workers. In some cases, temporary workers are in such demand that they may receive benefits, bonuses, and the same hourly wages as equivalent permanent employees. Some temporary agencies are even joining with companies to create long-term career paths for their temporary workers.

MARKETING YOURSELF

An employer's first impression of you is likely to be based on the way you present yourself on print. Whether it is in an application form or on a resume, you will want to make a good impression so that employers will be interested in giving you a personal interview. A potential employer is likely to equate a neat, well-written presentation with good work habits, and a sloppy, poorly written one with bad work habits.

Writing an Effective Resume

When you write to a company to follow up a lead or to ask about job openings, you should send information about yourself. The accepted way of doing this is to send a resume with a cover letter.

The work resume is derived from the French word résumer, meaning "to summarize." A resume does just that—it briefly outlines your education, work experience, and special abilities and skills. A resume may also be called a curriculum vitae, a personal profile, or a personal data sheet. This summary acts as your introduction by mail or e-mail, as your calling card if you apply in person, and as a convenient reference for you to use when filling out an application form or when being interviewed.

DO YOU KNOW YOUR RIGHTS?

JOB DISCRIMINATION—WHAT IT IS

Federal and State Law

An employer cannot discriminate against you for any reason other than your ability to do the job. By federal law, an employer cannot discriminate against you because of your race, color, religion, sex, or national origin. The law applies to decisions about hiring, promotion, working conditions, and firing. The law specifically protects workers who are over the age of forty from discrimination on the basis of age.

The law also protects workers with disabilities. Employers must make their workplaces accessible to individuals with disabilities—for example, by making them accessible to wheelchairs or by hiring readers or interpreters for blind or deaf employees.

Federal law offers additional protection to employees who work for the federal government or for employers who contract with the federal government. State law can also provide protection, for example by prohibiting discrimination on the basis of marital status, arrest record, political affiliations, or sexual orientation.

Affirmative Action

Affirmative action programs are set up by businesses that want to make a special effort to hire women and members of minority groups. Federal employers and many businesses that have contracts with the federal government are required by law to set up affirmative action programs. Employers with a history of discriminatory practices may also be required to establish affirmative action programs.

Discrimination against Job Applicants

A job application form or interviewer may ask for information that can be used to discriminate against you illegally. The law prohibits such questions. If you are asked such questions and are turned down for the job, you may be a victim of discrimination. However, under federal law, employers must require you to prove that you are an American citizen or that you have a valid work permit.

Discrimination on the Job

Discrimination on the job is illegal. Being denied a promotion for which you are qualified or being paid less than coworkers are paid for the same job may be forms of illegal discrimination.

Sexual, racial, and religious harassment are forms of discrimination and are prohibited in the workplace. On-the-job harassment includes sexual, racial, or religious jokes or comments. Sexual harassment includes not only requests or demands for sexual favors but also verbal or physical conduct of a sexual nature.

JOB DISCRIMINATION— WHAT YOU CAN DO

Contact Federal or State Commissions

If you believe that your employer practices discrimination, you can complain to the state civil rights commission or the federal Equal Employment Opportunity Commission (EEOC). If, after investigating your complaint, the commission finds that there has been discrimination, it will take action against the employer. You may be entitled to the job or promotion you were denied or to reinstatement if you were fired. You may also receive back pay or other financial compensation.

Contact a Private Organization

There are many private organizations that can help you fight job discrimination. For example, the American Civil Liberties Union (ACLU) works to protect all people from infringement on their civil rights. The National Association for the Advancement of Colored People (NAACP), National Organization

A resume is a useful tool in applying for almost any job, even if you use it only to keep a record of where you have worked, for whom, and the dates of employment. A resume is required if you are being considered for professional or executive jobs. Prepare it carefully. It's well worth the effort.

The goal of a resume is to capture the interest of potential employers so they will call you for a personal interview. Since employers are busy people, the resume should be as brief and as neat as possible. You should, however, include as much relevant information about yourself as you can. This is usually presented under at least two headings: "Education" and "Experience." The latter is sometimes called "Employment History." Some people add a third section titled "Related Skills," "Professional Qualifications," or "Related Qualifications."

If you prepare a self-inventory such as the one described earlier, it will be a useful tool in preparing a resume. Go through your inventory, and select the items that show your ability to do the job or jobs in which you are interested. Plan to highlight these

for Women (NOW), and Native American Rights Fund may negotiate with your employer, sue on your behalf, or start a class action suit—a lawsuit brought on behalf of all individuals in your situation.

WHAT TO DO IF YOU LOSE YOUR JOB

Being Fired and Being Laid Off

In most cases, an employer can fire you only if there is good cause, such as your inability to do the job, violation of safety rules, dishonesty, or chronic absenteeism.

Firing an employee because of that employee's race, color, religion, sex, national origin, or age (if the employee is over forty) is illegal. Firing an employee for joining a union or for reporting an employer's violation (called whistle-blowing) is also prohibited. If you believe you have been wrongfully discharged, you should contact the EEOC or the state civil rights commission.

At times, employers may need to let a number of employees go to reduce costs. This reduction in staff is called a layoff. Laying off an employee has nothing to do with the employee's job performance. Federal law requires employers who lay off large numbers of employees to give these employees at least two months' notice of the cutback.

Unemployment Compensation

Unemployment insurance is a state-run fund that provides payments to people who lose their jobs through no fault of their own. Not everyone is entitled to unemployment compensation. Those who quit their jobs or who worked only a few months before losing their jobs may not be eligible.

The amount of money you receive depends on how much you earned at your last job. You may receive unemployment payments for only a limited period of time and only so long as you can prove that you are actively looking for a new position.

Each claim for unemployment compensation is investigated before the state makes any payments. If the state unemployment agency decides to deny you compensation, you may ask the agency for instructions on how to appeal that decision.

OTHER PROTECTIONS FOR EMPLOYEES

Honesty and Drug Testing

Many employers ask job applicants or employees to submit to lie detector tests or drug tests. Lie detector tests are permitted in the hiring of people for high security positions, such as police officers. Some states prohibit or restrict the testing of applicants or employees for drug use. Aptitude and personality tests are generally permitted.

Other Federal Laws

The Fair Labor Standards Act prescribes certain minimum wages and rules about working hours and overtime payments. Workers' compensation laws provide payment for injuries that occur in the workplace and wages lost as a result of those injuries.

The Occupational Safety and Health Act sets minimum requirements for workplace safety. Any employee who discovers a workplace hazard should report it to the Occupational Safety and Health Administration (OSHA). The administration will investigate the claim and may require the employer to correct the problem or pay a fine.

Rights Guaranteed by Contract

Not every employee has a written contract. If you do, however, that contract may grant you additional rights, such as the right to severance pay in the event you are laid off. In addition, employees who are members of a union may have certain rights guaranteed through their union contract.

Before you sign any contract, make sure you understand every part of it. Read it thoroughly and ask the employer questions. Checking the details of a contract before signing it may prevent misunderstanding later.

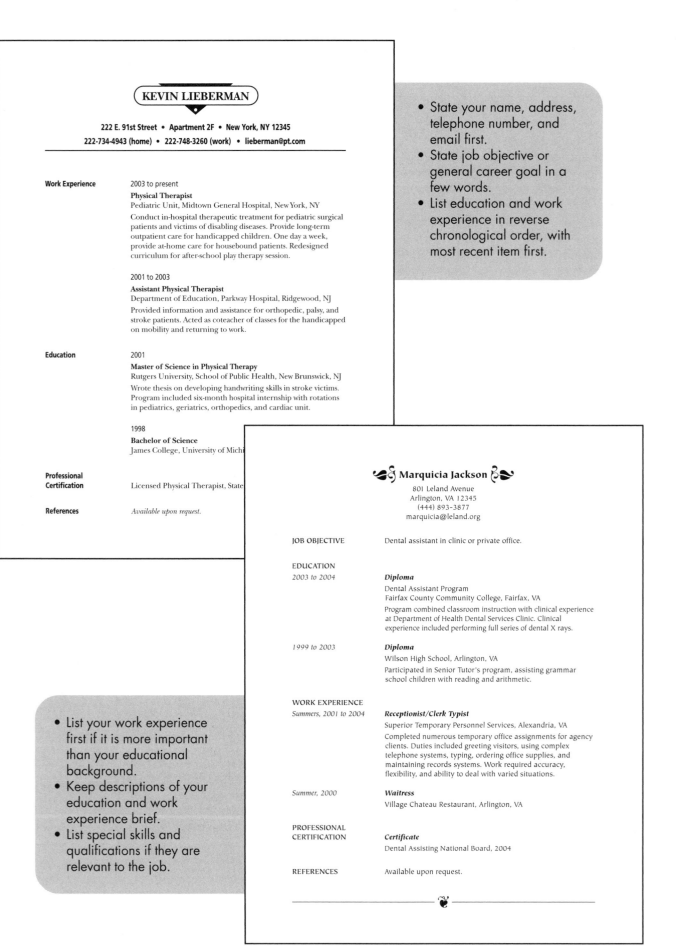

KEVIN LIEBERMAN

222 E. 91st Street • Apartment 2F • New York, NY 12345
222-734-4943 (home) • 222-748-3260 (work) • lieberman@pt.com

Work Experience

2003 to present
Physical Therapist
Pediatric Unit, Midtown General Hospital, New York, NY
Conduct in-hospital therapeutic treatment for pediatric surgical patients and victims of disabling diseases. Provide long-term outpatient care for handicapped children. One day a week, provide at-home care for housebound patients. Redesigned curriculum for after-school play therapy session.

2001 to 2003
Assistant Physical Therapist
Department of Education, Parkway Hospital, Ridgewood, NJ
Provided information and assistance for orthopedic, palsy, and stroke patients. Acted as coteacher of classes for the handicapped on mobility and returning to work.

Education

2001
Master of Science in Physical Therapy
Rutgers University, School of Public Health, New Brunswick, NJ
Wrote thesis on developing handwriting skills in stroke victims. Program included six-month hospital internship with rotations in pediatrics, geriatrics, orthopedics, and cardiac unit.

1998
Bachelor of Science
James College, University of Michi

**Professional
Certification**
Licensed Physical Therapist, State

References
Available upon request.

- State your name, address, telephone number, and email first.
- State job objective or general career goal in a few words.
- List education and work experience in reverse chronological order, with most recent item first.

Marquicia Jackson
801 Leland Avenue
Arlington, VA 12345
(444) 893-3877
marquicia@leland.org

JOB OBJECTIVE
Dental assistant in clinic or private office.

EDUCATION

2003 to 2004
Diploma
Dental Assistant Program
Fairfax County Community College, Fairfax, VA
Program combined classroom instruction with clinical experience at Department of Health Dental Services Clinic. Clinical experience included performing full series of dental X rays.

1999 to 2003
Diploma
Wilson High School, Arlington, VA
Participated in Senior Tutor's program, assisting grammar school children with reading and arithmetic.

WORK EXPERIENCE

Summers, 2001 to 2004
Receptionist/Clerk Typist
Superior Temporary Personnel Services, Alexandria, VA
Completed numerous temporary office assignments for agency clients. Duties included greeting visitors, using complex telephone systems, typing, ordering office supplies, and maintaining records systems. Work required accuracy, flexibility, and ability to deal with varied situations.

Summer, 2000
Waitress
Village Chateau Restaurant, Arlington, VA

**PROFESSIONAL
CERTIFICATION**
Certificate
Dental Assisting National Board, 2004

REFERENCES
Available upon request.

- List your work experience first if it is more important than your educational background.
- Keep descriptions of your education and work experience brief.
- List special skills and qualifications if they are relevant to the job.

items on your resume. Select only those facts that point out your relevant skills and experience.

Once you have chosen the special points to include, prepare the resume. At the top, put your name, address, and phone number. After that, decide which items will be most relevant to the employer you plan to contact.

State Your Objective Some employment counselors advise that you state a job objective or describe briefly the type of position for which you are applying. The job objective usually follows your name and address. Don't be too specific if you plan to use the same resume a number of times. It's better to give a general career goal. Then, in a cover letter, you can be more specific about the position in which you are interested.

Describe What You've Done Every interested employer will check your educational background and employment history carefully. It is best to present these sections in order of importance. For instance, if you've held many relevant jobs, you should list your work experience first, followed by your educational background. On the other hand, if you are just out of school with little or no work experience, it's probably best to list your educational background first and then, under employment history, to mention any part-time and summer jobs you've held or volunteer work you've done.

Under educational background, list the schools you have attended in reverse chronological order, starting with your most recent training and ending with the least recent. Employers want to know at a glance your highest qualifications. For each educational experience, include years attended, name and location of the school, and degree or certificate earned, if any. If you have advanced degrees (college and beyond), it isn't necessary to include high school and elementary school education. Don't forget to highlight any special courses you took or awards you won, if they are relevant to the kind of job you are seeking.

Chronological and Functional Resumes Information about your employment history can be presented in two ways. The most common format is the chronological resume. In a chronological resume, you summarize your work experience year by year. Begin with your current or most recent employment and then work backward. For each job, list the name and location of the company for which you worked, the years you were employed, and the position or positions you held. The order in which you present these facts will depend on what you are trying to emphasize. If you want to call attention to the type or level of job you held, for example, you should put the job title first. Regardless of the order

you choose, be consistent. Summer employment or part-time work should be identified as such. If you held a job for less than a year, specify months in the dates of employment.

It is important to include a brief description of the responsibilities you had in each job. This often reveals more about your abilities than the job title. Remember, too, that you do not have to mention the names of former supervisors or how much you earned. You can discuss these points during the interview or explain them on an application form.

The functional resume, on the other hand, emphasizes what you can do rather than what you have done. It is useful for people who have large gaps in their work history or who have relevant skills that would not be properly highlighted in a chronological listing of jobs. The functional resume concentrates on qualifications—such as familiarity with particular equipment, organizational skills, or managerial experience. Specific jobs may be mentioned, but they are not the primary focus of this type of resume.

Explain Special Skills You may wish to include a third section called "Related Skills," "Professional Qualifications," or "Related Qualifications." This is useful if there are points you want to highlight that do not apply directly to educational background or work experience. Be sure these points are relevant to the kind of work you are seeking. This section is most effective if you can mention any special recognition, awards, or other evidence of excellence. It is also useful to mention if you are willing to relocate or can work unusual hours.

Have References Available Employers may also want to know whom they can contact to find out more about you. At the start of your job search, you should ask three or four people if you may use them as references. If you haven't seen these people for a while, you may want to send them a copy of your resume and let them know what kind of position you're seeking. Your references should be the kind of people your potential employer will respect, and they should be able to comment favorably on your abilities, personality, and work habits. You should indicate whether these people are personal references or former work supervisors. Avoid using any relatives. You can list the names and addresses of your references at the end of your resume or in a cover letter. Or, you can simply write, "References available upon request." Just be sure you have their names, addresses, and phone numbers ready if you are asked.

Present Yourself Concisely Tips for making your resume concise include using phrases instead of sentences and omitting unnecessary words. When

KEVIN LIEBERMAN

222 E. 91st Street • Apartment 2F • New York, NY 12345
222-734-4943 (home) • 222-748-3260 (work) • lieberman@pt.com

February 19, 2005

Mr. Johnson Tellory
Personnel Department
St. Mary's Hospital
13 E. 49th Street
New York, NY 12345

Dear Mr. Tellory:

I am writing in response to the notice for a Director of Physical Therapy posted on the employees' bulletin board at St. Mary's Hospital. The opening was brought to my attention by Dr. Wong (surgery department). I am interested in taking on responsibility for a physical therapy program and would like to learn more about the position.

I understand that the therapy division at St. Mary's is structured so that physical, occupational, and speech therapists consult weekly on each patient. I feel that this type of coordination is essential, and I would be eager to take an active role in the system. I have recently trained two new members of our department at Midtown General, and as a result, I have become interested in training and staff supervision.

I enclose my resume and would be free to meet with you an[...]
I would also be interested in meeting members of the physi[...]

Very truly yours,

Kevin Lieberman

Kevin Lieberman

Enclosure

Marquicia Jackson

801 Leland Avenue
Arlington, VA 12345
(444) 893-3877
marquicia@leland.org

December 2, 2005

Patricia Gomez, D.M.D.
Jefferson Medical Building
Jefferson Boulevard
Arlington, VA 12345

Dear Dr. Gomez:

Henry Martin, who has recently joined your office as a dental assistant, is a former classmate of mine from the Fairfax County Dental Assistant Program. He mentioned that you are looking for a second dental assistant to work evenings and weekends. I would like to apply for the position.

During my training, I had the opportunity to participate in clinical practice on patients of all ages. I especially enjoyed working with children and adolescents. I understand that your practice specializes in orthodontics for young people. This would suit me very well. Evening and weekend hours would present no problem for me.

I enclose my resume. I am available for an interview at your convenience. I look forward to hearing from you.

Very truly yours,

Marquicia Jackson

Marquicia Jackson

Enclosure

appropriate, start a phrase with a verb, such as "maintained" or "coordinated." There is no need to say "I"—that is obvious and repetitive.

Present Yourself Well Employment counselors often recommend that resumes be no longer than one page because employers won't take the time to read a second page. If you've held many positions related to your occupation, go on to the second page, but don't include beginning or irrelevant jobs. If you have a lot of work experience, limit the education section to just the essentials.

You should also concentrate on the appearance of your resume. A traditional resume should be printed on a good grade of 8½" x 11" white paper. Consult a resume preparation guide for specific information about the best ways to format a resume that will be processed by e-mail or other electronic means. If you don't have access to a computer and printer, you can pay someone to type your resume, but it is up to you to read it carefully and ensure that it is error-free. Be sure that it is neatly typed with adequate margins. The data should be spaced and indented so that each item stands out. This enables a busy executive or personnel director to see at a glance the facts of greatest interest.

These suggestions for writing a resume are not hard-and-fast rules. Resumes may be adapted to special situations. For example, people with a variety of work experience often prepare several versions of their resumes and use the experience that's most relevant when applying for a particular job.

If this is your first resume, show it to someone else, perhaps a guidance counselor, for constructive advice. Make sure there are no spelling or punctuation mistakes anywhere on the page. No matter what, be truthful while emphasizing your assets. You can do that by showing the abilities, skills, and specific interests that qualify you for a particular job. Don't mention any weaknesses or deficiencies in your training. Do mention job-related aptitudes that showed up in previous employment or in school. Don't make things up; everything that's in your resume can, and often will, be checked.

Writing Cover Letters

Whenever you send your resume to a prospective employer, whether it's on paper or in e-mail form, you should send a cover letter with it. This is true whether you are writing to apply for a specific job or just to find out if there are any openings.

A good cover letter should be neat, brief, and well written, with no more than three or four short paragraphs. Since you may use your resume for a variety of job openings, your cover letter should be very specific. Your goal is to get the person who reads it

to think that you are an ideal candidate for a particular job. If at all possible, send the letter to a specific person—either the personnel director or the person for whom you would be working. If necessary, call the company and ask to whom you should address the letter.

Start your letter by explaining why you are writing. Say that you are inquiring about possible job openings at the company, that you are responding to an advertisement in a particular publication, or that someone recommended that you should write. (Use the person's name if you have received permission to do so.) Let your letter lead into your resume. Use it to call attention to your qualifications. Add information that shows why you are well suited for that specific job.

Completing the Application Form

Many employers ask job applicants to fill out an application form. This form usually duplicates much of the information on your resume, but it may ask some additional questions. Give complete answers to all questions except those that are discriminatory. If a question doesn't apply to you, put a dash next to it.

You may be given the application form when you arrive for an interview, or it may be sent to your home. When filling it out, print neatly in ink. Follow the instructions carefully. For instance, if the form asks you to put down your last name first, do so.

The most important sections of an application form are the education and work histories. As in your resume, many applications request that you write these in reverse chronological order, with the most recent experience first. Unlike your resume, however, the application form may request information about your earnings on previous jobs. It may also ask what rate of pay you are seeking on the job you are applying for.

Be prepared to answer these and other topics not addressed on your resume. Look at the sample application form, and make note of the kinds of questions that you are likely to be asked—for example, your Social Security number, the names of previous supervisors, your salary, and your reason for leaving. If necessary, carry notes on such topics with you to an interview. You have a responsibility to tell prospective employers what they need to know to make an informed decision.

Neatness Counts Think before you write on an application form so you avoid crossing things out. An employer's opinion of you may be influenced just by the general appearance of your application form. A neat, detailed form may indicate an orderly mind and the ability to think clearly, follow instructions, and organize information.

1 Always print neatly in blue or black ink. When completing an application at home, type it, if possible.

2 Read the application carefully *before* you start to fill it out. Follow instructions precisely. Use standard abbreviations.

3 If you aren't applying for a specific job, indicate the kind of work you're willing to do.

4 You don't have to commit to a specific rate of pay. Write "open" or "negotiable" if you are uncertain.

5 Traffic violations and so on do not belong here. Nor do offenses for which you were charged but not convicted.

6 If a question doesn't apply to you, write "NA" (for not applicable) or put a dash through the space.

7 Take notes along to remind you of school names, addresses, and dates.

8 If you're short on "real" employment, mention jobs such as babysitting, lawn mowing, or any occasional work.

9 Your references should be people who can be objective about you, such as former employers, teachers, and community leaders.

10 Under the heading "Reason for Leaving," a simple answer will do. Avoid saying "better pay"—even if it's so.

APPLICATION FOR EMPLOYMENT

NAME (LAST)	(FIRST)	(MIDDLE)	SOCIAL SECURITY NO.

PRESENT ADDRESS	CITY	STATE	ZIP CODE	AREA CODE	TELEPHONE NO.

PERMANENT ADDRESS	(IF DIFFERENT FROM ABOVE)	AREA CODE	TELEPHONE NO.

POSITION APPLIED FOR	DATE AVAILABLE	E-MAIL

SALARY OR WAGE DESIRED	WILL YOU RELOCATE?	REFERRED BY

ARE YOU A U.S. CITIZEN? YES _____ NO _____   IF NOT A U.S. CITIZEN, LIST VISA NUMBER AND EXPIRATION DATE: NUMBER _____ DATE _____

WITHIN THE LAST FIVE YEARS HAVE YOU BEEN CONVICTED OF A FELONY?	☐ YES ☐ NO	IF YES, GIVE DETAILS ON BACK PAGE	HAVE YOU EVER BEEN EMPLOYED BY OUR COMPANY? IF YES, GIVE DETAILS ON BACK PAGE	☐ YES ☐ NO

EDUCATION	INSTITUTION NAME AND ADDRESS	DID YOU GRADUATE?	MAJOR FIELD OF STUDY	CLASS STANDING
HIGH SCHOOL				
COLLEGE OR UNIVERSITY				
GRADUATE STUDY				
OTHER				

EMPLOYMENT RECORD

PLEASE LIST ALL EMPLOYMENT STARTING WITH MOST RECENT. ACCOUNT FOR ALL PERIODS (INCLUDING U.S. ARMED FORCES, PERIODS OF UNEMPLOYMENT, AND VOLUNTARY SERVICES).

LIST YOUR MOST RECENT POSITION HELD	MAY WE CONTACT YOUR PRESENT EMPLOYER?	☐ YES ☐ NO

EMPLOYER'S NAME AND COMPLETE ADDRESS/PHONE	DATES EMPLOYED	POSITION TITLE
	FROM TO	NAME AND TITLE OF SUPERVISOR
	SALARY	
	START FINAL	REASON FOR LEAVING
EMPLOYER'S NAME AND COMPLETE ADDRESS/PHONE	DATES EMPLOYED	POSITION TITLE
	FROM TO	NAME AND TITLE OF SUPERVISOR
	SALARY	
	START FINAL	REASON FOR LEAVING
EMPLOYER'S NAME AND COMPLETE ADDRESS/PHONE	DATES EMPLOYED	POSITION TITLE
	FROM TO	NAME AND TITLE OF SUPERVISOR
	SALARY	
	START FINAL	REASON FOR LEAVING

PERSONAL REFERENCES

NAME	ADDRESS	PHONE NUMBER
1.		
2.		
3.		

Know Your Rights Under federal and some state laws, an employer cannot demand that you answer any questions about race, color, creed, national origin, ancestry, sex, marital status, age (with certain exceptions), number of dependents, property, car ownership (unless needed for the job), or arrest record. Refer to the information on job discrimination in this essay for more information about your rights.

PRESENTING YOURSELF IN AN INTERVIEW

If your qualifications, as presented in your resume, cover letter, and application, are a strong match for the requirements of the job, you may be invited to a job interview. On the basis of this meeting, the prospective employer will decide whether or not to hire you, and you will decide whether or not you want the job.

Prepare in Advance

Before an interview, there are a number of things you can do to prepare. Begin by giving thought to why you want the job and what you have to offer. Then review your resume and any lists you made when you were evaluating yourself so that you can keep your qualifications firmly in mind.

Learn as much as you can about the organization. Check with friends who work there, read company brochures, search the Internet, or devise other information-gathering strategies. Showing that you know something about the company and what it does will indicate your interest and demonstrate that you are a well-informed job candidate.

Try to anticipate some of the questions an interviewer may ask and think about how you would answer. For example, you may be asked: Will you work overtime when necessary? Are you ready to go to night school to improve some of your skills? Preparing answers in advance will make the process easier for you. It is also wise to prepare any questions you may have about the company or the position for which you are applying. The more information you have, the better you can evaluate both the company and the job.

Employers may want you to demonstrate specific skills for some jobs. An applicant for a job in a lumber mill or a mine, for example, might be required to demonstrate mechanical ability. Prospective technicians might be expected to demonstrate mathematical skills.

On the appointed day, dress neatly and in a style appropriate for the job you're seeking. When in doubt, it's safer to dress on the conservative side, wearing a shirt and tie rather than a turtleneck or wearing a dress or blouse and skirt rather than pants and a T-shirt. Be on time. Find out in advance exactly where the company is located and how to get there. Allow extra time in case you get lost, get caught in a traffic jam, can't find a parking spot, or encounter another type of delay.

Maintain a Balance

When your appointment begins, remember that a good interview is largely a matter of balance. Don't undersell yourself by sitting back silently, but don't oversell yourself by talking nonstop about how wonderful you are. Answer all questions directly and simply, and let the interviewer take the lead.

Instead of saying, "I'm reliable and hardworking," give the interviewer an example. Allow the interviewer to draw conclusions from your example.

It's natural to be nervous before and during a job interview. However, you need to try to relax and be yourself. You may even enjoy the conversation. Your chances of being hired and being happy if you get the job are better if the employer likes you as you are.

Avoid discussing money until the employer brings it up or until you are offered the job. Employers usually know in advance what they are willing to pay. If you are the one to begin a discussion about the salary you want, you may set an amount that's either too low or too high.

Be prepared to ask questions, but don't force them on your interviewer. Part of the purpose of the interview is for you to evaluate the company while you are being evaluated. For instance, you might want to ask about the company's training programs and its policy on promotions.

Don't stay too long. Most business people have busy schedules. It is likely that the interviewer will let you know when it's time for the interview to end.

Don't expect a definite answer at the first interview. Employers usually thank you for coming and say that you will be notified shortly. Most employers want to interview all the applicants before they make a hiring decision. If the position is offered at the time of the interview, you can ask for a little time to think about it. If the interviewer tells you that you are not suitable for the job, try to be polite. Say, "I'm sorry, but thank you for taking the time to meet with me." After all, the company may have the right job for you next week.

Follow Up after the Interview

If the job sounds interesting and you would like to be considered for it, say so as you leave. Follow up after the interview by writing a brief thank-you note to the employer. Express your continued interest in the position and thank the interviewer for taking the time to meet with you.

It's a good idea to make some notes and evaluations of the interview while it is still fresh in your mind. Write down the important facts about the job—the duties, salary, promotion prospects, and so on, which will help you make a decision should you be offered the job. Also evaluate your own performance in the interview. List the things you wish you had said and things you wish you had not said, which will help you prepare for future interviews.

Finally, don't hesitate to contact your interviewer if you haven't heard from the company after a week or two (unless you were told it would be longer). Write a brief note or make a phone call in which you ask when a decision might be reached. Making such an effort will show the employer that you are genuinely interested in the job. Your call will remind the interviewer about you and could work to your advantage.

TAKE CHARGE

Job hunting is primarily a matter of organizing a well-planned campaign. Scan the classified ads, search through online job banks, watch for trends in local industry that might be reported in the news, and check with people you know in the field. Take the initiative. Send out carefully crafted resumes and letters. Respond to ads. Finally, in an interview, state your qualifications and experience in a straightforward and confident manner.

TRADE AND PROFESSIONAL JOURNALS

The following is a list of some of the major journals in the field of health. These journals can keep you up to date with what is happening in your field of interest. These publications can also lead you to jobs through their own specialized classified advertising sections.

Dentists, Dental Assistants, and Dental Technicians

Journal of the American Dental Association, ADA Publishing, 211 East Chicago Avenue, Chicago, IL 60611.
http://jada.ada.org

Health Administration and Education

Hospitals and Health Networks, One North Franklin, Chicago, IL 60606.
http://www.hospitalconnect.com/hhnmag/jsp/hhnonline.jsp

Nursing

Journal of Practical Nursing, P. O. Box 25647, Alexandria, VA 22313.
http://www.napnes.org/journal.htm
The Nurse Practitioner: The American Journal of Primary Health Care, 323 Norristown Road, Suite 200, Ambler, PA 19002.
http://www.tnpj.com
Nursing Outlook, Elsevier Inc., 360 Park Avenue South, New York, NY 10010.
http://journals.elsevierhealth.com

Physicians and Specialized Practitioners

American Family Physician, 11400 Tomahawk Creek Parkway, Leawood, KS 66211-2672.
http://www.aafp.org
American Journal of Psychiatry, 1000 Wilson Blvd., Suite 1825, Arlington, VA 22209-3901.
http://ajp.psychiatryonline.org
American Journal of Public Health, American Public Health Association, 800 I Street NW, Washington, DC 20001-3710.
http://www.apha.org
The Gerontologist, 1030 15th Street NW, Suite 250, Washington, DC 20005.
http://gerontologist.gerontologyjournals.org
JAMA: The Journal of the American Medical Association, 515 N. State Street, Chicago, IL 60610-0946.
http://jama.ama-assn.org
Journal of the National Cancer Institute, 8120 Woodmont Avenue, Suite 500, Bethesda, MD 20814-2743.
http://jncicancerspectrum.oxfordjournals.org
New England Journal of Medicine, 860 Winter Street, Waltham, MA 02451-1413.
http://content.nejm.org

Psychology and Mental Health

American Psychologist, American Psychological Association, 750 First Street, NE, Washington, DC 20002-4242.
http://www.apa.org/journals/amp

Community Mental Health Journal, Plenum US, 233
Spring Street, New York, NY 10013-1578.
http://www.springer.com
Monitor on Psychology, American Psychological
Association, 750 First Street, NE, Washington, DC
20002-4242.
http://www.apa.org/monitor
Psychology Today, 115 East 23rd Street, 9th Floor,
New York, NY 10010.
http://www.psychologytoday.com

Therapists

American Journal of Occupational Therapy, 2901
Oak Shadow Drive, Oak Hill, VA 20171.
Journal of Speech, Language, and Hearing Research,
10801 Rockville Pike, Rockville, MD 20852.
http://jslhr.asha.org
Physical Therapy, 1111 North Fairfax Street,
Alexandria, VA 22314-1488.
http://www.ptjournal.org/Apr2006/toc.cfm

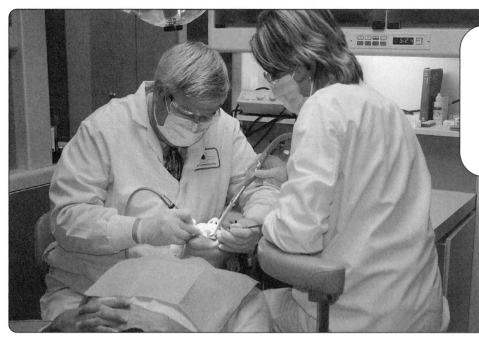

A dental assistant performs chair-side duties that include handing the dentist the proper tools and operating the suction hose that keeps the patient's mouth dry. *(Photograph by Kelly A. Quin. Thomson Gale. Reproduced by permission.)*

private clinics. To get a job with the government, apply to take the necessary civil service test. Check with state and private employment agencies. Also check newspaper want ads and job banks on the Internet.

Advancement Possibilities and Employment Outlook

Dental assistants can advance with experience and further training. In a large dental office, they may become supervisors of other assistants. By taking further dental courses, they can qualify to become dental hygienists or dental laboratory technicians.

The outlook is excellent through the year 2014, with employment expected to grow much faster than average. More assistants should be needed as the field of dental care continues to grow. In addition to new jobs being created, assistants will be needed to replace those who retire. Expanding population, the growing awareness of the importance of dental care, and increasing availability of dental insurance should also add to the demand for dental assistants.

Working Conditions

Most dental offices are comfortable and clean. Dental assistants deal with many kinds of people. They may have to comfort frightened children or calm worried parents. They must also be careful in their work, especially when handling X-ray and dental equipment.

Dental assistants generally work forty hours a week. Some work part time. Assistants are often expected to work on Saturdays.

Earnings and Benefits

Dental assistants earn a median wage of $13.62 per hour. Benefits usually include paid holidays and vacations. Other benefits vary, depending on the employer. Publicly employed dental assistants generally receive the same benefits as other hospital or health agency workers.

Where to Go for More Information

American Dental Assistants Association
35 E. Wacker Dr., Ste. 1730
Chicago, IL 60601-2211
(312) 541-1550
http://www.dentalassistant.org

American Dental Association
211 E. Chicago Ave.
Chicago, IL 60611-2678
(312) 440-2500
http://www.ada.org

National Association of Dental Assistants
900 S. Washington St., Ste. G13
Falls Church, VA 22046-4020
(703) 237-8616

Dialysis Technician

Education and Training
High school

Salary
$25,682 to $32,413
per year

Employment Outlook
Very good

Definition and Nature of the Work

Dialysis technicians work with people whose kidneys no longer work properly or at all. These technicians, who are sometimes called hemodialysis technicians or patient care technicians (PCTs), operate machines that remove wastes, salt, and extra water from patients' blood while keeping safe levels of certain chemicals. Dialysis patients generally use the machine for about four hours, three times a week. The technicians prepare patients for dialysis, monitor them and the machine during dialysis, and perform required procedures when dialysis is completed. Dialysis technicians help patients feel comfortable during the procedure and keep the machine in good working condition.

Most dialysis technicians work in hospitals under the supervision of a registered nurse. Others work in dialysis units run by private companies.

Education and Training Requirements

You need a high school diploma to become a dialysis technician. Various community colleges, vocational schools, and training centers across the country offer programs leading to certification. Courses in science and health are useful, as is volunteer or part-time work in a hospital. Mechanical ability is also important in this job.

Dialysis technicians train on the job. In a hospital they are taught how to operate the machine by a registered nurse. Companies that have dialysis units may also offer training.

Getting the Job

You can apply directly to hospitals or companies that have dialysis units. In addition, check state and private employment services for job listings and information.

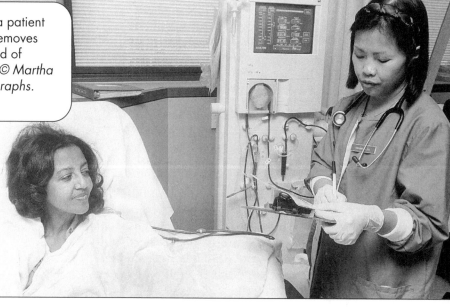

A dialysis technician monitors a patient on a dialysis machine, which removes waste substances from the blood of people with kidney problems. (© Martha Tabor/Working Images Photographs. Reproduced by permission.)

Advancement Possibilities and Employment Outlook

Advancement is possible with education and experience. Technicians working in large dialysis units may become chief technicians. With further training, some dialysis technicians become biomedical equipment technicians.

The employment outlook is very good through the year 2012. The field is growing steadily and there is a need for qualified workers.

Working Conditions

Technicians work forty hours a week. They often work with people who need understanding and encouragement. They must be careful workers who can keep calm in a medical emergency.

Earnings and Benefits

Salaries vary with experience. In 2005 salaries for dialysis technicians ranged from $25,682 to $32,413. Benefits include paid holidays and vacations, sick leave, and health insurance.

Where to Go for More Information

National Association of Nephrology
  Technicians/Technologists
PO Box 2307
Dayton, OH 45401-2307
(877) 607-6268
http://www.dialysistech.org

National Kidney Foundation
30 E. 33rd St.
New York, NY 10016
(800) 622-9010
http://www.kidney.org

Home Health Aide

Definition and Nature of the Work

Home health aides provide health care services in homes. Their clients include the elderly or people with long-term illnesses or disabilities. Home health aides work for hospitals and health care agencies.

Health aides provide a variety of services for their clients. They give them baths and massages and change bandages if necessary. Sometimes they help them to get dressed, do exercises, and get in and out of bed. Aides see that their clients take their medicine, although they cannot prescribe drugs themselves.

Aides often help with household chores. They may change bed linens and do some light laundry or cleaning. Sometimes they take clients for walks or rides. They may read to them or just keep them company.

In some cases, home health aides instruct clients and their families in health care. For example, they may teach a new mother how to care for her baby, or they may show parents how to help a handicapped child. Sometimes aides move into a client's home for a period of time.

Education and Training
Varies—see profile

Salary
Median—$8.81 per hour

Employment Outlook
Excellent

Education and Training Requirements

Some employers prefer to hire high school graduates, but a high school diploma is not necessary to enter this field. Volunteer work and part-time or summer jobs in hospitals are good experience. Training courses for home health aides are generally about two to three weeks long. Hospitals, adult education schools, health departments, and volunteer agencies offer these courses. Many home health

aides receive on-the-job training under the supervision of a registered nurse. Federal law suggests seventy-five hours of both classroom and practical training. Some states require home health aides to be certified. The federal government also has guidelines for home health aides whose employers receive reimbursement from Medicare. They must pass a competency test covering twelve areas that include reading and recording vital signs, basic nutrition, personal hygiene and grooming, and knowledge of emergency procedures. Aides must be in good health. They should also be patient, understanding, and cheerful.

Getting the Job

Apply to local health care agencies or to hospitals for jobs. You can also check newspaper want ads and job banks on the Internet. State and private employment agencies may also list openings for home health aides.

Advancement Possibilities and Employment Outlook

With further education, a home health aide can become a teaching health aide or a licensed practical nurse. The employment outlook for home health aides is expected to grow faster than the average through the year 2014. In fact, it is expected to be one of the fastest-growing occupations. This trend reflects several developments. First, hospitals are making an increased effort to contain costs by moving patients out of hospitals quickly without compromising their health. Second, studies have shown that treatment often proves to be more effective in familiar rather than clinical surroundings. Third, improvements in portable medical technology have made in-home treatment a feasible alternative to hospitalization. Finally, an increase in the elderly population is certain in the years ahead. This should provide many openings in this field and a shortage of workers.

Working Conditions

Home health aides generally work a forty-hour week. They might spend four hours at one home in the morning and four hours at another in the afternoon.

Part-time work is sometimes available. Aides are sometimes needed on weekends and overnight. Aides work with many different kinds of people and in many different kinds of homes. Some aides might live with a client for a period of time to provide round-the-clock care.

Earnings and Benefits

Earnings vary depending on experience. In 2004 the median hourly earnings for aides was $8.81 per hour. Most aides are paid on a per-visit basis, and most employers do not supply benefits. Aides are not usually paid for their travel time going from one client to another.

Where to Go for More Information

American Hospital Association
325 7th St. NW
Washington, DC 20004-2802
(202) 638-1100
http://www.aha.org/aha

National Association for Home Care & Hospice
228 7th St. SE
Washington, DC 20003
(202) 547-7424
http://www.nahc.org

Laboratory Animal Care Worker

Definition and Nature of the Work

Laboratory animal care workers take care of animals that are used in scientific research. Laboratory animal care workers include assistant laboratory animal technicians, laboratory animal technicians, and laboratory animal technologists.

Scientists use laboratory animals for a variety of purposes. Sometimes laboratory animals are used in the classroom for teaching purposes. They are also used for testing drugs and other substances, and for basic medical and non-medical scientific research. Some scientists study animals to learn about animal behavior and intelligence. Animal care workers help scientists and carry out their instructions.

Laboratory animal care workers look after a wide variety of animals, including mice, guinea pigs, rats, rabbits, monkeys, dogs, birds, insects, frogs, snakes, and fish. Animal care workers provide food and water for the animals and keep their cages clean. They check for signs of illness, injury, or disease. They also maintain careful records on each animal regarding such things as diet, weight, medication, and behavior. They may also order food and supplies for the animals. Sometimes they take samples from the animals and help scientists or medical doctors perform experiments.

Some laboratory animal care workers are veterinarian's assistants. They may administer medication orally or by injection, treat minor wounds, and prepare animals for surgery.

Education and Training Requirements

A high school education is usually required for unskilled jobs in laboratories. Courses in science, particularly biology, are helpful. Some laboratories provide on-the-job training. Many community colleges and technical schools offer two-year programs in animal care. Certification is available from the American Association for Laboratory Animal Science (AALAS), but it is not required for work. There are three levels of certification: assistant laboratory animal technician, laboratory animal technician, and laboratory animal technologist. For each level of certification there are age, education, experience, and examination requirements.

Education and Training
High school

Salary
Median—$7.86 per hour

Employment Outlook
Very good

Laboratory animal care workers need a knowledge of animals' eating and sleeping habits. They should enjoy working with animals and be able to follow directions carefully.

Getting the Job

You can apply directly to medical schools, drug companies, research centers, universities, or animal hospitals. Your school placement office may also have a list of openings. Some laboratories place want ads in the newspapers or in job banks on the Internet.

Advancement Possibilities and Employment Outlook

With training and experience, laboratory animal care workers can become supervisors, research assistants, or animal breeders. The employment outlook is expected to grow faster than the average through the year 2014. Drug companies, medical schools, and research centers are employing increasing numbers of technicians to help them with experiments. At the same time, a growing concern for animal welfare is leading many commercial product companies to limit or eliminate their animal-testing activities.

Working Conditions

Laboratory animal care workers usually work forty hours a week. Sometimes they must work nights and weekends. Working areas are usually well lighted and pleasant. However, animal care workers are exposed to unpleasant smells. They spend most of their time working with animals rather than with people.

Earnings and Benefits

Salaries vary depending on education and experience. In 2004 the median salary for laboratory animal care workers was $7.86 per hour. Benefits include paid holidays and vacations, health insurance, sick leave, and sometimes retirement plans and free tuition.

Where to Go for More Information

American Association for Laboratory
 Animal Science
9190 Crestwyn Hills Dr.
Memphis, TN 38125-8538
(901) 754-8620
http://www.aalas.org

American College of Laboratory Animal
 Medicine
96 Chester St.
Chester, NH 03036
(603) 887-2467
http://www.aclam.org

Nursing Aide and Orderly

Education and Training
High school

Salary
Average—$10.09 per hour

Employment Outlook
Very good

Definition and Nature of the Work

Nursing aides and orderlies help nurses care for patients by doing routine tasks. They help keep patients comfortable and tend to their basic needs. Aides and orderlies generally spend most of their time with patients, carrying meal trays to them, answering call lights when patients signal for help, and helping to move them when necessary. Aides and orderlies make beds, give baths and massages, and fill water pitchers and ice bags. They may also perform routine tests, such as taking a patient's temperature, pulse, and blood pressure. Sometimes aides and orderlies do light cleaning, distribute linens, set up equipment, deliver messages, and assemble meal trays for patients who are on special diets.

Many nursing aides and orderlies work in hospitals. An increasing number work in nursing homes and long-term care facilities for elderly people. Some work with psychiatric patients and are called psychiatric aides.

Some nursing aides are hospice workers. They provide terminally ill patients with services that range from companionship to personal care. Most hospice programs offer patients care in either their homes or in a residential facility, so the hospice nursing aide may work in either environment.

Education and Training Requirements

Often there are no specific educational requirements for these jobs, but in many cases a high school diploma is required. Aides and orderlies are usually trained on the job under the supervision of a registered nurse or a licensed practical nurse. Training generally lasts from one week to three months. Some high schools, vocational institutions, community colleges, and nursing care facilities also offer courses. Volunteer jobs in hospitals are good experience, as are courses in home nursing and first aid.

Federal regulations require all nursing aides who work in nursing homes that receive Medicare and Medicaid to complete a state-approved training program, pass a competency test, and receive certification from the state in which they work. The training program must be at least seventy-five hours, including sixteen hours of supervised clinical training, and be state-approved. Each year, certified nursing aides must complete twelve hours of continuing education to maintain their certification. Hospice workers almost always must be listed on the state's Nurse Aide Registry, which requires passing the state competency test. In addition, hospice nursing aides usually have specialized instruction in caring for terminally ill patients.

Nursing aides assist with many tasks including recording information about changes in patients' conditions. (© Julie Fisher Photography Limited/ zefa/Corbis.)

Getting the Job

Apply directly to the hospitals or nursing homes in which you want to work. Contact hospices in your area if you choose hospice work. You can also check newspaper want ads and job banks on the Internet. State and private employment agencies sometimes list openings for nursing aides and orderlies.

Advancement Possibilities and Employment Outlook

Aides and orderlies can advance with further education. Some train to be licensed practical nurses while working part time as aides or orderlies. Others may learn to operate specialized equipment, such as electrocardiograph machines.

The number of positions is expected to grow faster than average through 2014 as the elderly population increases and the demand for health care services continues to grow. High turnover in this occupation also creates frequent openings.

Working Conditions

Nursing aides and orderlies generally work forty hours a week. This usually includes some night or weekend work. The surroundings are generally quiet and clean. Aides perform many tasks and may spend much of their day standing and walking. They often have unpleasant duties and may have to deal with uncooperative patients. However, helping others can be a rewarding experience.

Since they work with sick people, aides and orderlies need to be patient and understanding. They should be healthy and responsible. They should also be able to stay calm in emergencies.

Earnings and Benefits

Salaries vary with experience and place of employment. In 2004 the median salary for nursing aides and orderlies was $10.09 per hour. Benefits usually include health insurance and paid holidays and vacations.

Optometric Assistant

Education and Training
High school

Salary
$12,000 to $30,000
per year

Employment Outlook
Excellent

Definition and Nature of the Work

Optometric assistants perform routine tasks in optometrists' offices. Their work enables optometrists to devote their time to patient care that requires specialized training. Optometric assistants do clerical work, such as bookkeeping and scheduling appointments. They also help the optometrist during eye examinations.

Optometrists give their patients eye examinations for vision, color blindness, and eye pressure. When the tests are completed, an optometrist can prescribe the necessary eyeglasses for the patient. Optometric assistants often prepare patients for the tests. They may put drops in patients' eyes or direct and seat patients at eye-testing machines.

Assistants may explain eye exercises to patients or teach them how to use contact lenses. In some offices, optometric assistants help people choose the frames for their glasses. When the eyeglasses are made, optometric assistants adjust them for a proper fit.

Some assistants work in laboratories that fill prescriptions for eyeglasses. They put lenses into frames or repair broken frames. Most optometric assistants work in private offices. Some work in health clinics or for government agencies. Others are employed by companies that make optical instruments.

Education and Training Requirements

Optometric assistants should have a high school diploma or its equivalent. Most are trained on the job. Optometrists prefer applicants who are accurate and able to work well with delicate and breakable tools and materials.

There are also formal training programs for this work. Some technical schools, community colleges, and colleges of optometry offer one-year programs. Training for optometric assistants generally includes secretarial and office skills as well as medical procedures. The Paraoptometric Section of the American Optometric Association certifies optometric assistants who pass their written exams.

Getting the Job

If you attend a training program, your school placement office can give you job information. If you do not have training, contact optometrists in your community and ask about on-the-job training. To get a government job, apply to take the necessary civil service test. State and private employment offices can also provide information about employment opportunities. You should also check newspaper want ads and job banks on the Internet for listings.

Advancement Possibilities and Employment Outlook

An assistant may train with an optometrist who specializes in a field such as contact lenses. Learning a specialty will enable the assistant to get a better-paying job.

The employment outlook is excellent through the year 2010. Job openings will be created by the coverage of eye care services through public and private insurance programs and the new, more economical eye care chains. Also, the growth of the older population is certain to assure the need for qualified optometric assistants. Opportunities will be best for people who have completed a formal training program.

Working Conditions

Most optometric assistants work in modern, well-lighted offices and laboratories. Offices can be very busy at times. However, the work area is usually quiet and clean. Optometric assistants work under the direct supervision of an optometrist. They must enjoy working with people because they usually have a lot of contact with patients. Work hours vary, but assistants typically work about forty hours a week. They may be required to work on evenings and Saturdays. Many optometric assistants work part time.

Earnings and Benefits

According to a 2002 American Optometric Association survey, annual salaries for optometric assistants ranged from less than $12,000 to more than $30,000. More than half of survey respondents reported annual salaries above $20,000. Benefits generally include paid holidays and vacations and health insurance.

Where to Go for More Information

American Optometric Association
243 N. Lindbergh Blvd.
St. Louis, MO 63141-7851
(314) 991-4100
http://www.aoanet.org

Psychiatric Aide

Definition and Nature of the Work

Psychiatric aides provide routine care for mentally impaired or emotionally disturbed patients. Psychiatric aides are also called mental health assistants or psychiatric nursing assistants. They work under the supervision of a mental health team that may include psychiatrists, psychologists, and social workers.

Aides help patients bathe, dress, and eat. They escort patients to examinations, treatments, therapy, and recreation. Aides also spend a great deal of time socializing with patients. They may play cards or games with patients, watch television with them, or lead group outings. Since psychiatric aides spend so much time interacting with patients, their observations on patient behavior are valuable to the rest of the staff.

Education and Training Requirements

There are no formal educational requirements to become a psychiatric aide, although many employers prefer to hire high school graduates. High school courses in the social and biological sciences are beneficial.

Some employers, especially hospitals, require job applicants to have previous training or experience. Other employers provide informal on-the-job training. Some states require psychiatric aides to complete a formal training program and obtain certification.

Getting the Job

School placement officers or counselors can offer assistance in finding job openings. The local office of the state employment agency can provide current listings of available jobs. You also can apply directly to the personnel offices of mental health facilities or hospitals.

Advancement Possibilities and Employment Outlook

Advancement opportunities for psychiatric aides/technicians are somewhat limited. After gaining experience, psychiatric aides may become senior aides, helping to train new workers. Most advancement, however, requires additional formal training and education.

Employment of psychiatric aides is expected to grow more slowly than average through the year 2014. However, employment will rise due to the increase in the number of older people, who often require mental health services, and to a more accepting attitude toward those needing mental health care. Employment for psychiatric aides is likely to decline in hospitals, due to attempts to cut costs by limiting in-patient treatment. As a result, job growth should increase in residential psychiatric facilities and with home health care agencies.

Working Conditions

Most psychiatric aides work in the psychiatric units of hospitals, private psychiatric facilities, state or county mental institutions, or community mental health clinics. They generally work a forty-hour week, but often must be available to work night, weekend, and holiday shifts. Many aides work only on a part-time basis.

Work as a psychiatric aide can be physically and emotionally demanding. Aides stand for long hours and may have to lift or move patients. Sometimes they must deal with disoriented, disturbed, or even violent patients. It is important for aides to be calm, patient, and caring.

Earnings and Benefits

Salaries vary depending on the type of employer and the geographic location. Median earnings for full-time psychiatric aides was $11.19 per hour in 2004. Aides who work night or weekend shifts generally earn more than those on day shifts. Most full-time aides employed by hospitals or state facilities receive medical benefits, paid holidays, sick leave, and paid vacation time.

Where to Go for More Information

National Institute of Mental Health
6001 Executive Blvd., Rm 8184,
   MSC 9663
Bethesda, MD 20892-9663
(866) 615-6464
http://www.nimh.nih.gov

Substance Abuse Counselor

Definition and Nature of the Work

Substance abuse counselors help people who have problems related to alcohol and other drugs. They counsel addicts as well as those who are afraid they might become addicts. They also help former addicts. Sometimes they counsel the families, friends, and loved ones of addicts, whose lives are inevitably affected by the problem.

Addiction counselors, as they are sometimes called, usually help with practical problems. For example, a counselor might help a former addict find a job. Counselors do not prescribe medicine or provide medical or psychological therapy. Substance abuse counselors are often supervised by doctors, psychologists, or social workers.

Some of these counselors work in halfway houses, where addicts live while they are under treatment. Counselors may also work in outpatient clinics where people come in on a regular basis for treatment. Other counselors work in hospitals, treatment centers, or human service agencies. Sometimes these counselors are former substance abusers themselves who have learned from their mistakes and want to help others. Substance abuse counselors hold counseling sessions for one person or for a group of people. At these sessions counselors try to help addicts talk about, understand, and cope with their problems.

Education and Training Requirements

A minimum of a high school diploma is usually required for this field of work. Counselors generally are trained on the job. Training programs vary in length from six weeks to two years. Some colleges also offer training programs for counselors. These programs usually last two years and include courses on the effects of alcohol and other drugs. Students may also learn crisis intervention—a way of handling emergency situations. Emergencies may involve emotional or medical problems. Graduates of these programs usually receive an associate's degree. Certification is also available from the National Board for Certified Counselors. For some positions, a bachelor's degree or higher in sociology, psychology, or a related field may be required. An increasing number of substance abuse counselors are getting their master's degrees in mental health counseling.

Education and Training
High school

Salary
Median—$32,960 per year

Employment Outlook
Very good

Substance abuse counselors help people who have alcohol or drug dependencies talk about, understand, and cope with their problems. (© Martha Tabor/ Working Images Photographs. Reproduced by permission.)

Getting the Job

You can apply for a job at a halfway house, treatment center, hospital, or clinic that offers substance abuse counseling. Your school placement office may be able to give you job information. Also check state and private employment agencies. Newspaper want ads and job banks on the Internet sometimes list jobs for substance abuse counselors.

Advancement Possibilities and Employment Outlook

Substance abuse counselors who have a high school diploma or an associate's degree can advance to the position of director of a halfway house. However, most other advanced jobs in the field of substance abuse, such as rehabilitation counselors or social workers, require at least a bachelor's degree. For other jobs, such as psychologist, the minimum education requirement is a master's degree. The employment outlook is expected to grow faster than the average for counselors through the year 2014 because addicts are increasingly being sent for therapy and rehabilitation rather than to jail.

Working Conditions

Most substance abuse counselors work a forty-hour week. Some live in halfway houses. The work can be tense and sometimes frustrating. Counselors work closely with other people and should enjoy helping others.

Where to Go for More Information

National Association of Alcoholism and
   Drug Abuse Counselors
901 N. Washington St., Ste. 600
Alexandria, VA 22314
(800) 548-0497
http://naadac.org

Earnings and Benefits

The median annual earnings of substance abuse counselors in 2004 was $32,960. Salaries vary depending on education, experience, and level of responsibility. The lowest 10 percent earned less than $21,060, while the highest 10 percent, who held bachelor's and master's degrees, earned more than $49,600. Benefits usually include paid holidays and vacations, health insurance, and retirement plans.

AIDS Counselor

Definition and Nature of the Work

AIDS (acquired immunodeficiency syndrome) is a disorder of the immune system caused by infection with the human immunodeficiency virus (HIV). There is no cure for AIDS. Although research is ongoing, there is no vaccine that can protect people from infection. HIV is transmitted via contaminated blood or blood products. There are a variety of ways to become infected. The two most frequent ways are by having unprotected sexual intercourse with an infected person or by sharing contaminated needles during intravenous (IV) drug use. A baby can be infected by an infected mother during birth. Medical personnel and law enforcement officials can be infected by the contaminated blood of patients or criminals.

AIDS counselors provide information about AIDS and instruction for AIDS prevention to the public and in the workplace. AIDS counselors help individuals determine their risk of acquiring and transmitting HIV. Some AIDS counselors talk to people who are about to have an AIDS test. They help patients understand the meaning of the test results. Others support and assist those diagnosed with AIDS, leading individual and family counseling sessions. Still others lead support groups for those who have lost friends and family to the disease, and for those who feel they are at risk.

Education and Training
Varies—see profile

Salary
Median—$34,820 per year

Employment Outlook
Varies—see profile

An AIDS counselor provides support and assistance to a man suffering from AIDS. (© Martha Tabor/Working Images Photographs. Reproduced by permission.)

One of the responsibilities of an AIDS counselor is to provide practical advice to people with AIDS on how to cope with their daily lives and the problems they may encounter. This may include finding housing, medical services, and legal advisers.

Volunteers play an important part in assisting organizations that counsel people with AIDS. They may become "buddies," visiting AIDS patients in their homes and assisting with household tasks. Others work for telephone hotlines and provide information about AIDS testing. Many are involved in administrative tasks that help these organizations operate.

Education and Training Requirements

There is no formal training to become a volunteer AIDS counselor. Experience is often more important than education. The best way to gain experience is to become a volunteer with an organization that cares for people with AIDS. Most organizations provide initial training for volunteers, and many provide follow-up sessions. Paid positions are usually filled by people with master's degrees in the field of mental health or social work. These people often have counseling experience in substance abuse.

Getting the Job

Organizations that work with people who have AIDS rely on volunteers. The best way to get a job in this field is to apply directly to these organizations as a volunteer. Your school placement office may be able to give you information about paid positions. You can also apply to hospitals and hospices in areas where there are large numbers of AIDS patients.

Advancement Possibilities and Employment Outlook

Experienced AIDS counselors with master's degrees can advance to administrative positions. Some may become AIDS educators who write, organize, and deliver information to the public. Others become training specialists and design training programs for volunteers and professionals. Within organizations counselors may become project coordinators, project directors, or regional directors.

The number of new AIDS cases each year has leveled off in the past decade. Advances in drug regimens for AIDS patients allow AIDS patients to live longer. Therefore, the cumulative number of persons living with AIDS has been increasing each year. Thus, the demand for volunteer AIDS counselors remains high, but paid positions will depend on private and government funding. Job opportunities will be most plentiful for those with master's degrees and experience in a related field.

Working Conditions

AIDS counselors in paid positions usually work a forty-hour week. Some work in hospitals and mental health clinics. Those who work in hospices work in pleasant surroundings. Many volunteers and counselors also visit AIDS patients in their homes, which may be in poor inner-city areas.

People suffering from AIDS are under severe emotional and physical stress, which often affects their interaction with AIDS counselors. Therefore, AIDS counselors must be able to work with people who are very ill and severely depressed due to the effects of the disease.

Earnings and Benefits

Many AIDS counselors are volunteers and do not receive a salary. For those in paid positions, salaries are similar to those of other social workers. In 2004 the median salary of social workers was $34,820 per year. Salaries are generally higher for private practitioners, administrators, and researchers. Benefits for those working for hospitals and public health departments generally include paid vacations and holidays, health insurance, and retirement plans.

Where to Go for More Information

American Psychological Association
Office on AIDS
750 First St. NE
Washington, DC 20002-4242
(202) 336-6052
http://www.apa.org/pi/aids

American Public Health Association
800 I St. NW
Washington, DC 20001-3710
(202) 777-APHA
http://www.apha.org

Ambulance Driver

Definition and Nature of the Work

Ambulance drivers and other ambulance personnel are often the first members of the medical team to reach a person in need of medical attention. Ambulance drivers operate vehicles that carry sick people and accident victims to hospitals. Ambulance drivers work for hospitals and for police, fire, and community first aid squads. They also work for private ambulance companies that provide emergency or invalid carrier service. Invalid carrier service is provided in a variety of situations, such as bringing a recovering patient from a hospital to a nursing home. In some communities, a large percentage of the ambulance drivers are volunteers. Some drivers, however, are salaried.

Education and Training
License and training

Salary
Median—$24,722 per year

Employment Outlook
Excellent

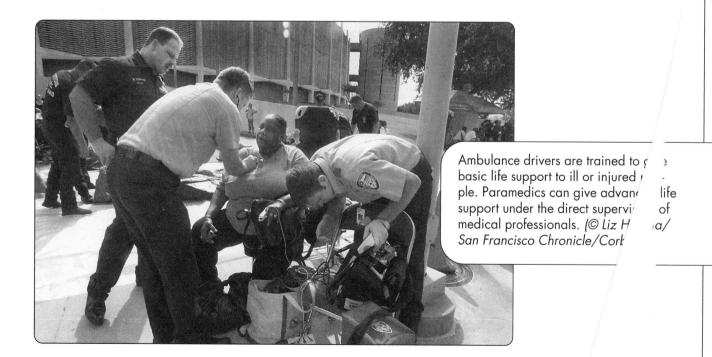

Ambulance drivers are trained to give basic life support to ill or injured people. Paramedics can give advanced life support under the direct supervision of medical professionals. (© Liz H___a/ San Francisco Chronicle/Cork___

Ambulance drivers are often trained to serve as emergency medical technicians (EMTs). EMTs are able to give certain kinds of emergency care, which is called basic life support, when they reach a patient. Various levels of EMT training provide workers with basic, intermediate, or advanced skills. The most highly skilled EMTs are called paramedics.

Education and Training Requirements

Ambulance drivers must be at least eighteen years old, licensed to drive a bus, and have a good driving record. Some are required to have the Red Cross first-aid training certificate. To become an EMT or paramedic as well, ambulance drivers must complete a formal training program and become certified. They must be recertified every two years.

Getting the Job

You can apply directly to your local ambulance service or hospital for a job. If you are in school, ask your school's placement office for help in finding a job.

Advancement Possibilities and Employment Outlook

Ambulance drivers can advance to become EMTs or paramedics with the appropriate training and certification.

The employment of ambulance drivers, EMTs, and paramedics is expected to grow much faster than average through 2014. Municipal government and private ambulance services will provide the best opportunities for qualified ambulance drivers.

Where to Go for More Information

American Ambulance Association
8201 Greensboro Dr., Ste. 300
McLean, VA 22102
(800) 523-4447
http://www.the-aaa.org

National Association of Emergency
  Medical Technicians
PO Box 1400
Clinton, MS 39060-1400
(800) 34-NAEMT
http://www.naemt.org

Working Conditions

Ambulance drivers usually work forty hours a week. They work irregular hours including nights, weekends, and holidays. Since many ambulance calls involve matters of life and death, drivers work under intense pressure. Ambulance drivers may have to perform physically strenuous duties. The work is demanding and requires a high degree of commitment.

Earnings and Benefits

In early 2006 ambulance drivers earned a median salary of $24,722. Benefits usually include paid holidays and vacations, health insurance, and retirement plans.

Biomedical Equipment Technician

Definition and Nature of the Work

Biomedical equipment technicians specialize in the use, maintenance, and repair of medical equipment such as heart-lung machines, dialysis machines, medical imaging machines, and defibrillators. Unlike electrocardiograph and electroencephalograph technicians, who specialize in one type of equipment, biomedical equipment technicians are familiar with many different kinds of machines. Biomedical equipment technicians work in hospitals and research organizations. They also work for manufacturers' sales departments and for research and development departments. Most technicians work under the direction of biomedical engineers.

In hospitals, biomedical equipment technicians may become experts at using certain pieces of equipment. Some technicians work in several departments with many different kinds of equipment. Technicians teach nurses, therapists, and other members of the hospital staff to operate the machines. They inspect new equipment to make sure that the machinery operates properly.

Technicians make minor repairs on equipment at the hospital. When equipment must be sent back to the manufacturer for major repairs, they write an analysis of the problem so the manufacturer can fix and return the equipment quickly. Technicians also maintain detailed records on the use and condition of all equipment.

Education and Training Requirements

You need one to three years of training after high school to become a biomedical equipment technician. Training courses are available at junior and community colleges. These colleges generally work closely with local hospitals and medical equipment manufacturers. During the training period, students learn how to operate and repair many different types of medical equipment. After they have completed their formal training, technicians must keep up with new developments in the field.

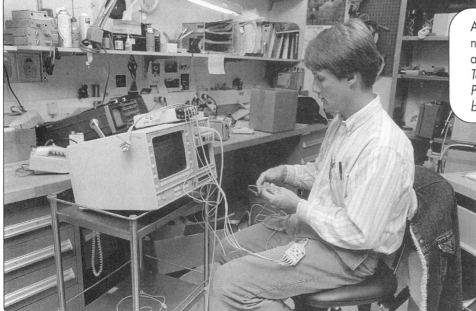

A biomedical equipment technician repairs a heart monitor at a hospital. (© Martha Tabor/Working Images Photographs. Reproduced by permission.)

The Association for the Advancement of Medical Instrumentation issues certification for biomedical equipment technicians. In order to qualify, technicians must pass a test given by the association. Many employers prefer to hire technicians who have certification.

Getting the Job

Your school placement office can help you find a job. You can also apply directly to hospitals, biomedical equipment manufacturers, and research organizations. Your state employment office may list openings. Also check newspaper want ads and job banks on the Internet for employment opportunities.

Advancement Possibilities and Employment Outlook

Biomedical equipment technicians can become biomedical engineers with at least a bachelor's degree and specialized biomedical training. Biomedical engineers research and design biomedical equipment.

The employment outlook is expected to grow as fast as the average through the year 2014. Research and development expenditures are expected to increase, and the rapid development and wide use of biomedical equipment should increase the need for biomedical equipment technicians. The companies that make the equipment have the greatest need for these technicians. Trained workers will also be needed in hospitals and research organizations.

Working Conditions

Technicians work with highly trained doctors and engineers. They must be able to communicate their mechanical knowledge to others. Most technicians work in or near large cities where medical facilities and companies are located.

Hours vary for technicians depending on where they work. Hospital technicians generally work eight-hour shifts. They may have to work at night or on weekends. Those employed by research organizations or manufacturing companies usually work regular hours.

Earnings and Benefits

Earnings vary depending on the employer and the type of work done. The median salary for technicians who service equipment was $17.90 per hour in 2004. Benefits include paid holidays and vacations, health insurance, and retirement plans.

Where to Go for More Information

Association for the Advancement of
   Medical Instrumentation
1110 N. Glebe Rd., Ste. 220
Arlington, VA 22201-4795
(800) 332-2264
http://www.aami.org

Biomedical Engineering Society
8401 Corporate Dr., Ste. 140
Landover, MD 20785-2224
(310) 459-1999
http://www.bmes.org

Cardiac Monitor Technician

Definition and Nature of the Work

Cardiac monitor technicians check the heart rhythm patterns of patients to detect abnormal pattern variations. They usually work in the intensive care or cardiac care units of hospitals. These technicians are responsible for reviewing patients' records to determine normal heart rhythms. They monitor current patterns and note any deviations. To do this, technicians use instruments called calipers to measure the length and height of a patient's heart rhythm pattern on graphic tape readouts. Cardiac monitor technicians observe the cardiac monitor screen and listen for an alarm to identify any abnormal heart rhythm variation. They notify nurses and doctors when medical attention is needed.

Education and Training Requirements

Most cardiac monitor technicians are trained on the job in hospital programs that last from one month to a year. A high school diploma or its equivalent is required for acceptance into a hospital's training program. Courses in health, biology, and computer technology are recommended.

Getting the Job

You can consult high school guidance counselors for information on job openings at hospitals, or you can contact hospitals directly. Students who have participated in field internships may be hired upon graduation by the hospital where they trained.

Advancement Possibilities and Employment Outlook

Cardiac monitor technicians advance by learning to perform more complex specialty procedures. With additional training, education, and experience, cardiac monitor technicians can become cardiovascular or cardiopulmonary technicians or cardiology technologists. Advancement to supervisory or training positions is also possible.

Job openings for cardiac monitor technicians are expected to decline through the year 2010. This decline is due primarily to the increased efficiency of the machines and equipment used, which require fewer technicians to perform an increasing number of tests. Those with the most training and experience will have the best opportunities.

Working Conditions

Technicians usually work a standard five-day, forty-hour week, in clean and quiet surroundings. Occasionally they are expected to work weekends and evenings, and those in smaller hospitals may be on twenty-four-hour call for emergencies.

Because they work with people who are ill or anxious about their health, technicians must be patient, reassuring, alert to emergencies, and able to cope with responsibility. Most of all, they must be able to remain calm under pressure.

Education and Training
High school plus training

Salary
Median—$26,513 per year

Employment Outlook
Poor

Where to Go for More Information

American College of Cardiology
9111 Old Georgetown Rd.
Bethesda, MD 20814-1699
(800) 253-4636
http://www.acc.org

Alliance of Cardiovascular Professionals
Thalia Landing Offices, Bldg. 2
4356 Bonney Rd., Ste. 103
Virginia Beach, VA 23452-1200
(757) 497-1225
http://www.acp-online.org

Earnings and Benefits

In early 2006 the median salary for cardiac monitor technicians was $26,513 per year. Cardiac monitor technicians usually receive benefits that include hospitalization insurance, paid sick leave, and paid vacations. Some hospitals also provide pension plans, uniform allowances, and tuition assistance for further education.

Cardiology Technologist

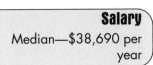

Education and Training
High school plus training

Salary
Median—$38,690 per year

Employment Outlook
Excellent

Definition and Nature of the Work

Cardiology technologists work in hospital cardiology departments, cardiac rehabilitation centers, clinics, doctors' offices, or medical schools. They help doctors diagnose and treat disorders of the heart and blood vessels. Cardiology technologists specialize in invasive procedures—those in which the body is entered—and help doctors with cardiac catheterizations. In these procedures, a small tube (catheter) is threaded through a patient's artery from the groin to the heart. The procedure can determine whether a vessel that supplies blood to the heart is blocked. Part of the procedure may involve treating blockages.

Cardiology technologists prepare patients for cardiac catheterization. After positioning the patient on an examining table, the technologist shaves, cleans, and numbs the top of the leg near the groin. During the procedure, the technologist monitors the patient's blood pressure and heart rate. Technologists also may prepare and monitor patients during open-heart surgery and other heart-related procedures. Some cardiac technologists run noninvasive tests as well, such as the electrocardiogram (EKG).

To take an EKG, a cardiology technologist (also known as an EKG technician) fastens disk-like electrodes to the patient's chest, arms, and legs. During this process, the technologist explains the procedure to the patient and tries to make the patient feel comfortable. This helps to limit faulty readings, which can be caused by stress, among other things. Once the electrodes are in place, the technologist operates the controls on the EKG machine, allowing the electrodes to pick up electronic signals from the heart and transmit them to the machine. The machine is equipped with a special pen, or stylus, that records the heartbeat patterns on graph paper.

EKG technicians with additional training can administer more advanced types of cardiovascular tests. Holter monitoring involves a twenty-four- to forty-eight-hour surveillance of a patient going about a normal daily routine—sitting, standing, eating, and sleeping. Electrodes are placed on the patient's chest, and a portable cassette monitor is strapped to the patient's waist. At the end of the testing period, the cassette is scanned and printed for a physician to interpret.

EKG technicians with additional training may also administer the treadmill stress test. After taking a patient's medical history, resting heartbeat, and blood pressure, the technologist asks the patient to start walking slowly on a treadmill. The technologist gradually increases the treadmill's speed while monitoring the performance of the patient's heart. The treadmill stress test is a way of determining the effect of increased exertion on a patient's heart.

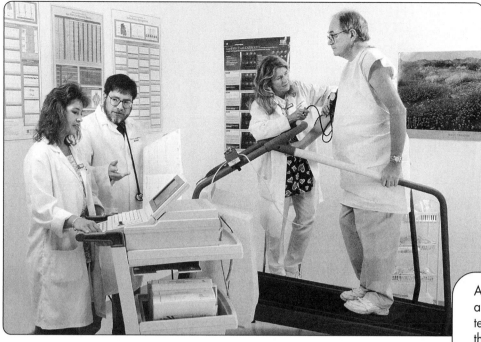

A cardiology technologist administers a treadmill stress test. This determines the effect that increased exertion has on a patient's heart. (© Brownie Harris/Corbis.)

Education and Training Requirements

You must have a high school diploma to become a cardiology technologist. Some cardiology technologists get on-the-job training in hospitals, which generally lasts from eight to sixteen weeks. However, most graduate from two-year community college or technical school programs, and some from four-year programs. Recommended high school courses include health, biology, anatomy, and mathematics. Certification is offered by the American Cardiology Technologists Association.

Getting the Job

You can apply directly to hospitals, cardiac rehab centers, clinics, doctors' offices, or medical schools for job openings. Check with your school placement office. Also check state and private employment services for openings for cardiology technologists.

Advancement Possibilities and Employment Outlook

Doctors are using EKGs more frequently as part of routine physical examinations. In large hospitals, cardiology technologists can become supervisors of other technologists. As they gain more experience and training, they can move into better-paying jobs as skilled technicians. Opportunities are best for cardiology technologists who learn how to do more complex procedures.

The employment outlook for cardiology technologists is excellent, with job growth expected to be much faster than average through the year 2014. Growth will occur as the population ages, because people who are middle-aged and older have more heart problems than young people do. Registered nurses and other office personnel in hospitals are being trained to perform basic EKG procedures because newer equipment is more efficient and easier to use. Opportunities will be best for technologists who have training in the more advanced tests such as Holter monitoring and stress testing.

Working Conditions

Cardiology technologists generally work forty hours a week, sometimes on weekends. They may also be on call at night and on weekends. They usually work in clean, pleasant surroundings and are recognized as an important part of the medical team. They work closely with doctors and nurses as well as with patients. An important part of a cardiology technologist's job is putting patients at ease before and during the procedure. A technologist should be calm, confident, and sympathetic.

Earnings and Benefits

Salaries vary with education and experience. Registered cardiology technologists earned a median income of $38,690 in 2004. Those with more experience and those who are trained to perform more advanced tests can earn more. Most employers offer paid vacations, sick leave, pensions, and health insurance.

Where to Go for More Information

Association for the Advancement of Medical Instrumentation
1110 N. Glebe Rd., Ste. 220
Arlington, VA 22201-4795
(800) 332-2264
http://www.aami.org

National Health Council
1730 M St. NW, Ste. 500
Washington, DC 20036
(202) 785-3910
http://www.nationalhealthcouncil.org

Clinical Laboratory Technician

Education and Training
High school plus training

Salary
Median—$30,840 per year

Employment Outlook
Excellent

Definition and Nature of the Work

Clinical laboratory technicians are also known as medical technicians or medical laboratory technicians. They conduct laboratory tests that aid in the detection, diagnosis, and treatment of disease. Clinical laboratory technicians are supervised by clinical laboratory technologists and physicians, such as pathologists. (Pathologists specialize in the diagnosis of disease.)

Most clinical laboratory technicians work in hospitals. Some work in research institutes and clinics. Others are employed in commercial medical laboratories that run tests for doctors and hospitals on a fee basis.

Clinical laboratory technicians perform routine tasks in the laboratory. For example, they collect samples of blood and urine, label them, and conduct simple tests on them. They sterilize instruments; prepare, stain, and label slides; and keep records of tests. Clinical laboratory technicians also perform tests involved in blood banking. For example, they may help to determine a donor's blood type. They may work in several areas of the clinical laboratory or specialize in just one.

Histotechnicians prepare slides of body tissue for examination by clinical laboratory technologists and pathologists. They freeze tissue so that it can be cut into paper-thin slices. They also stain the slides so that the tissue can be seen clearly under a microscope.

Education and Training Requirements

You must have a high school diploma or its equivalent to be a clinical laboratory technician. High school courses in science and math offer good preparation. You generally need specialized training after high school—either an associate degree from a community or junior college or a certificate from a hospital, a vocational or technical school, or one of the U.S. Armed Forces. A few technicians learn their skills on the job. Certification is not required to work. However, it can be an advantage in finding a job or advancing in the field. Manual dexterity and normal color vision are generally required.

The best way to acquire training as a clinical laboratory technician is to take a two-year accredited training program offered in community and junior colleges, four-year colleges, and universities. The Committee on Allied Health Education and Accreditation has accredited more than one hundred of these programs, while the National Accrediting Agency for Clinical Laboratory Sciences (NAACLS) has accredited more than four hundred and fifty programs. Several organizations also offer certification for technicians.

In some states, technicians must be licensed to work. The requirements vary, but usually include a written examination. Accredited training programs are also available for histotechnicians.

It is very important that clinical laboratory technicians carefully research training programs before choosing one. Selecting the right program can help during job hunting because certain areas of medicine have different training requirements.

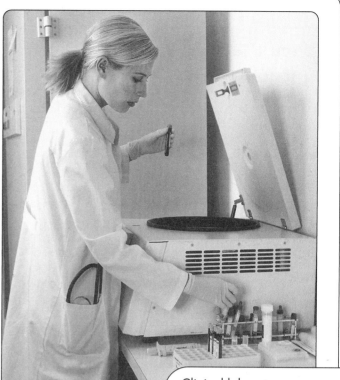

Clinical laboratory technicians perform procedures on blood and other bodily fluids that are crucial to the detection, diagnosis, and treatment of disease. (© Stock4B/ Corbis.)

Getting the Job

Your school placement office can help you find a job. You can also apply directly to hospitals, clinics, laboratories, and research institutions at which you would like to work. Check newspaper want ads, job banks on the Internet, and professional journals as well.

Advancement Possibilities and Employment Outlook

Additional training is usually required to advance. Clinical laboratory technicians may study to become technologists. A master's degree is generally required for teaching and research positions.

The outlook for clinical laboratory technicians is excellent through the year 2014, with employment expected to increase faster than average. As the older population grows, so will the volume of testing and the number of clinical laboratories. The probability of new and more powerful diagnostic tests and research laboratories working to find the cause, treatment, and cure for AIDS (acquired immunodeficiency syndrome) also should create jobs.

Working Conditions

Working conditions for clinical laboratory technicians vary depending on their specialty. However, in all cases the work is very detailed. Laboratory technicians sit for much of the day. They rarely have contact with patients. Their tasks are generally routine, but they perform a wide range of tests.

Histotechnicians perform many different tasks. Generally, they work under the supervision of several people. Histotechnicians may be under pressure to work quickly. At times, tissue samples of a person who is being operated on are sent to the technicians, and they must prepare the slides immediately.

Clinical laboratory technicians usually work forty hours per week. Those who work in hospitals may be required to work some evenings and weekends. Laboratory technicians may be required to wear uniforms and protective clothing.

Earnings and Benefits

Clinical laboratory technicians earn a median salary of $30,840. Experienced workers can earn more. Benefits generally include paid holidays and vacations. Some workers have pension plans.

Dental Hygienist

Education and Training
Two-year college; license

Salary
Median—$28.05 per
hour

Employment Outlook
Excellent

Definition and Nature of the Work

Dental hygienists are licensed professionals who help dentists provide treatment and care of the mouth, teeth, and gums. State laws limit the duties that hygienists may perform. Hygienists examine patients' teeth and gums. They remove stains and tartar, a hard, yellow deposit. They also perform root planing, a procedure that smooths and cleans the root of the tooth. In addition, dental hygienists take and develop dental X-rays to help diagnose problems and apply fluorides and sealants to help prevent cavities. Hygienists teach patients how to prevent dental problems, emphasizing the importance of good nutrition, proper brushing, and regular dental checkups.

In small dental offices, a hygienist may also act as the office assistant or the laboratory technician. Hygienists may schedule appointments and do laboratory work, such as polishing gold inlays and making models from dental impressions. However, not all dental hygienists work in dental offices. There are also job opportunities in clinics and public health agencies.

Education and Training Requirements

To practice, dental hygienists must be licensed by the state in which they wish to work. To qualify for licensure, hygienists must graduate from a school of dental hygiene accredited by the Commission on Dental Accreditation and pass both a written and a clinical examination administered by the state. To enter a school of dental hygiene, you must have at least a high school education. Many schools require that you take an aptitude test given by the American Dental Hygienists Association. Two-year associate's degree programs qualify you to work in a private office. Four-year bachelor's degree programs qualify you to do research, teach, or work in public or school health programs.

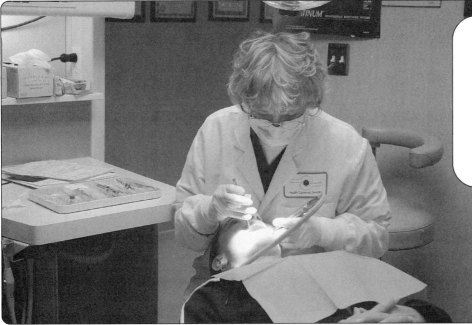

Dental hygienists usually clean patients' teeth, teach patients how to prevent dental problems, and inform the dentist about possible problem areas in the patients' mouths. *(Photograph by Kelly A. Quin. Thomson Gale. Reproduced by permission.)*

Getting the Job

Your school placement office can help you find a job. Check the want ads in trade and professional journals, as well as in local newspapers or job banks on the Internet. Apply directly to dentists' offices or clinics in which you would like to work. If you want to work for a school or public health program, apply to take the necessary civil service test.

Advancement Possibilities and Employment Outlook

Advancement possibilities are best for dental hygienists who work in public, hospital, or school health programs. Those who have a bachelor's or master's degree may take on supervisory or administrative jobs. Hygienists with master's degrees may teach in dental hygiene schools.

The employment outlook for dental hygienists is expected to grow much faster than the average through 2014. Employment prospects should be favorable as the demand for dental care increases with public awareness of the importance of oral health. Older dentists are being replaced by younger dentists, who are more likely to employ dental hygienists.

Working Conditions

Most dental hygienists work in dentists' offices. These offices are generally clean, pleasant, and well lighted. Dental hygienists work with a small staff and usually enjoy a close relationship with their fellow workers. Hygienists often attend to a number of different patients in the course of a day. The work is especially varied in schools and in public health positions.

In general, hygienists work between thirty-five and forty hours a week. Part-time employment is also common. Hygienists who work in dentists' offices may work some evenings and Saturdays. School hygienists work during school hours.

Earnings and Benefits

Salaries vary depending on education, experience, and geographical location. In 2004 the median income for dental hygienists was $28.05 per hour. Benefits generally include paid holidays and vacations. Hygienists who work for government health agencies receive the same benefits that other government workers receive.

Where to Go for More Information

American Dental Association
211 E. Chicago Ave.
Chicago, IL 60611-2678
(312) 440-2500
http://www.ada.org

American Dental Hygienists Association
444 N. Michigan Ave., Ste. 3400
Chicago, IL 60611
(312) 440-8900
http://www.adha.org

National Health Council
1730 M St. NW, Ste. 500
Washington, DC 20036
(202) 785-3910
http://www.nationalhealthcouncil.org

Dental Laboratory Technician

Education and Training
High school plus training

Salary
Median—$14.93 per hour

Employment Outlook
Fair

Definition and Nature of the Work

Dental laboratory technicians fill prescriptions from dentists. They construct and repair dentures (false teeth), bridges, crowns, and other artificial tooth replacement devices (prosthetics) that dentists order for patients. They work from the dentist's written instructions and from plastic or wax impressions of the patient's mouth.

Dental laboratory technicians work with plaster, wax, porcelain, and plastic, as well as with gold and other metals. They use many different kinds of tools and equipment. They use hand tools for carving and shaping. Then they use electric drills, presses, lathes, and high-heat furnaces for completing each dental piece.

Some dental laboratory technicians specialize. They may work chiefly on crowns and bridges, or with porcelain. Generally these specialists work in large laboratories. Workers in smaller laboratories or in dentists' offices usually perform all laboratory work that is needed.

Education and Training Requirements

A person usually needs a high school diploma to become a dental laboratory technician. High school courses in art, ceramics, metalwork, and chemistry are helpful. Many technicians are trained on the job or in apprenticeship programs. Dental laboratory trainees work under the supervision of experienced technicians. They start by doing simple jobs, such as mixing plaster and pouring it into molds. Apprentices also receive classroom training. The training period generally lasts three or four years.

An increasing number of technicians are entering formal training programs after high school. These programs usually last two years and are followed by about

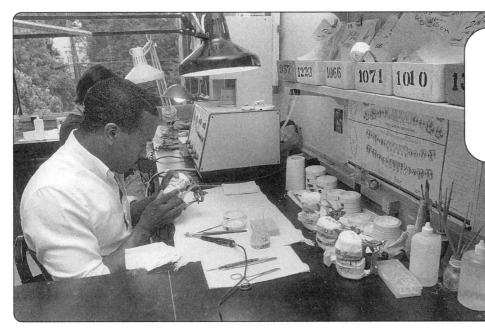

Dental lab technicians use hand tools to carve and shape dentures, bridges, crowns, and other dental devices. (© Martha Tabor/Working Images Photographs. Reproduced by permission.)

three years of practical experience. Technicians can become certified dental technicians by passing tests given by the National Board for Certification established by the National Association of Dental Laboratories.

Dental laboratory technicians should have good vision and color sense. They also need manual dexterity for handling the tiny pieces of material they use in their work. Because the work demands precision, technicians should have patience and should enjoy detail work.

Getting the Job

Interested individuals can apply directly to dentists' offices and laboratories for jobs and training. If candidates are attending school, they can ask their placement office for help in finding a job. Private and state employment agencies sometimes list openings for dental laboratory technicians. Job seekers should also check the newspaper want ads and job banks on the Internet.

Advancement Possibilities and Employment Outlook

Dental laboratory technicians can advance as they gain experience. They can become experts in a specialized kind of laboratory work. In large laboratories, some technicians become managers or supervisors. Some technicians start their own laboratories. To do this, they need capital or financing to buy equipment. They also need knowledge about running a business.

Employment opportunities are expected to grow slower than average through the year 2014, according to the U.S. Bureau of Labor Statistics. Although employers find entry-level positions hard to fill, job prospects are only fair. Dental care is better in the aging population than decades ago, and the need for dentures has lessened. The demand for cosmetic dental devices, however, is on the rise.

Working Conditions

Dental laboratories are found mostly in large cities and heavily populated states. Most are very small, but a few employ more than fifty technicians. Technicians

Where to Go for More Information

American Dental Association
Commission on Dental Accreditation
211 E. Chicago Ave.
Chicago, IL 60611-2678
(312) 440-2500
http://www.ada.org

National Association of Dental Laboratories
325 John Knox Rd., Ste. L103
Tallahassee, FL 32303
(800) 950-1150
http://www.nadl.org

National Board for Certification in Dental
    Technology
325 John Knox Rd., Ste. L103
Tallahassee, FL 32303
(800) 684-5310
http://www.nbccert.org

National Dental Association
3517 16th St. NW
Washington, DC 20010
(202) 588-1697
http://www.ndaonline.org

usually work forty hours per week. Those who are self-employed may work longer hours.

Technicians generally work independently. Because each job in a laboratory is different, the work is diverse and interesting. It is not strenuous work, but it does require close attention to detail. Dental laboratories are generally pleasant places in which to work, although there is sometimes pressure when deadlines must be met.

Earnings and Benefits

Salaries vary depending on technicians' experience and area of specialization. Trainees in dental laboratories average only slightly above the minimum wage. However, earnings in this field increase greatly with experience. The median salary for dental technicians was $14.93 per hour in May 2004, according to the Bureau of Labor Statistics. Self-employed technicians can earn more.

Benefits usually include paid holidays and vacations, as well as health insurance and pension plans. Self-employed dental laboratory technicians must provide their own benefits.

Dental and Medical Secretary

Education and Training
High school plus training

Salary
Median—$26,540 per year

Employment Outlook
Good

Definition and Nature of the Work

Dental secretaries and medical secretaries perform clerical and secretarial duties for dentists and physicians, respectively. They take shorthand, type, and file patients' records. To do their jobs, they must have an understanding of the procedures and terms that physicians and dentists use. Secretaries may also keep track of patients' payments, so they must be familiar with insurance rules and billing practices.

Secretaries sometimes take a patient's medical history before the physician or dentist sees the patient. Secretaries may also ask what the patient's symptoms are and how long a condition has lasted. If this information is collected in advance, physicians and dentists can devote their time to diagnosing and treating patients.

Medical and dental secretaries also arrange appointments for patients. They make sure that people who need immediate care are able to see the doctor or dentist without delay. When there are emergencies that make the physician or dentist late, secretaries must tactfully explain the delay to patients who are waiting.

Most secretaries work in the private offices of physicians and dentists. Some work in hospitals and clinics. Secretaries with knowledge of medical terms are also employed by the medical information and medical emergency departments of large companies. Other dental and medical secretaries work in the research laboratories of drug companies. They may also work for health organizations or government agencies.

Education and Training Requirements

Most medical and dental secretarial positions require a high school education. Candidates need skills in word processing, filing, and bookkeeping. Some employers provide on-the-job training in medical or dental terminology, but most prefer to hire candidates who have secretarial training. Computer and word processing skills have become increasingly important in this field. Training courses are given in business and vocational schools and in junior and community colleges. Courses last from a few months to two years.

Getting the Job

Check with your school placement office. Physicians, dentists, hospitals, and clinics often advertise jobs in local newspapers or job banks on the Internet. For a government job, apply to take the necessary civil service test.

Dental and medical secretaries talk to patients on the phone and arrange appointments for them. They make sure that patients who need immediate care see the dentist or doctor with minimal delay. *(Photograph by Kelly A. Quin. Thomson Gale. Reproduced by permission.)*

Advancement Possibilities and Employment Outlook

Advancement is possible with further education and experience. Secretaries may go on to become medical or dental assistants or technicians. The field is expected to experience average growth through the year 2014.

Working Conditions

Medical and dental secretaries work in clean and comfortable offices. Much of their time is spent at desks. They have a great deal of contact with a variety of people both in person and on the telephone. Sometimes their days are hectic. They must be prepared to move quickly from one situation to another. Medical and dental secretaries must be calm and capable of dealing with all kinds of problems. They should also be responsible, organized, and efficient.

Medical and dental secretaries work thirty-five to forty hours a week. Because their hours match those of physicians and dentists, many secretaries have some evening and weekend work.

Earnings and Benefits

Salaries vary greatly depending on education, experience, and location. Medical and dental secretaries earned a median income of $26,540 per year in 2004. Benefits may include paid vacations, holidays, health insurance, and sick leave.

Where to Go for More Information

American Association of Medical Assistants
20 N. Wacker Dr., Ste. 1575
Chicago, IL 60606
(312) 899-1500
http://www.aama-ntl.org

National Health Council
1730 M St. NW, Ste. 500
Washington, DC 20036
(202) 785-3910
http://www.nationalhealthcouncil.org

International Association of Administrative
  Professionals
10502 NW Ambassador Dr.
P.O. Box 20404
Kansas City, MO 64195-0404
(816) 891-6600
http://www.iaap-hq.org

Dispensing Optician

Education and Training
High school plus training

Salary
Median—$27,950 per year

Employment Outlook
Good

Definition and Nature of the Work

Dispensing opticians, sometimes called prescription opticians or ophthalmic dispensers, examine written prescriptions to determine the specifications of lenses. They recommend eyeglass frames, lenses, and lens coatings after considering the prescription and the customer's occupation, habits, and facial features. Dispensing opticians also make sure that the lenses and frames fit the patient properly.

Most dispensing opticians work in stores that sell eyeglasses. They measure each patient's face to decide exactly where the lenses should be placed. Then they send information on the size, color, shape, and prescription of the lenses to the optical laboratory. When the eyeglasses have been made, the dispensing optician measures and adjusts the glasses for the patient until they fit properly. They instruct clients about adapting to, wearing, or caring for eyeglasses.

Dispensing opticians with additional training fit patients for contact lenses by measuring the shape and size of the eye, selecting the type of contact lens material, and preparing work orders for the laboratory. Dispensing opticians also teach patients proper insertion, removal, and care of contact lenses.

Dispensing opticians also perform administrative tasks. They keep prescription records, work orders, and payment records. They also track inventory and sales.

Education and Training Requirements

Most dispensing opticians are trained on the job or through apprenticeships. Both types of training usually take two to four years to complete. Formal training is increasingly preferred. Community colleges offer training programs that lead to an associate degree.

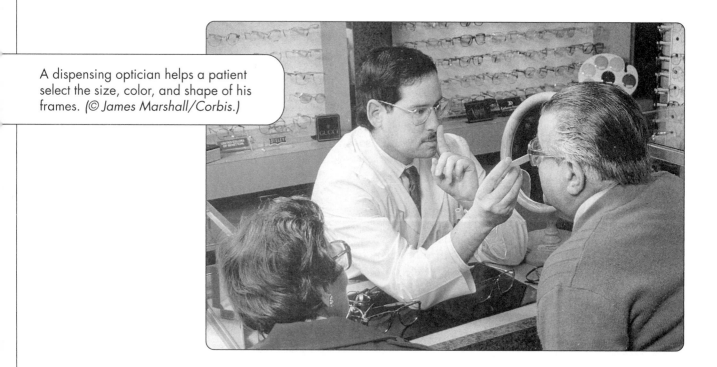

A dispensing optician helps a patient select the size, color, and shape of his frames. (© James Marshall/Corbis.)

Some states require dispensing opticians to be licensed. Licensing requirements usually include meeting educational and training standards and passing a written or practical test. In some states an individual must pass both tests. Dispensing opticians may become certified by the American Board of Opticianry (ABO) and the National Contact Lens Examiners (NCLE). To maintain their certification, dispensing opticians must participate in continuing education.

Getting the Job

A school placement office can help students find a job. Interested individuals can apply directly to companies and private dispensing opticians for on-the-job training. In addition, a person can apply to companies that operate apprenticeship programs.

Advancement Possibilities and Employment Outlook

Dispensing opticians may advance by becoming the managers of their stores. Some open up their own businesses. Others may become sales representatives for wholesalers or manufacturers of eyeglasses or lenses.

Employment of dispensing opticians is expected to grow as fast as the average through the year 2014, according to the U.S. Bureau of Labor Statistics. The anticipated growth of the middle-aged and elderly populations requiring health and vision care will create a need for dispensing opticians. Also, as more customers buy contact lenses or more than one pair of glasses, the number of jobs for opticians is expected to increase.

Working Conditions

Dispensing opticians work in clean, quiet offices. Dispensing opticians must have a talent for sales and enjoy working with people. They generally work forty hours per week. Dispensing opticians may work some evenings and Saturdays.

Earnings and Benefits

Earnings vary depending on education, experience, and place of employment. In May 2004 the median annual salary of a dispensing optician was $27,950 per year, according to the Bureau of Labor Statistics. Owners, managers, and certified graduates of optician programs can earn more. Benefits for salaried dispensing opticians generally include paid holidays and vacations, health insurance, and pension plans.

Where to Go for More Information

American Board of Opticianry/National
   Contact Lens Examiners
6506 Loisdale Rd., Ste. 209
Springfield, VA 22150
(703) 719-5800
http://www.abo-ncle.org

National Academy of Opticianry
8401 Corporate Dr., Ste. 605
Landover, MD 20785
(800) 229-4828
http://www.nao.org

Opticians Association of America
441 Carlisle Dr.
Herndon, VA 20170
(800) 443-8997
http://www.oaa.org

Electroneurodiagnostic Technologist

Education and Training
High school plus training

Salary
Median—$44,621 per year

Employment Outlook
Fair

Definition and Nature of the Work

Electroneurodiagnostic (END) technology enables health care professionals to record and study the electrical activity of the brain and nervous system. END technologists use a variety of techniques and instruments to record electrical activity arising from a patient's brain, spinal cord, peripheral nerves, and other parts of the nervous system. END technologists work with specially trained physicians who interpret the data and determine treatment based on the information. Data gathered with END technology are used for medical research and to diagnose health problems such as brain tumors, strokes, epilepsy, sleep disorders, and Alzheimer's disease.

END technologists maintain END equipment, obtain medical histories, prepare patients for procedures, record patients' electric potentials, and calculate results. A major part of the job is interacting with patients undergoing END procedures.

END technologists apply electrodes to a patient's head. They must choose the most appropriate combination of instrument controls and electrodes to receive accurate data. Many END technologists work in operating rooms. Therefore, they must also understand the effects of anesthesia on a patient's responses.

END technologists may perform a variety of common procedures in the course of their work. The electroencephalogram (EEG) is a recording of the ongoing activity in the brain. It is the most well-known END procedure. In fact, many END departments still carry the title "EEG Lab."

Another common END procedure is the evoked potential (EP) test. This test records electrical activity in the nervous system that occurs in response to an outside stimulus. END technologists also evaluate sleep disorders with the polysomnogram (PSG) test.

Senior END technologists may have supervisory duties in addition to their regular jobs. They may manage an END lab, keep records, set work schedules, train

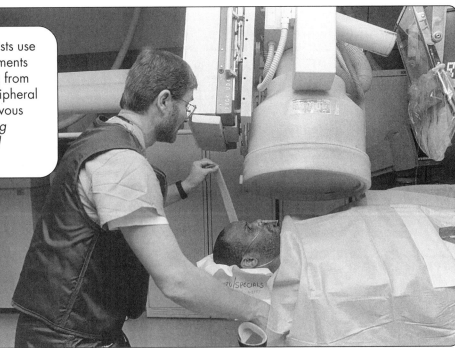

Electroneurodiagnostic technologists use a variety of techniques and instruments to record electrical activity arising from a patient's brain, spinal cord, peripheral nerves, and other parts of the nervous system. (© Martha Tabor/Working Images Photographs. Reproduced by permission.)

other END technologists, and schedule patients' appointments. END technologists must have above-average intelligence, the desire to learn, the ability to manipulate the equipment, and a sympathetic personality.

Education and Training Requirements

Generally, END technologists have a high school diploma and many have post-secondary training in the field. Many current END technologists learned their skills while on the job. The trend, however, is hiring candidates with some formal training. High school students interested in the field should study biology, anatomy, mathematics, and English.

Many two-year colleges, hospitals, and vocational schools offer training in END technology. Interested students should seek out programs accredited by the Commission on Accreditation of Allied Health Education Programs. Another professional group, the American Board of Registration of Electroencephalographic and Evoked Potential Technologists, awards the credentials "registered EEG technologist" and "registered evoked response technologist" to qualified applicants.

Getting the Job

Local hospitals are the best source of information for training and employment opportunities. High school students interested in END technology should work as hospital volunteers to become familiar with hospital procedures.

Advancement Possibilities and Employment Outlook

Employment of END technologists is expected to grow slower than the average through the year 2010. New technologies and cross-trained employees will limit employment growth.

An experienced END technologist can work toward a position managing a hospital or clinic's END department as chief technologist. Typically, a chief technologist reports directly to a physician.

Working Conditions

END technologists work in hospitals, neurology clinics, and psychiatric facilities. Their surroundings are clean and well lighted. Some technologists work in specific designated rooms, whereas others move equipment to perform tests in patients' rooms. Technologists work standard forty-hour workweeks and spend about half of their time on their feet. Technologists working in a hospital may be on call during evenings, weekends, and holidays.

Because END technologists often work with critically ill patients, they need great tact and emotional strength. The job also may require physical strength in helping to move patients who are unable to move on their own.

Earnings and Benefits

Salaries vary according to an END technologist's education and experience. Data collected from END laboratories in Spring 2003 showed the average annual salary for all END technologists across the United States was $44,621.

Where to Go for More Information

American Board of Registration of
    Electroencephalographic and Evoked
    Potential Technologists
1904 Croydon Dr.
Springfield, IL 62703
(217) 553-3758
http://www.abret.org

American Society of Electroneurodiagnostic
    Technologists
6501 E. Commerce Ave., Ste. 120
Kansas City, MO 64120
(816) 931-1120
http://www.aset.org

EEG and Clinical Neuroscience Society
    (ECNS)
Wayne State University
Department of Psychiatry and Behavioral
    Neurosciences
2751 E. Jefferson
Detroit, MI 48207
(313) 577-6687
http://www.ecnsweb.com

Emergency Medical Technician/Paramedic

Definition and Nature of the Work

Emergency medical technicians (EMTs) offer immediate aid to victims of accidents or critical illnesses. They may provide their services at the scene of the crisis, en route to the hospital, and in the emergency room. Usually an EMT's first contact with a victim is at the scene of the crisis. EMTs work on-call and are dispatched to an emergency site when needed. They must be able to quickly yet accurately determine the nature and extent of the problem and decide how it should be treated. In many cases they must treat the victim instantly if his or her life is to be saved. After giving the appropriate emergency care at the site, EMTs usually transport victims to proper medical facilities. They report their observations and care given, and they often stay on hand to provide any additional assistance.

The duties and capabilities of an emergency medical technician depend on their training. All EMTs are qualified to give cardiopulmonary resuscitation (CPR), control bleeding, and administer oxygen. They can also deliver babies, subdue people displaying violent behavior, treat allergic reactions, apply splints and antishock suits, and treat wounds.

The National Registry of Emergency Medical Technicians (NREMT) registers emergency medical service (EMS) providers at four levels: First Responder, EMT-Basic, EMT-Intermediate, and EMT-Paramedic. The First Responder designation is not for EMTs but for police, firefighters, and other emergency workers. As mentioned previously, those with EMT-Basic training (or EMT-1) can assess a patient's condition and manage breathing, heart, and trauma emergencies. In addition to these skills, the EMT-Intermediate (EMT-2 and EMT-3) is trained to administer intravenous fluids and use defibrillators to shock a stopped heart. The EMT-Intermediate also knows advanced airway techniques to help people who are having trouble breathing. EMT-Paramedics (EMT-4) are trained to provide the most extensive prehospital care. In addition to the skills already listed, paramedics may administer drugs, interpret electrocardiograms (EKGs), place a tube into the windpipe to help breathing, and use monitors and other complex equipment. Emergency medical technicians work for fire and police departments, hospitals, and private and public ambulance services.

Emergency medical technicians must arrive quickly at the scene of a crisis, diagnose the problem, and decide how it should be treated. Some EMTs in major cities ride bicycles to avoid delays caused by traffic. (© Martha Tabor/Working Images Photographs. Reproduced by permission.)

Education and Training Requirements

A person needs a high school diploma to enter a formal EMT training program. Training programs prepare students for EMT registration with the NREMT, for state certification, or both. To maintain certification, EMTs and paramedics must work as an EMT or paramedic, meet a continuing education requirement, and re-register every two years.

Fire departments and colleges offer most of the EMT courses available. Certification involves both written and practical tests. Refresher courses for EMTs are available at all levels.

Getting the Job

Volunteer technicians are always needed, and this is an excellent way for interested individuals to find out if they are suited to the work. To volunteer, candidates must take the training courses and pass the tests. For jobs, individuals should check with their local police or fire department or apply directly to a local first aid squad. Prospective EMTs can also apply to hospitals and private ambulance services.

Advancement Possibilities and Employment Outlook

Competent technicians can advance fairly quickly to the paramedic level if they are willing to meet training requirements mandated by their states. The employment outlook is expected to grow much faster than the average through the year 2014, according to the U.S. Bureau of Labor Statistics, as more highly trained, salaried workers replace volunteers. In addition, as the population ages, the need for emergency medical services should increase. Opportunities for paramedics will be best in communities that are just setting up advanced rescue teams. Although job stress and turnover will produce many openings, keen competition is expected for those jobs.

Working Conditions

The work is demanding and unpredictable, requiring physical stamina, manual dexterity, emotional stability, compassion, good judgment, and the ability to react quickly under stressful conditions. Some EMTs work on rotating shifts, working a twenty-four-hour shift followed by two days off. Others work a single shift each day, totaling anywhere from forty to more than fifty-five hours per week. Night and weekend work is often required, and many EMTs are on call for emergencies.

Earnings and Benefits

The Bureau of Labor Statistics reports that the median salary for EMTs was $25,310 per year in 2004. Those with more experience and training can earn up to $43,240 per year.

Benefits for EMTs employed by city or local governments include paid vacations and holidays, retirement plans, and health insurance. Benefits for EMTs working for private companies vary and may not include retirement plans.

Where to Go for More Information

National Association of Emergency
  Medical Technicians
PO Box 1400
Clinton, MS 39060-1400
(800) 34-NAEMT
http://www.naemt.org

Environmental Health Specialist

Definition and Nature of the Work

Environmental health specialists monitor health and safety conditions in residential, industrial, commercial, and recreational settings. A person who works as an environmental health specialist may also be called an environmental health or safety inspector, or a health and safety specialist. The main responsibilities of the position are to determine the existence of possible health hazards and to take steps to correct them.

Most environmental safety specialists work for government agencies that monitor local, state, and federal safety and environmental regulations. This includes checking plants and factories for pollution or industrial waste; inspecting restaurants for cleanliness; and inspecting schools, day care centers, and nursing homes for harmful substances such as radon or lead paint. Environmental safety specialists also monitor how hospitals handle biological waste and ensure that swimming pools and other recreational facilities are safe for public use. Government-employed environmental safety specialists issue permits and certificates stating that a particular residence, place of business, or recreational facility has met minimum acceptable health and safety standards.

As part of the inspection process, environmental health specialists may collect samples of soil, air, water, and possible pollutants from the places they inspect. They then test the samples to determine whether there are dangerous levels of any hazardous substances. If possible health problems are discovered, the specialists draw up a plan to monitor the facility to determine the source and nature of the hazard. This may involve setting up equipment at the inspection site to monitor air or water quality and checking the records periodically to ensure that health and quality standards are met. The environmental health specialist then evaluates the success of any steps taken to resolve the problem and finds alternative solutions if necessary.

Environmental health specialists who work for private companies are responsible for keeping the firm's facilities up to government standards. They need to make sure that government inspectors who monitor the company find no problems or violations. Because the job is preventative in nature, the environmental health specialist must be aware of all the areas in which health or safety problems are likely to arise and develop plans to help employees reduce the possibility of violations. For this reason, they must be familiar with current government and industry regulations.

Education and Training Requirements

Most positions for environmental health specialists require at least a bachelor's degree. Significant course work in chemistry, biology, public health, physical sciences, as well as environmental engineering is usually needed as well. Those who want to work for the government have to complete a certification course administered by the appropriate local, state, or federal agency. Most states have licensing boards that examine potential candidates and grant certification to qualified applicants. The type of training and certification needed depends on the types of facilities being inspected. Credentialing is also available through the National Environmental Health Association (NEHA). It is possible to receive specialist certification for dealing with certain types of hazardous materials.

Getting the Job

Private companies post openings for environmental health specialists in newspaper classified sections and on Internet job search sites. Government agencies may also have job listings at local government offices.

Advancement Possibilities and Employment Outlook

Environmental health specialists who work for government agencies typically advance along a specified career ladder in which they receive salary increases according to a set schedule. When the top salary level is reached, further advancement leads to supervisory positions. There is a good deal of competition for these positions, which are based on the needs of the agency as well as the qualifications of the candidate.

Increasing concern for environmental health and safety is balanced by public concern for reductions in the size and regulatory power of the government. For this reason, the employment outlook for government-employed environmental safety inspectors is about average. Most job openings in government work will come as a result of retirement of existing employees or their transfer to other fields of work. The demand for environmental health specialists in private industry should grow as more companies turn toward self-enforcement of regulations to avoid government sanctions.

Working Conditions

Environmental health specialists work in a very wide range of settings. The inspection work may take place in modern homes and offices, industrial plants, private businesses, and even parks and wildlife refuges. Analysis of materials collected during inspections occurs in a laboratory setting. The job may entail exposure to potentially dangerous materials including industrial pollution, medical and nuclear waste, airborne and waterborne germs or other contaminants, and substances such as lead and asbestos.

Earnings and Benefits

The salaries of environmental health specialists depend on their levels of general education, specific training, and experience. In 2006 most salaries ranged from $37,300 to $57,551 per year. Both government positions and jobs in private industry offer paid vacation, medical, and retirement benefits.

Where to Go for More Information

Institute of Environmental Sciences and
   Technology
5005 Newport Dr., Ste. 506
Rolling Meadows, IL 60008-3841
(847) 255-1561
http://www.iest.org

National Environmental Health Association
720 S. Colorado Blvd., Ste. 970-S
Denver, CO 80246-1925
(303) 756-9090
http://www.neha.org

Licensed Practical Nurse

Education and Training
High school plus training; license

Salary
Median—$33,970 per year

Employment Outlook
Good

Definition and Nature of the Work

Licensed practical nurses (LPNs) help physicians and registered nurses (RNs) care for patients. They have the technical knowledge to perform routine nursing duties, but they may also make appointments, maintain patient records, and perform basic clerical duties. Their work allows doctors and registered nurses to devote their time to patient care that requires specialized knowledge. Most licensed practical nurses work in hospitals, nursing homes, other health care institutions, and private homes. Some are employed in doctors' offices, clinics, and public health agencies. Still others work in large businesses. They care for workers who have accidents or become ill on the job. Licensed practical nurses are also called licensed vocational nurses.

Licensed practical nurses have a great deal of contact with their patients. It is important that nurses keep patients in good spirits. They also take patients' blood pressures, check temperatures, and apply bandages. In some cases LPNs may give their patients drugs that doctors have prescribed. Licensed practical nurses watch for changes in their patients' condition. If there is a change, they report it to the doctors immediately.

Licensed practical nurses sometimes work in special units of a hospital. These include cardiac, burn, and maternity units. LPNs may be trained to use special equipment and may direct nurse's aides.

On occasion, patients who are recovering from an illness hire licensed practical nurses to work in their homes. The nurses provide basic bedside care as well as follow the specific instructions of a patient's doctor. For example, they may give drugs on schedule or change bandages. In addition, they may prepare meals for patients.

A licensed practical nurse works under the direction of registered nurses or doctors. (© Hulshizer, Jen/ Star Ledger/Corbis.)

Education and Training Requirements

Most schools that train licensed practical nurses prefer to admit high school graduates. Admission requirements usually include passing an aptitude test and taking a physical exam.

Training programs currently take one year to complete and include both classroom study and supervised patient care. Junior and community colleges, technical and vocational schools, and hospitals offer these programs. The armed services also offer state-approved courses. However, there is a move to two levels of nursing. Technical nurses, such as LPNs, will be required to have an associate degree. Professional nurses, such as RNs, will be required to have a bachelor's degree. Those interested in careers in nursing should check current state regulations. All LPNs must be licensed. To qualify for a license, a person must complete a state-approved course and pass a written test.

Getting the Job

The school placement office may be able to help students find a job. Interested individuals can apply directly to hospitals, clinics, and other institutions. They can also check with private employment agencies that specialize in medical job placements. Newspaper want ads and job banks on the Internet often carry listings for licensed practical nurses.

To get a job in home health care, candidates can contact local hospitals and clinics. These facilities usually maintain lists of practical nurses. When a patient needs private care, hospitals suggest someone from their lists.

Advancement Possibilities and Employment Outlook

Licensed practical nurses can take extra courses to specialize in one field, such as the care of newborn infants. With further training, they may become registered nurses. However, this training may be extensive.

The outlook for licensed practical nurses is good, with employment expected to increase as fast as the average through the year 2014, according to the U.S. Bureau of Labor Statistics. These jobs will be concentrated in clinics, rehabilitation hospitals, and long-term care facilities. There will also be increasing demand for skilled LPNs to work in home health care.

Working Conditions

Licensed practical nurses can usually choose where they work, from hospitals to private homes. LPNs must keep an even temper, especially when caring for difficult and unhappy patients. They must stand for long periods and often have to help patients move in bed, stand, walk, or dress. Licensed practical nurses always work under the direction of registered nurses or doctors.

Practical nurses generally work forty hours per week. Sometimes they work at night and on weekends, earning premium pay for these shifts. Jobs in private homes often involve longer hours. Each case places different demands on the practical nurse's time.

Earnings and Benefits

Salaries vary with experience and place of employment. Full-time licensed practical nurses earned a median annual salary of $33,970 per year in 2004, according to the Bureau of Labor Statistics. In most hospitals salary increases are given at regular intervals. Benefits include paid holidays and vacations, health insurance, and pension plans.

Where to Go for More Information

National Association for Practical Nurse
   Education and Service
PO Box 25647
Alexandria, VA 22313
(703) 933-1003
http://www.napnes.org

National Federation of Licensed Practical
   Nurses
605 Poole Dr.
Garner, NC 27529
(919) 779-0046
http://www.nflpn.org

National League for Nursing
61 Broadway, 33rd Fl.
New York, NY 10006
(212) 363-5555
http://www.nln.org

Medical Assistant

Education and Training
High school plus training

Salary
Median—$24,610 per year

Employment Outlook
Excellent

Definition and Nature of the Work

Medical assistants aid physicians by performing administrative duties and handling basic clinical tasks. They work in doctors' offices, hospitals, and medical clinics, helping to keep operations running smoothly and efficiently. The job description of a medical assistant varies from office to office. Some assistants do patient and laboratory work exclusively. Others are responsible for medical records, bookkeeping, and answering phones. In most small offices, medical assistants may handle all these tasks.

Most medical assistants work in private offices. Clinical duties vary according to state law. Some medical assistants may help doctors examine and treat patients. They may check the height, weight, temperature, and blood pressure of each patient. Assistants write down patients' medical histories and run simple laboratory tests. Sometimes they answer patients' questions about medicines and treatment at home. Assistants may also give injections, apply bandages, and take X-rays. Many assistants take electrocardiograms, which measure the electrical impulses of the heart.

Medical assistants are sometimes in charge of buying and maintaining medical equipment and furniture for the doctor's office. They may also act as office managers. They plan the doctor's schedule, greet patients, file records and correspondence, and type letters and bills. Assistants keep medical records up to date and handle tax and insurance forms. At the doctor's request they arrange for laboratory tests or for a patient's admission to the hospital. In a large group practice or in a hospital clinic, the duties of the medical assistant may be divided among several assistants.

Education and Training Requirements

A high school diploma is required to enter this field. Although medical assistants can be trained on the job, most employers prefer to hire graduates of formal training programs. Vocational schools offer one-year programs resulting in a certificate or diploma. Community colleges offer two-year programs leading to an

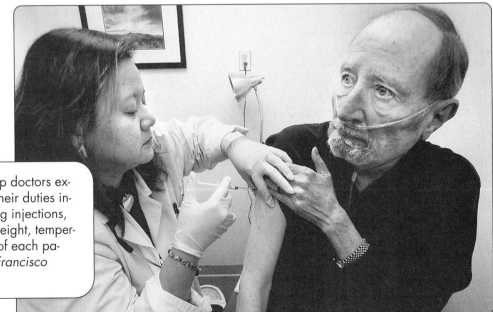

Most medical assistants help doctors examine and treat patients. Their duties include drawing blood, giving injections, and checking the height, weight, temperature, and blood pressure of each patient. (© Darryl Bush/San Francisco Chronicle/Corbis.)

About half of all states require technologists to be licensed. Most employers prefer to hire certified or registered technologists, so many technologists obtain a voluntary professional certification or registration from the Nuclear Medicine Technology Certification Board or the American Registry of Radiologic Technologists.

Getting the Job

Most nuclear medicine technologists work in hospitals, which hire only certified or registered technologists. Sometimes individuals with a bachelor's degree in an accepted specialty or those who have completed an accredited training program can obtain entry-level positions in doctors' offices or clinics.

Advancement Possibilities and Employment Outlook

Nuclear medicine technologists can advance to supervisory positions such as chief technologist or department administrator. Some technologists advance through specialization, such as nuclear cardiology, or move on to work in research laboratories. Those technologists with advanced degrees may become teachers in nuclear medicine technology programs.

Employment of nuclear medicine technologists is expected to grow faster than the average through the year 2014, according to the U.S. Bureau of Labor Statistics. Technological innovations may increase the diagnostic use of nuclear medicine, especially for the nation's aging population. However, the occupation is small, and only a few openings each year are expected in this field. Opportunities will be best for technologists trained in both nuclear medicine and radiologic procedures.

Working Conditions

Nuclear medicine technologists usually work in clean, well-lighted environments. They generally work a forty-hour week, although evening and weekend hours, on-call duty, and shift work may be expected. Technologists must possess strong physical stamina, since they stand most of the day and may have to lift or position patients.

Earnings and Benefits

The median annual salary for nuclear medicine technologists was $56,450 in 2004, according to the Bureau of Labor Statistics. Those with more experience and training can earn more. Full-time technologists usually receive benefits that include health insurance and paid vacation time.

Where to Go for More Information

American College of Nuclear Medicine
101 W. Broad St., Ste. 614
Hazleton, PA 18201
(570) 501-9661
http://www.acnucmed.com

The Society of Nuclear Medicine
1850 Samuel Morse Dr.
Reston, VA 20190-5316
(703) 708-9000
http://www.snm.org

Occupational Therapist Assistant

Definition and Nature of the Work

Occupational therapist assistants, also known as occupational therapy assistants, provide rehabilitative services to people with mental, emotional, physical, or developmental impairments. They work under the supervision of occupational therapists. Many occupational therapist assistants work in hospitals. Others work in homes for the aged, clinics, special schools, or occupational workshops.

Assistants help patients work through rehabilitative exercises and activities outlined in a treatment plan by an occupational therapist. Assistants may help patients learn how to feed and dress themselves, compensate for lost motor skills, or achieve a more independent lifestyle.

Occupational therapist assistants may be responsible for ordering supplies and taking care of the equipment used in therapy. They may write up observation and progress reports on the patients and do other paperwork. Sometimes they may handle clerical duties.

Education and Training Requirements

To enter a training program for occupational therapist assistants, a person must have a high school diploma or its equivalent. Courses in crafts, health, science, and typing are helpful. Work experience in summer camps or hospitals is useful.

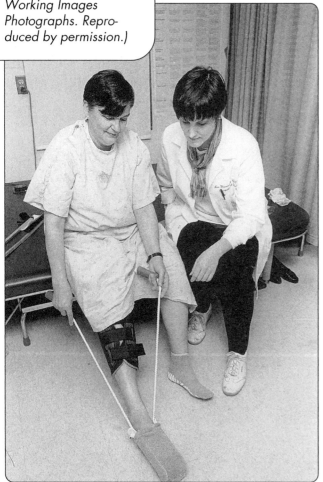

An occupational therapist assistant helps a patient work through rehabilitative exercises and activities. (© Martha Tabor/ Working Images Photographs. Reproduced by permission.)

Training for occupational therapist assistants is given in community colleges and vocational and technical schools. Most programs last two years and lead to an associate degree. Some lead to a certificate only. Courses may include basic medical terminology, anatomy, mental health, and pediatrics. If individuals graduate from a program accredited by the American Occupational Therapy Association and pass a test, they can become a certified occupational therapist assistant (COTA).

Getting the Job

Interested individuals can apply directly to hospitals or clinics for a job. Job openings are sometimes listed in newspaper want ads or job banks on the Internet. School placement offices can also help candidates find a job, as can state and private employment agencies.

Advancement Possibilities and Employment Outlook

In large hospitals and clinics, assistants can become supervisors. With further training and experience, and by passing an examination, a certified occupational therapist assistant can become a registered occupational therapist (OTR).

The employment outlook for occupational therapist assistants is expected to grow much faster than the average through the year 2014, according to the

U.S. Bureau of Labor Statistics. Due to the increasing numbers of persons with disabilities, the aging population, and children with sensory disorders, there will be a demand for rehabilitation services and long-term care. Also, there is an anticipated high rate of turnover among occupational therapist assistants, which should result in openings. The employment outlook is best for graduates of approved programs.

Working Conditions

Occupational therapist assistants usually work forty hours per week. Some weekend or evening hours may be required. Most occupational workshops are nicely decorated. Assistants should be friendly and understanding. They often work with people who are in pain or who need to be cheered up. Assistants should be good at working with their hands and should enjoy helping others.

Earnings and Benefits

Salaries vary with education and experience. The Bureau of Labor Statistics reports that in May 2004 the median salary for occupational therapist assistants was $38,430 per year. Benefits include paid holidays and vacations, health insurance, and pension plans.

> **Where to Go for More Information**
>
> American Occupational Therapy Association
> 4720 Montgomery Ln.
> PO Box 31220
> Bethesda, MD 20824-1220
> (301) 652-2682
> http://www.aota.org

Ophthalmic Laboratory Technician

Definition and Nature of the Work

Ophthalmic laboratory technicians prepare eyeglass lenses or contact lenses from an eye doctor's (optometrist's or ophthalmologist's) prescription. Some make precision lenses for cameras, microscopes, telescopes, and military equipment. Ophthalmic laboratory technicians are also called manufacturing opticians, optical mechanics, or optical goods workers.

Ophthalmic laboratory technicians cut, grind, edge, and finish lenses. Although some technicians still grind lenses by hand, most use automated equipment to make lenses. The technician must choose the correct blank lens with which to begin, mark the lenses for grinding, place them in the machine, and set the dials for proper grinding. The lenses are finished and polished in other machines.

After the lenses are ground and polished, the ophthalmic laboratory technician checks the curvature of the lenses by using a lensometer. The lenses must fit the prescription or specifications exactly. The technician then fits the lenses to the glasses frame to produce a finished pair of glasses, or fits the lenses into optical equipment such as microscopes.

> **Education and Training**
> High school plus training
>
> **Salary**
> Median—$11.40 per hour
>
> **Employment Outlook**
> Fair

Education and Training Requirements

Most ophthalmic laboratory technicians are trained on the job. Employers filling trainee jobs generally prefer high school graduates. Interested individuals should take courses in science, mathematics, and computers. It generally takes at least six months to learn all phases of the job.

A small number of ophthalmic laboratory technicians learn the trade in the U.S. Armed Forces. A few vocational–technical institutes or trade schools offer programs in optical technology. Programs are from six months to one year.

Getting the Job

School placement offices can help students find jobs. Prospective technicians can apply directly to companies and private dispensing opticians for on-the-job training.

Advancement Possibilities and Employment Outlook

Optical laboratory technicians may advance in their careers by becoming supervisors or managers.

The outlook for ophthalmic laboratory technicians is expected to grow slower than average through the year 2014, according to the U.S. Bureau of Labor Statistics. Although the middle-aged and elderly populations requiring vision care will increase, so will the use of automated equipment, which will limit job growth for ophthalmic laboratory technicians.

Working Conditions

Ophthalmic laboratory technicians have limited contact with the public. They generally work in clean, well-lighted, and well-ventilated laboratories, but they may stand much of the day. At times, laboratory technicians wear protective eyewear, gloves, or masks. They must be precise and exacting in their work. Ophthalmic laboratory technicians generally work forty hours per week.

Where to Go for More Information

Commission on Opticianry Accreditation
8665 Sudley Rd., Ste. 341
Manassas, VA 20110
(703) 940-9134
http://www.coaccreditation.com/

Earnings and Benefits

Earnings vary depending on education, experience, and place of employment. The Bureau of Labor Statistics reports that in 2004 the median hourly earnings of ophthalmic laboratory technicians were $11.40. Benefits for salaried workers generally include health insurance and paid holidays and vacations.

Pharmaceutical Sales Representative

Education and Training
Two to four years of college and on-the-job training

Salary
Median—$60,130 per year

Employment Outlook
Good

Definition and Nature of the Work

Pharmaceutical sales representatives are employed by drug companies. They distribute information about their companies' products to physicians, hospital nurses, and medical technicians. They do not take drug orders from these health care practitioners but instead try to persuade doctors to prescribe more of their companies' drugs. Patients then buy the drugs.

Most doctors are very busy, and sales representatives usually have no more than five or six minutes with them. In that time the representative must describe their company's newest products. They outline what a drug is designed to do and how it works. They also explain its advantages over older drugs, attempting to convince doctors as to why their product is better than others.

Sales representatives must have a basic knowledge of how the human body works. They must also have some understanding of disease and pharmacology (the study of drugs and their effects on humans), because doctors will question sales representatives about drugs and their side effects. Sales representatives must also know which drugs will be of interest to doctors in different specialties.

A pharmaceutical sales representative discusses information about a drug with doctors. Representatives must speak clearly and concisely under pressure, because they only spend a few minutes at each medical site.
(© Jim Craigmyle/Corbis.)

Sales representatives are assigned territories based on postal zip codes. They make up their own itineraries, concentrating on doctors who write the most prescriptions. This information is available from surveys of pharmacists. Sales persons may leave samples of new drugs with doctors and must keep careful records concerning the samples they leave.

Sales representatives must be able to speak clearly and concisely under pressure. They must have pleasant personalities and be able to build long-lasting relationships with doctors. In addition, sales representatives must be able to accept rejection. About 40 percent of doctors refuse to see sales persons. Others will not see them when they are very busy.

Education and Training Requirements

To become a pharmaceutical sales person, a person must have a high school diploma. Most employers prefer to hire college graduates, preferably with a bachelor's degree in science. However, two years of college should be sufficient to qualify for most jobs. Drug companies provide on-the-job training, selecting trainees on the basis of their verbal and social skills. Training consists of intensive study followed by supervised field work.

Representatives must keep abreast of current medical and product knowledge throughout their careers. They attend regular meetings to get product information. They must maintain a general knowledge of advances in medicine. Correspondence courses are available through their company and the Certified Medical Representatives Institute, which offers certification.

Getting the Job

College students should ask their college placement office for information about applying to become a pharmaceutical sales representative trainee. Representatives of drug companies may also visit campuses. Otherwise, interested individuals should write to major drug companies and request interviews. Once a person is selected as a trainee, a job is guaranteed.

Advancement Possibilities and Employment Outlook

Some representatives prefer to stay in the field. Some advance to supervisory and training positions. A few advance to administrative and planning posts. Occasionally a sales person will transfer to another department in the company or move into a related health occupation.

Employment of sales representatives is expected to grow as fast as average through 2014, according to the U.S. Bureau of Labor Statistics. The job outlook for pharmaceutical sales representatives is good. Some companies are expanding rapidly and will need to hire additional representatives.

Working Conditions

Pharmaceutical sales representatives set their own hours to fit doctors' schedules, often having appointments in the early morning, in the evening, or at lunch. Representatives may spend much time traveling and often have to wait to see doctors despite appointments. The general atmosphere in the drug industry is becoming increasingly competitive. Pharmaceutical sales representatives must be able to cope with stressful situations caused by competition with other sales representatives for access to doctors during their limited free time.

Earnings and Benefits

Commissions account for a large proportion of earnings for sales representatives. Depending on the company, roughly 10 to 20 percent of their earnings are derived from commissions based on the drugs ordered by doctors. The Bureau of Labor Statistics reports that in May 2004 the median salary for pharmaceutical sales representatives was $60,130 per year including commissions. Sales persons receive health insurance and paid vacations and holidays. They also receive free cars and some travel expenses.

Where to Go for More Information

Certified Medical Representatives
   Institute, Inc.
4423 Pheasant Ridge Rd., Ste. 100
Roanoke, VA 24014-5274
(800) 274-2674
http://www.cmrinstitute.org

Physical Therapist Assistant

Education and Training
High school and associate degree

Salary
Median—$37,890 per year

Employment Outlook
Very good

Definition and Nature of the Work

Physical therapist assistants work under the supervision of physical therapists. They use physical treatment procedures to help improve mobility and relieve pain and disability caused by disease or injury. Physical therapists and their assistants usually work in hospitals, nursing homes, or clinics. They are part of a health care team that includes doctors, occupational therapists, and social workers.

Physical therapist assistants work with people of all ages. Some work with elderly patients who have trouble moving about. Some work with handicapped children, and others work with patients who have lost an arm or a leg, have arthritis problems, or are paralyzed. Physical therapist assistants use many different types of equipment and procedures. They treat patients by using massage, exercise, heat, cold, and light. Assistants teach patients how to use and care for wheelchairs, braces, and artificial limbs.

Assistants have other duties that give physical therapists more time to put their special training to use. Assistants may do some office work, for example, or they

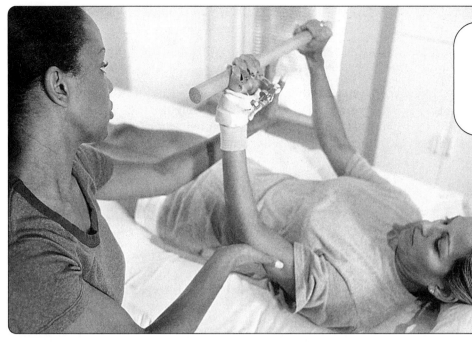

may get equipment ready for the therapist. They may also prepare a patient for a therapy session.

Education and Training Requirements

To become a physical therapist assistant, an individual must have a high school diploma or its equivalent. Candidates should take courses in mathematics and science in high school. Prospective physical therapist assistants can also get experience by volunteering part time in a hospital or clinic or working with handicapped children in summer camps.

Most physical therapist assistants have an associate degree from an accredited physical therapist assistant program. Some states require licensure or registration for the physical therapist assistant to practice. Most employers provide clinical on-the-job training.

Getting the Job

College placement offices can help students find jobs as physical therapist assistants. Interested individuals can also apply directly to hospitals or clinics. Another good source of job openings is newspaper want ads.

Advancement Possibilities and Employment Outlook

As physical therapist assistants gain experience, they are often given more responsibility and salary increases. Some assistants continue their education to become physical therapists.

The employment outlook for physical therapist assistants is expected to grow much faster than the average through the year 2014, the U.S. Bureau of Labor Statistics reports. Opportunities will be best for graduates of accredited training programs. The expansion of rehabilitation services for people with physical disabilities will create many new jobs. The need for physical therapy is expected to grow as the number of people over the age of seventy-five increases. Advances in rehabilitation medicine and therapeutic techniques are likely to create additional demands.

Working Conditions

Physical therapist assistants usually work in clean, pleasant places. Their patients may sometimes be depressed by their disabilities. Assistants can help them by being cheerful and encouraging. Physical therapist assistants should also be healthy and able to work well with their hands. Most physical therapist assistants work forty hours per week, but some work part time.

Earnings and Benefits

Salaries vary with experience and place of employment. The median yearly salary for physical therapist assistants was $37,890 in May 2004, according to the Bureau of Labor Statistics. Benefits include paid holidays and vacations, and health insurance.

Radiologic Technologist

Education and Training
Two-year or four-year college

Salary
Median—$43,350 per year

Employment Outlook
Good

Definition and Nature of the Work

Radiologic technologists, who are also called radiographers, take X-rays (radiographs), which are images of the inside of the human body. To take X-rays, radiographers position the patient, position the X-ray machine and other equipment, set controls, position the X-ray film, and remove and develop the film after the X-ray has been taken. Experienced radiographers may perform more complex imaging procedures, such as computed tomography (CT) or magnetic resonance imaging (MRI) scans. In addition, radiologic technologists are usually responsible for writing reports and maintaining their equipment.

Radiologic technologists work under the direction of radiologists, medical doctors who specialize in interpreting radiographs. The information from radiographs is helpful in the diagnosis and treatment of illness and injury. Most radiologic technologists work in hospitals, but some work in medical laboratories, clinics, or doctors' or dentists' offices. Others help staff mobile X-ray units or work in private industry.

Education and Training Requirements

A person can become a radiologic technologist by enrolling in a two- to four-year program in radiography that leads to a certificate, associate degree, or bachelor's degree. A high school diploma or its equivalent is needed to enter a program. Hospitals, colleges, medical schools, the U.S. Armed Forces, and vocational and technical schools offer these programs. After graduating from an approved program, individuals can take an exam leading to registration by the American Registry of Radiologic Technologists. With further training and experience, registered technologists can become certified in radiation therapy technology or nuclear medicine technology.

Getting the Job

Many hospitals will hire students that they have helped to train. School placement offices can also help interested individuals find jobs. The want ads in newspapers and professional journals are another good source of job leads.

Advancement Possibilities and Employment Outlook

Experienced radiologic technologists can become supervisors of other workers in large X-ray departments. They can also learn to operate other types of hospital equipment. Technologists who have a bachelor's degree can become instructors or administrators. Some technologists advance by getting jobs with the manufacturers of X-ray equipment. They may sell or service this equipment.

The employment outlook for the field of radiologic technology is expected to grow faster than average through the year 2014, according to the U.S. Bureau of Labor Statistics. However, the number of candidates going into the field is also increasing. Also, more hospitals are merging their radiologic and nuclear medicine departments in an effort to cut costs. Radiographers who are also trained in more than one type of imaging technology will have the best prospects. In the years ahead, a growing number of radiologic technologists will find jobs in offices of physicians, health maintenance organizations, diagnostic imaging centers, and freestanding cancer clinics.

A radiologic technologist processes films of patient X-rays at a hospital. Radiologic technologists are also responsible for writing reports and maintaining equipment.
(© Martha Tabor/ Working Images Photographs. Reproduced by permission.)

Working Conditions

Radiologic technologists generally work forty hours per week. Sometimes they must work night and weekend shifts. Part-time work is often available.

Radiologic technologists need manual dexterity and mechanical ability. They come in contact with a wide variety of people and should be sympathetic and friendly. Their working environment is usually clean and pleasant. Technologists should be in good health and must always work carefully to avoid exposing themselves and others to harmful radiation.

Earnings and Benefits

Salaries depend on education, experience, and location. The Bureau of Labor Statistics reported that radiologic technologists earned a median income of $43,350 per year in May 2004. Benefits include paid holidays and vacations, health insurance, and pension plans.

Where to Go for More Information

American Association for Women
 Radiologists
4550 Post Oak Place, Ste. 342
Houston, TX 77027
(713) 965-0566
http://www.aawr.org

American Society of Radiologic
 Technologists
15000 Central Ave. SE
Albuquerque, NM 87123-3917
(800) 444-2778
http://www.asrt.org

Radiological Society of North America
820 Jorie Blvd.
Oak Brook, IL 60523-2251
(800) 381-6660
http://www.rsna.org

Respiratory Therapist

Education and Training
Two-year or four-year degree

Salary
Median—$43,140 per year

Employment Outlook
Very good

Definition and Nature of the Work

Respiratory therapists are also known as inhalation therapists. They treat patients who have difficulty breathing and work with all types of patients, from premature infants to stroke victims to elderly patients with lung disease. They operate equipment such as respirators and ventilators. Most respiratory therapists work in hospitals under the supervision of physicians, but a growing number are contracted outside of hospitals in home health agencies and nursing homes.

Respiratory therapists often work in emergency situations resulting from injury or illness. They also work in ongoing treatment programs for patients with breathing disorders, such as emphysema.

Respiratory therapists operate machines that provide oxygen. Some kinds of equipment provide medicine in the form of a mist or gas. Usually physicians give respiratory therapists prescriptions stating the medicine and dosage to be given to the patient. It is generally up to the therapist to decide what equipment should be used. Respiratory therapists must be aware of the dangers and hazards involved in each kind of treatment. They observe patients during treatment and report any adverse reactions to the doctor.

In most hospitals respiratory therapists are responsible for having faulty equipment repaired. They may make small repairs themselves. Respiratory therapists are often called on to explain the equipment to nurses. Therapists must also know how to work in a sterile environment.

Education and Training Requirements

Training programs vary in length from two to four years. Technical schools and community and junior colleges offer two-year programs leading to an associate degree. Four-year colleges offer bachelor's degrees. Hospitals, medical schools, and the U.S. Armed Forces also offer training. To get into a program, a person must be a high school graduate with a background in mathematics and science.

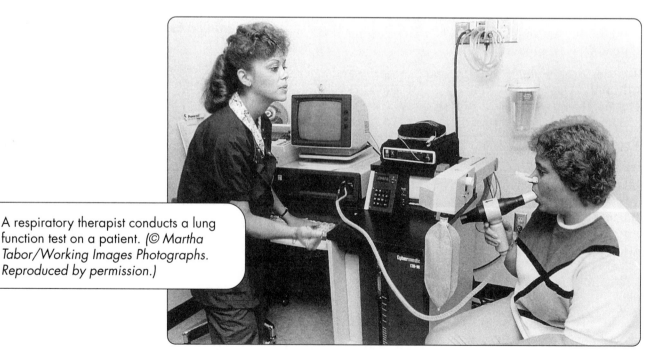

A respiratory therapist conducts a lung function test on a patient. (© Martha Tabor/Working Images Photographs. Reproduced by permission.)

A good background in English is also helpful, because respiratory therapists must keep very detailed records of the treatment they administer.

To become a Registered Respiratory Therapist (RRT) or Certified Respiratory Therapist (CRT), an individual must graduate from a program approved by the Commission on Accreditation of Allied Health Education Programs (CAAHEP) or the Committee on Accreditation for Respiratory Care (CoARC). After graduation, interested individuals can take the CRT exam. If candidates meet further requirements after CRT certification, they can take the RRT exam. Most employers require therapists to hold the CRT or at least be eligible to take the certification exam. Most states require respiratory therapists to obtain a license.

Getting the Job

School placement offices may be able to help students find jobs. If candidates receive their training in a hospital, they may be hired by that hospital. Trade and professional journals often carry listings for respiratory therapists. Interested individuals can also check newspaper want ads and job banks on the Internet.

Advancement Possibilities and Employment Outlook

Respiratory therapists may advance to supervisory positions. Those who have advanced degrees may get teaching positions. Advancement depends on training, personal qualifications, and performance.

The U.S. Bureau of Labor Statistics reports that the outlook for respiratory therapists is very good through the year 2014, with employment expected to increase faster than average. The projected growth of the middle-aged and elderly populations is expected to increase the risk of heart and lung disease, and more respiratory therapists will be needed to provide services for these individuals. Also, as respiratory therapists are required to perform a greater variety of duties, this could mean more jobs for respiratory therapists than currently expected.

Working Conditions

Respiratory therapists do most of their work in hospitals. In emergencies they may work in ambulances. However, because most therapy work can be scheduled in advance, respiratory therapists have fairly regular hours.

Therapists generally work forty hours per week. They may be expected to work some evenings and weekends. Many therapists work part time and hold another job as well.

Earnings and Benefits

Salaries vary with education and place of employment. The median income for experienced therapists was $43,140 per year in 2004, according to the Bureau of Labor Statistics. Benefits include paid holidays and vacations, health insurance, and retirement plans.

Where to Go for More Information

American Association for Respiratory Care
9425 N. MacArthur Blvd., Ste. 100
Irving, TX 75063-4706
(972) 243-2272
http://www.aarc.org

American Lung Association
61 Broadway, 6th Fl.
New York, NY 10006
(212) 315-8700
http://www.lungusa.org

Committee on Accreditation for Respiratory
Care
1248 Harwood Rd.
Bedford, TX 76021-4244
(817) 283-2835
http://www.coarc.com

Surgical Technologist

Education and Training
Community college or vocational/technical school

Salary
Median—$34,010 per year

Employment Outlook
Very good

Definition and Nature of the Work

Surgical technologists, also known as operating room technicians, are part of the surgical team. They assist the doctors, nurses, and other operating room workers. They help prepare patients for surgery by washing, shaving, and disinfecting the intended areas of operation. They clean and set up the surgical equipment. They also transport patients to the operating room, position them on the operating table, and cover them with surgical drapes.

Surgical technologists set up the operating room with instruments and supplies. They help the surgical team scrub in and put on their gowns, gloves, and masks. During surgery, they hand instruments and supplies to the proper surgeons. They may also monitor a patient's vital signs. Technicians help keep track of equipment. They may also help to prepare samples of tissues or organs that will be tested in a laboratory. At times they operate some of the machines in the operating room.

After an operation, technicians take patients to the recovery room. They help to clean and restock the operating room and get it ready for the next operation.

Education and Training Requirements

Surgical technologists usually need a high school diploma. Courses in health and science are helpful. Summer or volunteer work in a hospital is also good experience.

Most surgical technologists receive formal training in vocational and technical schools, hospitals, and community colleges. These training programs, which provide both classroom training and supervised clinical experience, last from nine months to two years. They lead to a certificate or a degree. Students take a variety of courses including anatomy, medical terminology, and professional ethics. They also learn procedures such as how to sterilize instruments, handle

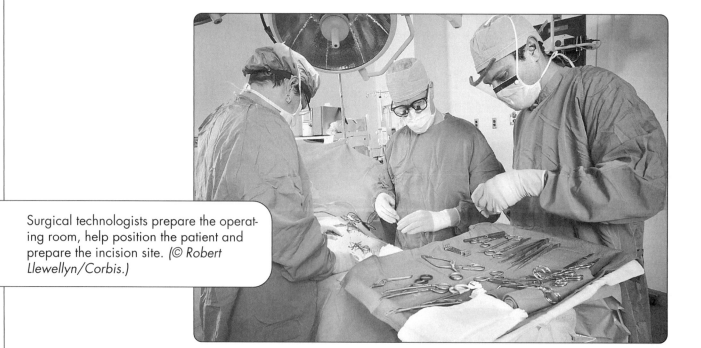

Surgical technologists prepare the operating room, help position the patient and prepare the incision site. (© Robert Llewellyn/Corbis.)

drugs, and control infections. Two organizations certify surgical technologists via national examinations to become either a Certified Surgical Technologist (CST) or a Tech in Surgery–Certified (TS-C). To maintain certification, the surgical technologist must become recertified on a regular basis. Certification is not required to get a job, but most employers prefer to hire certified surgical technologists.

Getting the Job

You can apply directly to the hospital in which you want to work. Also check job listings at state or private employment offices. Newspaper want ads and job banks on the Internet sometimes list jobs for surgical technologists.

Advancement Possibilities and Employment Outlook

Surgical technologists can advance to jobs with more responsibility as they gain experience. They can also specialize in a particular area of surgery such as neurosurgery. With further education they can also move into other health care jobs.

The employment outlook is expected to grow much faster than the average through the year 2014. Growth and aging of the population, advances in surgical techniques, and widespread insurance coverage are expected to increase the number of operations performed. Graduates of postsecondary school training programs will have the best opportunities.

Working Conditions

Surgical technologists generally work forty hours per week. Sometimes they must be on call for night and weekend work. They work with doctors, nurses, and other hospital workers. They must be on their feet for long periods of time and remain alert. Sometimes they can be exposed to diseases and to unpleasant sights and sounds. Surgical technologists need to be careful workers and remain calm in emergencies. They should also be in good health.

Earnings and Benefits

Salaries vary depending on education, experience, and location. In 2004 surgical technologists earned a median salary of $34,010 per year. Benefits include paid holidays and vacations, health insurance, and retirement plans.

Where to Go for More Information

Association of Surgical Technologists
6 W. Dry Creek Circle
Littleton, CO 80120
(303) 694-9130
http://www.ast.org

Acupuncturist

Education and Training
Minimum of some college plus additional training

Salary
Median—$50,000 per year

Employment Outlook
Good

Definition and Nature of the Work

Acupuncturists are alternative health care providers who use procedures that originated in China more than two thousand years ago. American acupuncture incorporates medical traditions from China, Japan, Korea, and other countries. Acupuncture includes procedures that stimulate anatomical points on the body primarily by penetrating the skin with thin, solid, metallic needles that are manipulated by hand or by electrical stimulation. Scientific evidence shows that stimulation by needles at acupuncture points releases hormones called endorphins in the brain, which block pain.

Many people visit acupuncturists for the treatment of headache pain, asthma, or arthritis. Acupuncture may also be useful to treat conditions such as addiction, stroke rehabilitation, menstrual cramps, tennis elbow, lower-back pain, and carpal tunnel syndrome.

After diagnosing the patient and discussing treatment, the practitioner performs the acupuncture. Taking various factors into account, the acupuncturist decides which size needles to use and where to insert them (there are 365 acupuncture points on the body). Several sessions may be necessary to achieve the desired result. The treatment is not generally painful.

Acupuncturists must be skillful and competent with their hands. They must accurately insert and manipulate needles because needles used incorrectly can potentially cause pain, infection, and punctured organs. Acupuncturists must sterilize the needles carefully to avoid infection or use disposable needles. They need great patience to perfect their skill and must relate well to other people.

Many acupuncturists are qualified in such fields as medicine, nursing, and physical therapy. A number of them offer acupuncture as an additional service while continuing in their original professions.

Education and Training Requirements

Acupuncture is a relatively new profession in the United States. Available training varies from apprenticeship to three-year postgraduate programs. About forty states have established training standards for acupuncture certification, but states have varied requirements for obtaining a license to practice acupuncture. In some states, you must first be a doctor of medicine (M.D.) or a chiropractor. However, in other states, a master's of acupuncture (C.A.) at an accredited postgraduate school provides the qualifications necessary for certification. This degree usually consists of two years of study plus a year of supervised practice. Most schools require previous undergraduate study with a focus in anatomy and physiology. The Accreditation Commission for Acupuncture and Oriental Medicine accredits acupuncture schools in the United States. Contact them for a list of accredited schools.

Getting the Job

Most acupuncturists are self-employed. Only a small percentage are affiliated with hospitals. Until recently, nearly all students in acupuncture schools came from careers in the medical field. Upon graduation, they were advised to continue their previous work and develop their acupuncture practices as second jobs. There is no established route for graduates to enter practice.

Advancement Possibilities and Employment Outlook

According to the Bureau of Labor Statistics, there is an increasing demand for alternative health care practitioners, such as acupuncturists. Acupuncture treatments are increasingly covered by insurance. As with doctors, advancement comes with building a practice.

Acupuncturists work in comfortable offices that must be kept quiet and clean. They can usually set their own hours. Some work late on certain evenings for the convenience of their patients. A few work in hospitals or clinics.

Earnings and Benefits

The median salary for acupuncturists in 2005 was $50,000 per year. However, the median salary was quite different in different parts of the country. In Texas, for example, the median salary in 2005 was $32,500, while in California it was $65,000. Acupuncturists in private practice must provide their own benefits.

Where to Go for More Information

American Academy of Medical
  Acupuncture
4929 Wilshire Blvd., Ste. 428
Los Angeles, CA 90010
(323) 937-5514
http://www.medicalacupuncture.org

Accreditation Commission for Acupuncture
  and Oriental Medicine
7501 Greenway Center Dr., Ste. 820
Greenbelt, MD 20770
(301) 313-0855
http://www.acaom.org

Anesthesiologist

Definition and Nature of the Work

Anesthesiologists are physicians who focus on surgical patients and pain relief. They administer anesthetics, which are medicines to prevent patients from feeling pain and sensations; closely monitor patients' vital signs during surgery and adjust anesthetics accordingly; monitor patients through the first recovery stages after an operation; and administer appropriate medications during recovery. In addition to helping patients through surgery, anesthesiologists may also help treat patients with conditions causing chronic pain. Many specialize in specific types of problems, such as respiratory or neurological illness. More than ninety percent of the anesthetics used in health care are administered by or under the direct supervision of an anesthesiologist.

An anesthesiologist's first contact with a surgical patient is usually during a "preoperative interview." At that time the anesthesiologist reviews the patient's medical history and medications, discusses the upcoming surgery, and reviews the options for anesthesia and pain-killing drugs. The anesthesiologist also becomes familiar with the patient's preexisting medical conditions, such as diabetes or heart disease, and plans how to manage those conditions during surgery.

The anesthesiologist is responsible for a patient's life functions as the surgeon and other members of the medical team operate. In the first phase of surgery,

Education and Training
College, medical school, and specialized medical training

Salary
Median—$321,686 per year

Employment Outlook
Very good

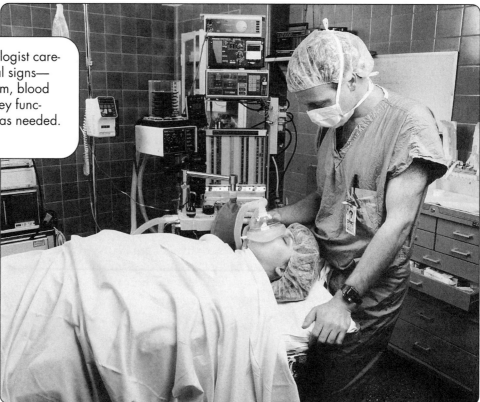

During surgery, an anesthesiologist carefully monitors the patient's vital signs—including heart rate and rhythm, blood pressure, breathing, and kidney function—and adjusts anesthetics as needed. (© Julian Calder/Corbis.)

the anesthesiologist applies the anesthesia. During the middle phase, as the surgery actually takes place, the anesthesiologist uses sophisticated electronic equipment to carefully monitor the patient's vital signs, including heart rate and rhythm, blood pressure, breathing, and brain and kidney functions. As the surgical procedure progresses, the anesthesiologist may have to adjust the patient's anesthesia to compensate for changes in the patient's physical state.

When surgery is finished, the recovery phase begins. The anesthesiologist administers medications to reverse the effects of the anesthetic, returning the patient to consciousness if a general anesthetic has been used. After surgery, patients are moved to a recovery room, where the anesthesiologist is still responsible for the patient's vital functions. In the recovery room, nurses and other specially trained staff closely monitor the patient under the supervision of the anesthesiologist. Eventually, the anesthesiologist determines when the patient has recovered sufficiently to leave the recovery room.

There are three main types of anesthesia administered during surgery: general, regional, and local. General anesthesia renders the patient unconscious and unable to feel pain or any other sensation. Many general anesthetics are gases or vapors administered through a mask or breathing tube, whereas others are liquid medicines introduced through a vein. Regional anesthesia numbs an entire area of the body requiring surgery. Local anesthesia is used to numb a specific part of the body (such as the foot or hand). Both regional and local anesthetics are administered via injections. In addition to anesthetics, patients requiring regional and local anesthetics often are given sedatives to help them relax during surgery and put them to sleep.

Anesthesiologists work in hospitals or outpatient medical facilities where surgery is performed. Some work in emergency rooms, where they handle victims of heart attacks, shock, drug overdoses, traumatic injuries, and other serious health problems requiring immediate care.

Anesthesiologists work as part of a team. In surgery, the team includes the surgeons performing the operation and the nurses supporting them. Anesthesiologists often work directly with a nurse anesthetist who helps administer medications to the patient during surgery.

The job of the anesthesiologist requires intelligence, perseverance, and years of sophisticated training. Besides great technical skills, an anesthesiologist needs a good bedside manner, especially during the preoperative interview when the anesthesiologist must be able to calm the patient while eliciting important information. Anesthesiologists must themselves keep calm during high-stress situations, and they need to be able to maintain peak levels of concentration during long surgical procedures.

Education and Training Requirements

Anesthesiologists are highly educated medical professionals. They must undergo extensive training in addition to their basic medical education.

Like any other physician, an anesthesiologist must successfully complete a four-year undergraduate degree and a four-year medical school program. After medical school, an anesthesiologist takes an additional four years of specialized training.

During the first year of specialized training, an anesthesiologist serves a general internship and is trained in diagnosis or treatment in other areas of medicine. This is followed by an intensive three-year residency program on the technology and medical aspects of anesthesiology. Besides anesthesiology, an anesthesiologist must also study cardiology, critical care medicine, internal medicine, pharmacology, and surgery. An anesthesiologist may choose to specialize in a particular field, such as neurosurgical anesthesiology, and undergo additional training in that field.

Once an anesthesiologist has completed college, medical school, and residency and specialized training, his or her education is by no means finished. New developments in the field of anesthesiology require anesthesiologists to continually update their knowledge and skills through professional seminars and continuing education courses. All students interested in pursuing anesthesiology need a strong background in physics, chemistry, biology, and mathematics.

Getting the Job

Like all physicians, anesthesiologists must be driven, self-motivated individuals willing to work long hours under intense pressure. In addition, a medical education is extremely costly and requires a huge financial commitment. An estimated 80 percent of all medical students borrow money to cover their education expenses.

Anyone interested in pursuing a career in medicine should consider volunteer work at a local hospital or health clinic. That is a good way to gain firsthand experience in working with patients, doctors, nurses, and health care managers.

Advancement Possibilities and Employment Outlook

Anyone who has made it through medical school and residency training to become a fully licensed and practicing anesthesiologist has already made it to the top of his or her chosen field. He or she may decide to pursue a position as the anesthesiology department head within a specific hospital or health care facility. Individuals wishing to quit their medical practice can often find work as teachers.

In 2003 anesthesiologists accounted for approximately 5.4 percent of the 567,000 physicians in the United States. The growing and aging population will increase demand for physicians' services in the coming years. Employment of physicians and surgeons will grow faster than average for all occupations through the year 2014. Opportunities for individuals interested in becoming physicians and surgeons are expected to be very good.

Working Conditions

Anesthesiologists work in hospitals and medical facilities offering inpatient and outpatient surgery. They divide their time between patients' rooms, operating theaters, and post-operation recovery rooms. The job can be extremely stressful and may demand long hours. Anesthesiologists are often "on call," during which time they must be prepared to show up for emergency procedures at all hours of the day and night.

Earnings and Benefits

Anesthesiologists are near the top of the pay scale among all physicians. In May 2004 the median annual income for anesthesiologists who had been in practice for more than one year was $321,686.

Where to Go for More Information

American Society of Anesthesiologists
520 N. Northwest Hwy.
Park Ridge, IL 60068-2573
(847) 825-5586
http://www.asahq.org

American Board of Medical Specialties
1007 Church St., Ste. 404
Evanston, IL 60201-5913
(847) 491-9091
http://www.abms.org

Audiologist

Education and Training
Master's or doctoral degree

Salary
Median—$51,470 per year

Employment Outlook
Good

Definition and Nature of the Work

Audiologists help people who have hearing, balance, and related ear problems. These problems may be a result of trauma at birth, viral infections, genetic disorders, exposure to loud noise, certain medications, or aging. Using various types of testing equipment, audiologists measure patients' ability to hear and distinguish between sounds. In addition, they use computers to evaluate and diagnose balance disorders. Audiologists analyze these test data along with educational, psychological, and other medical patient data to make a diagnosis and determine a course of treatment.

More than half the practicing audiologists work in health care facilities. Another significant portion provides services to schools. Some have private practices, and others work in colleges and universities, clinics, hospitals, special speech and hearing centers, government agencies, and private industry. Some audiologists are researchers.

Education and Training Requirements

A master's degree in audiology has been the standard in the profession. However, a clinical doctoral degree (doctor of audiology, or Au.D.) is becoming more common and will soon be the new standard. You must also achieve a passing score on the national examination on audiology offered through the Praxis Series of the Educational Testing Service. Other requirements typically are 300 to

375 hours of supervised clinical experience and nine months of postgraduate professional clinical experience. Audiologists can become certified by both the American Speech-Language-Hearing Association and the American Board of Audiology. Some states require a special license to dispense hearing aids.

Getting the Job

You can apply directly to the health care facility, school, clinic, or other institution in which you would like to work. Your school placement office or the American Speech-Language-Hearing Association can give you information about job openings. You can also check job listings in the want ads in newspapers and on the Internet.

Advancement Possibilities and Employment Outlook

Advancement depends on education and experience. Audiologists can become supervisors or heads of clinics. They can set up private practices. Those with the necessary training can work as consultants, do research, and write books or articles on hearing problems.

Employment of audiologists is expected to grow about as fast as the average for all occupations through the year 2014. Employment in health and rehabilitation services will increase as a result of advances in medical technology and growth in the elderly population. In addition, as awareness of the importance of the early recognition and treatment of hearing problems increases, so will the demand for professionals in elementary and secondary schools.

Working Conditions

Working conditions are usually pleasant. The job requires attention to detail and intense concentration.

Many audiologists work more than forty hours a week. Their hours are often flexible, and there are part-time jobs available. Audiologists may have contracts with various schools or other institutions and may spend time traveling among those facilities.

Earnings and Benefits

Salaries vary widely depending on education, experience, and location. Median annual earnings of audiologists were $51,470 in May 2004. Benefits usually include paid holidays and vacations, health insurance, and retirement plans.

Where to Go for More Information

American Speech-Language-Hearing
  Association
10801 Rockville Pike
Rockville, MD 20852
(800) 498-2071
http://www.asha.org

American Academy of Audiology
11730 Plaza American Dr., Ste. 300
Reston, VA 20190
(800) AAA-2336
http://www.audiology.org

Cardiac Perfusionist

Education and Training
College degree plus specialized training

Salary
Median—$96,144 per year

Employment Outlook
Excellent

Definition and Nature of the Work

Cardiac perfusionists set up and operate heart-lung machines, which take over the functions of a patient's heart and lungs during heart surgery. The word "perfusion" means to pump a liquid into an organ or tissue, usually via blood vessels. In this case, the liquid is blood with the heart-lung machine doing the pumping.

As part of their jobs, cardiac perfusionists must review patients' medical history and current status, and set up and test the heart-lung machine and related equipment. Perfusionists operate the machine to regulate blood circulation and composition, control body temperature, and administer any necessary drugs. They also communicate to the rest of the operating room team how the patient is doing.

Education and Training Requirements

To obtain employment, a cardiac perfusionist must have a Certified Clinical Perfusionist (CCP) credential from the American Board of Cardiovascular Perfusion. To obtain this credential, an applicant must have graduated from an accredited training program in cardiovascular perfusion by the time of the examination. He or she must also have performed at least seventy-five clinical perfusions during training and have received a letter of satisfactory clinical competency from their school. Certified perfusionists must recertify each year by meeting requirements for clinical activity and continuing education.

Requirements for entrance to a perfusionist training program is a bachelor's degree in science or nursing, or a certain number of undergraduate credits. In some colleges and universities, the program leads to a bachelor's degree. Other colleges and universities offer a graduate program leading to certification and possibly to a master's degree. Programs are not available in every state, admit only a few students, and are rigorous.

Cardiac perfusionists operate heart-lung machines to regulate blood circulation and composition during heart surgery.
(© Owen Franken/ Corbis.)

Getting the Job

In June 2005 there were only four thousand perfusionists employed throughout the United States. The school at which you receive your training may be able to help you obtain employment. You can also apply directly to hospitals, finding information about openings from newspapers and the Internet.

Advancement Possibilities and Employment Outlook

A perfusionist may advance to chief perfusionist with three to five years of experience. A chief perfusionist is an administrator who supervises other perfusionists and is responsible for budgeting.

Employment opportunities for perfusionists are excellent due to the high level of heart disease in the United States. As the population ages, perfusionists will be needed in increasing numbers. Further advancements in the technology used in cardiac surgery are also expected to increase career opportunities for cardiac perfusionists.

Working Conditions

Perfusionists work in well-lighted, sterile environments in hospital operating rooms. They may stand for six to eight hours per day and may have to lift machinery. The operating room environment can be stressful. Perfusionists work with physicians, nurses, and other operating room personnel.

Earnings and Benefits

In 2006 the salary range for most perfusionists was $87,569 to $105,609 per year. The median salary was $96,144. Perfusionists generally received health care, disability insurance, vacations, and retirement plans.

Where to Go for More Information

American Academy of Cardiovascular Perfusion
PO Box 3596
Allentown, PA 18106-0596
(610) 395-4853
http://users.aol.com/officeAACP/home.html

Perfusion.com Inc.
17080 Safety St., Ste. 108
Fort Myers, FL 33908
(866) 892-0265
http://www.perfusion.com

The American Board of Cardiovascular Perfusion
207 N. 25th Ave.
Hattiesburg, MS 39401
(601) 582-2227
http://www.abcp.org

American Society of Extra-Corporeal Technology
2209 Dickens Rd.
PO Box 11086
Richmond, VA 23230-1086
(804) 565-6363
http://www.amsect.org

Chiropractor

Definition and Nature of the Work

Chiropractors are alternative health care practitioners who diagnose and treat health problems associated with the muscular, nervous, and skeletal systems. Chiropractic philosophy holds that interference with these systems impairs the body's normal functions and lowers its resistance to disease. A main tenet of chiropractic philosophy is that dysfunction of the spine (the nerve cord that runs down the back) or vertebral column (the bones that surround that cord) alters many important body functions. In addition, skeletal "imbalance," especially in the vertebral column, can cause pain.

Chiropracters treat patients primarily by manipulating parts of the body, especially the spinal column. By means of this manipulation, chiropractors try to correct any disorders of the skeleton or spine that may interrupt the flow of nerve impulses to various parts of the body. They do not use drugs or surgery to treat patients.

Chiropractors use a variety of methods to learn about a patient's condition. They ask the patient questions and examine the patient carefully, determining whether body structures are out of place. They often use X-rays to get a picture of the patient's bone structure. In addition, chiropractors use laboratory tests, such as urinalysis or blood tests, as well as instruments, such as stethoscopes, to diag-

Education and Training
Advanced degree and license

Salary
Median—$69,910 per year

Employment Outlook
Good

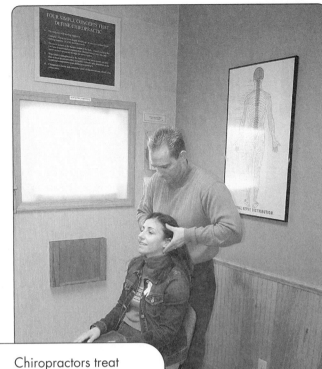

Chiropractors treat patients by manipulating parts of the body. They also treat patients with light, heat, cold, water, exercise, or other forms of physical therapy. *(Photograph by Kelly A. Quin. Thomson Gale. Reproduced by permission.)*

nose disorders. However, some patients need drugs, surgery, psychiatry, and other types of treatment that chiropractors do not provide. Chiropractors refer these patients to physicians.

In addition to performing manipulations, chiropractors treat patients with light, heat, cold, water, exercise, or other forms of physical therapy. In addition, chiropractors often advise their patients about diet and mental outlook to help promote good health.

Most chiropractors have private practices or share practice ownership with other chiropractors. Some teach chiropractic or do research in hospitals, clinics, health agencies, or private industry. Many chiropractors specialize in areas such as athletic injuries, diseases of children and women, and X-ray diagnoses.

Education and Training Requirements

Students usually need two years of college before they can enroll in a chiropractic college, but some states and schools require four years. They should take courses in science and other subjects required by the chiropractic college that they want to attend. After completing a four-year program in a chiropractic college, graduates receive a doctor of chiropractic (D.C.) degree. All states require that chiropractors be licensed. Requirements vary, however, from state to state. In all states chiropractors must pass a state board examination. In some states they must also pass a test in basic science.

Getting the Job

Nearly all newly licensed chiropractors enter private practice. Some of them open their own offices right away. Others buy an established practice from a chiropractor who is retiring. Still others join the office of a practicing chiropractor to get experience. Chiropractic colleges can provide information about setting up a practice.

Some chiropractors have salaried jobs in clinics, chiropractic colleges, or private industry. Job openings of this kind can be found through the want ads of newspapers, Internet job banks, or in professional publications.

Advancement Possibilities and Employment Outlook

Chiropractors usually advance by building their practices. The degree of their success depends on their skill and location as well as other factors. Some chiropractors advance by moving into high-level jobs in teaching, research, or administration.

The employment outlook is expected to grow faster than the average through the year 2014 due to growing use of chiropractic services. Demand for chiropractors is related to the ability of patients to pay, either directly or through health insurance, and to public acceptance of the profession, which is growing. However, more people are going into this field. There may be competition for jobs in some geographical areas.

Working Conditions

Chiropractors usually work in pleasant offices. If they are in private practice, they can set their own hours. To be successful, they need to have a good business sense and self-discipline. They should be able to work with all kinds of people. Chiropractors must also be able to work well with their hands.

Earnings and Benefits

The earnings of chiropractors vary greatly. The median annual salary was $69,910 in 2004. Since chiropractors are usually self-employed, they must provide their own benefits, such as pension funds and insurance policies.

Where to Go for More Information

American Chiropractic Association
1701 Clarendon Blvd.
Arlington, VA 22209
(800) 986-4636
http://www.amerchiro.org

International Chiropractors Association
1110 N. Glebe Rd., Ste. 650
Arlington, VA 22201
(800) 423-4690
http://www.chiropractic.org

Clinical Laboratory Technologist

Definition and Nature of the Work

Clinical laboratory technologists perform laboratory tests that are crucial to the detection, diagnosis, and treatment of disease. They look for evidence of the presence of illnesses and parasites, identify allergic reactions and changes in body chemistry, and type and cross-match blood. They prepare vaccines and serums. Technologists perform exacting microscopic chemical and bacteriological tests, much more complex than performed by clinical laboratory technicians. Clinical laboratory technologists also work as supervisors, teachers, and administrators.

Clinical laboratory technologists test blood, urine, other body fluids, and tissue samples that doctors send to the laboratory. For example, technologists analyze blood and urine to look for signs of diseases, such as hemophilia or diabetes. They are also responsible for matching blood samples so that patients are given the correct type of blood during transfusions. Clinical laboratory technologists identify parasites and bacteria through their tests. The technologist's work is important, because doctors depend on complex tests to diagnose and determine treatment for patients' illnesses.

Technologists may specialize in such areas as blood banking, virology (the study of viruses), cytology (analysis of body cells), and histology (tissue preparation and examination). In large hospitals most technologists specialize in one area. In smaller laboratories they usually perform a variety of duties.

Clinical laboratory technologists work in large hospital laboratories, laboratories of private physicians, public health laboratories, and in medical research institutes. Technologists also work in colleges and universities, companies that manufacture drugs and laboratory test equipment, and the armed services.

Education and Training Requirements

To become a clinical laboratory technologist, you need a bachelor's degree with a major in medical technology or in one of the life sciences. Colleges and uni-

Education and Training
Bachelor's degree plus training

Salary
Average—$45,730 per year

Employment Outlook
Excellent

versities offer medical technology programs accredited by the National Accrediting Agency for Clinical Laboratory Sciences (NAACLS).

Recent graduates who pass the appropriate examinations can become certified. Several organizations offer this certification. Certification is important for technologists, because it indicates that they have met recognized standards of competence. Some states require that technologists be licensed. Requirements for licensing vary but usually include a written examination.

Many universities offer graduate programs in medical technology and related subjects for technologists who want to do certain types of laboratory work or for those who want to work in teaching, administration, or research.

Getting the Job

The placement office of your school can give you job information. You may find employment where you received your clinical training. Newspaper want ads, Internet job banks, and medical journals sometimes list openings. It is a good idea to apply directly to hospitals and laboratories. You can also apply for a position with federal, state, and local health departments.

Advancement Possibilities and Employment Outlook

Technologists can advance with further training. They may choose to specialize in one form of laboratory work or do research. Technologists can also advance to positions as teachers or administrators. A master's degree is generally required for these jobs.

The employment outlook is expected to grow faster than average through 2014 because of increased volume of medical testing due to population growth and an increase in disease and disability among the older population. New, more powerful and accurate diagnostic tests and advances in biotechnology should create a need for qualified medical technologists. Workers will be needed to fill supervisory positions in all laboratories. However, because of advances in equipment, technicians can now do tests that once required the expertise of a technologist.

Where to Go for More Information

American Society for Clinical Laboratory
    Science
6701 Democracy Blvd., Ste. 300
Bethesda, MD 20817
(301) 657-2768
http://www.ascls.org

National Accrediting Agency for Clinical
    Laboratory Sciences (NAACLS)
8410 W. Bryn Mawr Ave., Ste. 670
Chicago, IL 60631
(773) 714-8880
http://www.naacls.org

Working Conditions

Working conditions for medical technologists are generally pleasant. Most laboratories are clean and well lighted. With careful training and proper handling of materials, technologists can keep hazards to a minimum. There are many opportunities for part-time work. Hospital workers may be on emergency call twenty-four hours a day at least once a month. Most technologists work a forty-hour week and may work day, evening, or night shifts.

Earnings and Benefits

Salaries vary depending on experience, location, and the type of laboratory. Median annual earnings of medical and clinical laboratory technologists were $45,730 in 2004. Benefits include paid holidays and vacations and health insurance.

Dentist

Definition and Nature of the Work

Dentists are health professionals who take care of the teeth, gums, and supporting bones of the mouth. They help their patients keep their teeth and gums healthy. They also treat diseased teeth and gums. Dentists sometimes detect general diseases of the body that can affect the condition of a patient's mouth.

Most dentists work as general practitioners in their own offices or with a group of dentists. They often have dental assistants and dental hygienists working for them. Under the dentist's direction, these helpers sometimes take X-rays, clean patients' teeth, and teach patients how to care for their teeth and gums at home. Dentists may take X-rays themselves. They examine patients' mouths for cavities, sores, swelling, or other signs of disease. They may fill cavities, pull teeth that cannot be saved, or replace missing teeth. Dentists use both hand and power tools. They may use a local or general anesthetic to keep patients comfortable during treatment. Some dentists do their own laboratory work. Others send this work out to dental laboratories. Sometimes general practitioners refer patients to specialists.

There are eight areas of specialization for dentists. Orthodontists straighten teeth by fitting them with wires or braces. Oral surgeons operate on the mouth and jaws. Endodontists treat diseases of the soft pulp inside the teeth. Oral pathologists diagnose and sometimes treat diseases of the mouth. Pedodontists specialize in dentistry for children and teenagers. Periodontists are concerned with problems of the gums. Prosthodontists replace missing teeth with artificial teeth. Public health dentists develop care programs. A small percentage of dentists also work in teaching, research, or administration jobs.

Education and Training Requirements

You need six to eight years of training after high school before you can work as a dentist. You must complete two to four years of college before entering a dental

Education and Training
College and dental college

Salary
Median—$129,920 per year

Employment Outlook
Good

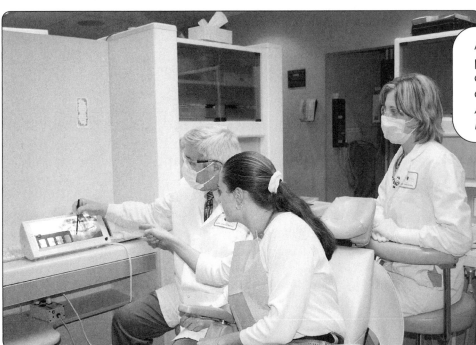

A dentist shows X-rays to a patient. There are several areas of specialization for dentists. *(Photograph by Kelly A. Quin. Thomson Gale. Reproduced by permission.)*

college. Most students have at least a bachelor's degree when they begin dental college. The four-year program at a dental college leads to degrees as either a doctor of dental surgery (DDS) or a doctor of dental medicine (DMD) degree. Dentists who decide to specialize need from two to four years of further training.

All states require dentists to be licensed. They must graduate from an approved dental college and then pass a state board examination.

Getting the Job

Most newly licensed dentists enter private practice. Since it is becoming more difficult to open new practices, many dentists start out by working with a dentist who is already established. Other dentists find salaried positions in hospitals or government agencies. Your dental college placement office can give you information on how to begin a practice.

Advancement Possibilities and Employment Outlook

Dentists usually advance by building their practices. Some become specialists. Others may go into high-level teaching, research, or administration jobs. Employment in dentistry is expected to grow about as fast as average for all occupations through the year 2014. Most jobs will result from the need to replace the large number of dentists projected to retire. Job prospects will be good and the demand for dentists will continue to grow as the population ages and requires more dental care. The provision of dental insurance is also expected to create some new jobs for dentists. At the same time, dentists are likely to hire more dental hygienists and dental assistants to handle some of the services they provide, rather than hiring more dentists.

Working Conditions

Dentists must spend long hours on their feet. They must take precautions against infectious diseases and be able to deal with tense patients. They are rewarded, however, by the prestige of their profession. Because they often have several helpers, dentists must be able to supervise the work of others. They should also have good business sense. They must be responsible and careful professionals who can work well with their hands.

Dentists usually set their own schedules. Many choose to work more than forty hours per week, including some evening and Saturday hours. Some dentists prefer a part-time schedule.

Earnings and Benefits

Earnings for dentists vary widely. They depend on the dentist's experience, skill, and willingness to work long hours. Earnings also depend on location and on the type of practice. In 2004 the median income for dentists was $129,920 per year. Since most dentists are self-employed, they must provide their own benefits.

Where to Go for More Information

American Dental Education Association
1400 K St. NW, Ste. 1100
Washington, DC 20005
(202) 289-7201
http://www.adea.org

American Dental Association
211 E. Chicago Ave.
Chicago, IL 60611-2678
(312) 440-2500
http://www.ada.org

Dermatologist

Definition and Nature of the Work

Dermatologists are physicians who diagnose and treat conditions and diseases of the skin, hair, and nails, such as fungal infections, acne (pimples), birthmarks, skin cancer, eczema (itching, scaling skin), warts, and psoriasis (red patches of skin covered with white scales). The dermatologist first examines the affected area and then may take blood samples, skin scrapings, or tissue samples. The dermatologist usually examines the samples under a microscope or analyzes them using chemical and biological tests. Once the diagnosis is made, the dermatologist treats conditions and diseases using various methods, including medication, surgery, and radiotherapy.

Dermatologists also perform cosmetic procedures on the skin. Some dermatologists may treat scars using methods such as dermabrasion, in which superficial layers of the skin are removed. Others may treat wrinkles using botox injections or other injectible preparations. They may also use laser therapy to remove age spots, treat visible veins, and reduce skin discolorations.

Education and Training Requirements

Like all physicians, dermatologists attend medical school after completing a bachelor's degree. After their internship, dermatology students complete a first-year residency program in one of the following: internal medicine, general surgery, family practice, obstetrics and gynecology, pediatrics, or emergency medicine. The next three years of residency must be in an accredited dermatology residency program. After their residencies are completed, dermatologists can take the certifying examination administered by the American Board of Dermatology (ABD). To maintain certification, dermatologists must take a recertification examination every ten years.

Getting the Job

Dermatologists work in private practice, for hospitals, and for private clinics. Professional associations and medical colleges can provide information about going into private practice or finding a salaried position.

Advancement Possibilities and Employment Outlook

Dermatologists advance as they gain experience in the field and their practice grows. They may specialize in areas such as pediatric or cosmetic dermatology. They can also move into supervisory, teaching, and research positions.

Employment of physicians and surgeons is projected to grow faster than average for all occupations through the year 2014 due to continued expansion of health care industries. The population is growing and aging, and the need for dermatologists to diagnose and treat skin cancers will continue to rise. In addition, there will continue to be a demand for cosmetic procedures.

Education and Training
College, medical school, and specialty training

Salary
Median—$193,870 per year

Employment Outlook
Excellent

Where to Go for More Information

American Academy of Dermatology
10531 I St. NW, Ste. 870
Washington, DC 20005-4355
(202) 842-3555
http://www.aad.org

Womens' Dermatologic Society
575 Market St., Ste. 2125
San Francisco, CA 94105
(415) 927-5727
http://www.womensderm.org

American Board of Dermatology
Henry Ford Health System
1 Ford Place
Detroit, MI 48202-3450
(313) 874-1088
http://www.womensderm.org

Working Conditions

Physicians generally work in clean, comfortable offices, clinics, or hospitals. Those who have their own practices can control some of their working conditions. Dermatologists who specialize in cosmetic procedures may have upscale offices with the latest equipment.

Earnings and Benefits

In 2006 the median salary of dermatologists was $193,870. Self-employed dermatologists arrange their own benefits. For those who are not self-employed, benefits generally include paid holidays and vacations, health insurance, and retirement plans.

Epidemiologist

Education and Training
College, graduate degree, and possibly medical school

Salary
Median—$54,800 per year

Employment Outlook
Good

Definition and Nature of the Work

Epidemiologists are medical scientists who investigate and describe factors that influence the development of disease, disability, and other health outcomes. They formulate means for prevention and control. Epidemiologists focus either on research or on clinical situations.

Research epidemiologists conduct studies to determine how to wipe out or control infectious diseases. They often focus on basic research as well, determining the incidence of a particular disease in a particular part of the world, for example. They may study many different diseases, such as tuberculosis, influenza, or cholera, often focusing on epidemics. Research epidemiologists work at colleges and universities, schools of public health, medical schools, and research and development services firms.

Clinical epidemiologists work mainly as consultants in hospitals, informing medical staff of infectious outbreaks and providing ways to control the spread of infection. In addition, clinical epidemiologists are usually the ones who develop a hospital's standards and guidelines for the treatment and control of infectious diseases.

Education and Training Requirements

To become an epidemiologist, you must have at least a master's degree from a school of public health. In some cases you might need a Ph.D. or medical degree depending on the work you will do. Clinical epidemiologists or research epidemiologists who work in hospitals and health care centers often must have a medical degree with specific training in infectious diseases. You will need to be a licensed physician (that is, you must have passed licensing examinations) if you are going to administer drugs in clinical trials. Epidemiologists who are not licensed physicians frequently work closely with those who are.

Getting the Job

The placement offices of medical and graduate schools will have information on available positions. Qualified individuals can also contact research facilities directly to inquire about research openings.

Advancement Possibilities and Employment Outlook

After gaining experience in epidemiology, individuals can become supervisors of epidemiology departments or directors of research facilities.

Opportunities in epidemiology are highly competitive because the number of available positions is limited. However, some new positions are being added in hospitals and health care centers. Epidemiologists are also needed to investigate outbreaks of new infectious diseases and diseases associated with bioterrorism.

Working Conditions

Epidemiologists generally work in clean, well-lighted offices and laboratories. In addition to hospitals, epidemiologists work in colleges and universities, schools of public health, medical schools, and research and development services firms. Many work for the Centers for Disease Control and Prevention in Atlanta, Georgia, or for other government agencies. A forty-hour, five-day week is the standard; however, a flexible schedule is often required.

Earnings and Benefits

Earnings vary depending on the type of employer and the experience and qualifications of the epidemiologist. Median annual earnings of epidemiologists were $54,800 in 2004. Epidemiologists are usually provided with medical insurance, paid vacations and holidays, and retirement plans.

Where to Go for More Information

International Society for Environmental Epidemiology
c/o JSI Research and Training Institute
44 Farnsworth St.
Boston, MA 02210
(617) 482-9485
http://www.iseepi.org

American College of Epidemiology
1500 Sunday Dr., Ste. 102
Raleigh, NC 27607
(919) 861-5573
http://www.acepidemiology2.org

International Epidemiological Association
http://www.IEAweb.org

Geriatric Social Worker

Definition and Nature of the Work

Social workers help people function in their environments, deal with their relationships, and solve personal and family problems. Geriatric social work is a division of social work concerned with the welfare of the elderly. Geriatric social workers try to improve the quality of life for senior citizens and help alleviate some of the negative aspects of aging. They help senior citizens enjoy happier, more productive lives.

Geriatric social workers are employed in a variety of settings and have a wide range of duties. Most geriatric social workers specialize in one of three areas. One of these areas is assessing the needs of senior citizens. These social workers are often associated with community organizations, such as family service agencies or day care centers, many of which have outreach programs. The social workers may help decide which senior citizens need home health aides, special transportation, or similar services. With the help of such services, some elderly people may be able to live in their own homes when otherwise they would need nursing home care. Geriatric social workers are trained to recognize normal and abnormal aging patterns. They can suggest when an elderly client needs to see a

Education and Training
Associate's, bachelor's, or master's degree

Salary
Median—$40,080 per year

Employment Outlook
Excellent

Geriatric social workers help senior citizens enjoy happier, more productive lives. They help the elderly deal with their problems and alleviate some of the pain of aging. (© Martha Tabor/Working Images Photographs. Reproduced by permission.)

doctor and can arrange for a visit. They can help a family decide whether it would be best to place the client in an institution.

Geriatric social workers also help the elderly deal with their problems. Many older adults are lonely. Social workers encourage clients to participate in group activities. Many workers are skilled in leading these activities or in arranging for others to lead. Some have a background in mental health. They may provide therapy for clients suffering from depression or anxiety (both common conditions among the elderly). Most social workers act as a link between their clients and the numerous confusing public and private programs designed for the aging. Social workers help their clients apply for appropriate services. They help sort out any problems in the delivery of these services. Social workers providing direct services can be found in many types of institutions, including retirement communities, nursing homes, hospitals, and employment programs for older adults.

A small number of geriatric social workers plan and organize services for the elderly. Every program or agency has an executive director or its equivalent. Large organizations may have many administrators. State and county long-range-planning bodies have no clients; their function is to estimate future needs and plan how these needs can best be met.

Geriatric social workers must enjoy working with older people and respect them. The reward of the occupation is having a strong rapport with the clients. Workers should be emotionally mature, objective, and sensitive to the needs of others. They must also be well organized and keep careful records.

Education and Training Requirements

Training in social work with a specialty in gerontology is available at the associate, bachelor's, and master's degree levels. A graduate degree with a specialization in aging is recommended. Some of the better jobs require advanced degrees.

Training requirements may vary with geographic region; they tend to be higher in metropolitan versus rural areas. Consult your local guidance counselor.

Getting the Job

Your college placement office may be able to help you find a job. Consult the job listings in your local newspapers and on the Internet. You can also contact the organizations providing services for senior citizens in your area and ask for information interviews.

Advancement Possibilities and Employment Outlook

Geriatric social workers can advance to supervisory and administrative positions. The director of a small program may go on to run a larger organization.

The outlook for geriatric social workers is excellent, especially for those with advanced degrees. Because the number of senior citizens is increasing rapidly, the need for geriatric social workers will also rise.

Working Conditions

Geriatric social workers are employed in a variety of settings. Their services may be needed at retirement communities, nursing homes, state and government agencies, or hospices. Since the locations of employment may differ, the social worker might be providing service in a modern, well-lighted building one day and an older inner-city facility the next.

Earnings and Benefits

Earnings vary widely. The median annual earnings of medical and public health social workers, such as geriatric social workers, were $40,080 in 2004. Benefits usually include medical insurance, life insurance, and paid vacations.

Where to Go for More Information

Association for Gerontology in Higher Education
1030 15th St. NW, Ste. 240
Washington, DC 20005-1503
(202) 289-9806
http://www.aghe.org

National Association of Social Workers
750 First St. NE, Ste. 700
Washington, DC 20002-4241
(202) 408-8600
http://www.socialworkers.org

Geriatrician

Definition and Nature of the Work

Geriatricians are physicians who work primarily with the elderly. Although they address their patients' multiple medical problems and chronic illnesses, geriatricians focus primarily on quality of life and functional ability. Geriatricians also determine when it is no longer medically safe for seniors to live alone and counsel them on alternative living arrangements. They also counsel patients and families on end of life care.

More than other physicians, geriatricians deal with diseases and conditions that often accompany old age, such as Alzheimer's disease, arthritis, memory loss, chronic heart and lung disease, incontinence, osteoporosis, Parkinson's disease, stroke, and vision and hearing problems. In addition, geriatricians work with

Education and Training
College, medical school, and specialty training

Salary
Median—$166,420 per year

Employment Outlook
Excellent

patients who take a variety of medications. They develop drug regimens that avoid negative drug interactions.

Education and Training Requirements

Geriatricians are typically internists with additional training in elder care. (Internists diagnose and non-surgically treat problems of the internal organs, such as the liver, heart, and lungs.) Like all physicians, geriatricians attend medical school after completing a bachelor's degree. Their internship and residency after medical school lasts from three to eight years. Requirements for licensing vary from state to state. (See the entry "Physician" for more detailed information.)

Getting the Job

Geriatricians work in private practice, for hospitals, nursing homes, and elder care facilities. Professional associations and medical colleges can provide information about going into private practice or finding a salaried position.

Advancement Possibilities and Employment Outlook

Geriatricians advance as they gain experience in the field and their practices grow. They can also move into teaching and research positions.

The employment outlook for geriatricians is excellent. When the baby boom generation enters its senior years, between 2010 and 2030, it is projected that one in five Americans will be over sixty-five. The aging population will generate a demand for geriatricians as well as physicians in other specialty areas.

Working Conditions

Physicians generally work in clean, comfortable offices, clinics, or hospitals. Those who have their own practices can control some of their working conditions. Many geriatricians work or visit patients in assisted living facilities and nursing homes.

Earnings and Benefits

Geriatricians have a salary comparable to internists. In 2004 the median salary for internists was $166,420.

Self-employed physicians arrange their own benefits. For those who are not self-employed, benefits generally include paid holidays and vacations, health insurance, and retirement plans.

Where to Go for More Information

American Geriatrics Society
The Empire State Building
350 Fifth Ave., Ste. 801
New York, NY 10018
(212) 308-1414
http://www.americangeriatrics.org

American Society on Aging
833 Market St., Ste. 511
San Francisco, CA 94103
(800) 537-9728
http://www.asaging.org

Health Educator

Definition and Nature of the Work

Health educators plan, organize, and direct health education programs for communities and groups such as civic organizations and labor unions. They work with other health professionals, civic groups, and community officials to determine health needs, develop desirable health goals, and evaluate the availability of health services. They focus on promoting good health and preventing disease, but they must also deal with social, behavioral, legal, and economic issues.

Public health educators prepare and distribute educational and informational materials on public health issues such as smoking, immunization, drug abuse, and AIDS. They may plan exhibits and health fairs, and may conduct forum discussions to motivate their audiences to understand health issues so they can act in ways that promote good health. Public health educators may also be involved in health-related issues, such as traffic safety and the design of community health facilities. Their goals are to help people adopt healthier lifestyles, make the most efficient use of health services, and practice self-care.

Education and Training Requirements

To be a health educator, you should have a master of public health (M.P.H.) or a master of science (M.S.) degree, preferably from one of the accredited schools of public health or an accredited graduate public health program offered at other educational institutions. Study for the M.P.H. or M.S. involves courses in public health practice and program management, behavioral sciences, and health education, among others.

Some health educators also have a medical degree and have worked in the medical field. Others have a bachelor's degree in a related field, such as sociology or anthropology, as well as related work experience. Practicing public health educators must continue to take courses to maintain and improve their skills, and many go on to earn doctoral degrees. You can become a Certified Health Education Specialist (CHES) if you meet the standards of competence established by the National Commission for Health Education Credentialing (NCHEC) and have successfully passed the CHES examination.

Health educators conduct classes on public health issues such as violence prevention, immunization, drug abuse, and smoking. (© Martha Tabor/Working Images Photographs. Reproduced by permission.)

Education and Training
Master's degree or higher

Salary
Median—$52,639 per year

Employment Outlook
Very good

Getting the Job

Graduates can consult the college placement office for job openings. Many entry-level jobs are available with federal, state, and local governments; health agencies; and volunteer health organizations.

Advancement Possibilities and Employment Outlook

A public health educator for a town or county can become the director of health education for a state's Department of Health and Human Services or, at the federal level, a director of the National Institutes of Health or the Health Resources and Services Administration. A public health educator can also advance by becoming a specialist in a particular area—such as international health issues—and by working for the Centers for Disease Control and Prevention.

Employment opportunities for public health educators are expected to increase faster than the average through 2014. The rise of communicable diseases such as AIDS, the need for prenatal and child health care programs, and the increasing complexity of medical technology have all contributed to this growing demand. Community-oriented health care is also becoming increasingly important.

Where to Go for More Information

National Commission for Health Education
   Credentialing
1541 Alta Dr., Ste. 303
Whitehall, PA 18052-5642
(888) 624-3248
http://www.nchec.org

American Public Health Association
800 I St. NW
Washington, DC 20001-3701
(202) 777-APHA
http://www.apha.org

Working Conditions

Public health educators generally work in comfortable offices. When they are conducting forums or giving presentations, they may have to work some evenings and weekends. Public health educators also frequently travel to other communities or states to explore health education programs.

Educators must have good communication skills and be comfortable working with people. They must also be able to adapt ideas to suit various situations.

Earnings and Benefits

In 2006 the median salary for a health educator was $52,639. Salaried educators usually receive health insurance, paid holidays and vacations, and retirement plans.

Medical and Health Services Manager

Education and Training
College plus graduate degree

Salary
Median—$67,430 per year

Employment Outlook
Good

Definition and Nature of the Work

Health care is one of the largest sectors of the American economy, and it is undergoing radical changes in order to meet the needs of a growing and aging population. Like other complicated businesses, health care institutions require skilled managers.

Currently, more than one-half of medical and health services managers (health care administrators) are employed by hospitals. Other medical and health services managers work for health maintenance organizations (HMOs), nursing homes, mental health institutions, outpatient facilities, home health care agencies, and independent group practices. As health care trends such as preventive

The ever-evolving health care industry requires skilled managers and administrators to make difficult decisions and face complex situations on a daily basis. (© Fred Prouser/Reuters/Corbis.)

medicine and managed care become more common, relatively fewer administrators will be employed by hospitals. (Managed care is a system that delivers health care services to covered individuals by arrangements with selected providers.) Other trends affecting health care administration include integrating various types of health care delivery systems, continual changes in technology, and the rapidly aging American population.

There are many different types of medical and health services managers. Generalists set the overall direction of the health care facility that they manage and do not specialize in any one facet of health care. Top managers or chief executive officers and assistant managers without specific titles are usually generalists. They must combine a basic understanding of clinical issues with business management expertise. Top managers are also often called on to represent their health care facilities to the general public and/or investors.

Specialist managers generally fall into one of two categories: clinical and nonclinical. Nonclinical managers are responsible for such nonhealth functions as finance, housekeeping, and human resources. Clinical managers specialize in functions unique to the health care industry, such as nursing, surgery, therapy, medical records, and outpatient services. Clinical managers usually have more narrowly defined responsibilities than generalists or nonclinical managers.

In addition to being employed at health care facilities, medical and health services managers are also employed by governments and insurance companies. Those employing managers include public health departments, health planning agencies, and the Veterans Administration (VA) health care system. Insurance companies need managers to help manage medical records and claims.

Certain tasks are common to most medical and health services managers regardless of their specialty or employer. Most managers evaluate personnel and their job performance; develop budgets; and implement policies, objectives, and procedures established for their various departments. All managers must also be able to coordinate their efforts with those of other managers and administrators in the best interests of their health care facility and its doctors, nurses, and patients.

The number of administrators employed by a given health care facility is determined by the size of the facility. A large hospital or HMO may employ dozens of managers, whereas a small group of physicians in a group practice may hire a single administrator to handle billing and other administrative duties.

Medical and health services managers often face difficult decisions and complex situations on a daily basis. The job requires good leadership and management skills, excellent problem-solving abilities, and the capacity to work long hours under stress.

Education and Training Requirements

A bachelor's degree from an accredited program and a Registered Health Information Administrator (RHIA) certification from the American Health Information Management Association is almost always a prerequisite for finding employment as a medical and health services manager. Candidates with bachelor's degrees can expect to compete for jobs as administrative assistants or assistant department heads. Becoming a health information manager requires a bachelor's degree. In 2005 there were forty-five accredited bachelor's programs in health information management, according to the Commission on Accreditation for Health Informatics and Information Management Education.

Department managers usually must have at least a master's degree. In addition, many clinical managers also have practical experience in their fields (for example as nurses or therapists) in addition to management training and experience. In 2005 seventy schools had accredited programs leading to the master's degree in health services administration, according to the Commission on Accreditation of Healthcare Management Education. Competition for entry in these programs is keen. Typically, the programs last two to three years and provide course work in hospital organization and management, marketing, accounting, budgeting, and human resources. Some programs offer students the chance to specialize in one type of health care facility or one aspect of health care management, while others offer a general education in health care administration.

Top managers, independent health care management consultants, and researchers have often earned doctoral degrees en route to achieving their positions.

Getting the Job

High school students interested in preparing for a career in medical and health services management should study sciences related to health care, such as biology, chemistry, and physics. In addition, they should take available courses in business management, accounting, and marketing. Volunteering at hospitals, nursing homes, and other health care facilities also provides important exposure to the field.

Upon earning a college degree and certification in medical and health services management, candidates can apply directly to health care facilities for entry-level positions. As mentioned previously, graduate degrees are almost always a prerequisite for top management jobs, so many low-level health care managers participate in continuing education programs in order to advance to the next level.

Advancement Possibilities and Employment Outlook

Medical and health services managers advance by moving into more responsible and higher-paying positions. They may advance within their places of employment or by moving on to larger facilities.

Employment of medical and health services managers is expected to grow faster than the average for all occupations through 2014 due to expansion and diversification in the health services industry. Expect to find relatively fewer positions in hospitals, and more positions in HMOs, home health care agencies, group practices, and long-term facilities.

Working Conditions

Medical and health services managers work long hours in modern facilities. Hospitals, nursing homes, and other health care facilities never "close," and managers are needed at all times to solve problems and handle day-to-day operations. Health care management is a high-stress occupation because managers must make decisions balancing the health of patients with the fiscal health of their facilities.

Earnings and Benefits

The median annual income of medical and health services managers were $67,430 in 2004. According to a survey by *Modern Healthcare* magazine, the median annual compensation in 2004 for hospital administrators of selected clinical departments was $76,800 in respiratory care, $81,100 in physical therapy, $87,700 in home health care, $88,800 in laboratory services, $90,200 in long-term care, $93,500 in medical imaging/diagnostic radiology, $94,400 in rehabilitation services, $95,200 in cancer treatment facilities, $96,200 in cardiology, $102,800 in nursing services, and $113,200 in pharmacies.

Where to Go for More Information

American College of Healthcare Executives
One N. Franklin St., Ste. 1700
Chicago, IL 60606-4425
(312) 424-2800
http://www.ache.org
http://www.healthmanagementcareers.org

American College of Health Care
  Administrators
300 N. Lee St., Ste. 301
Alexandria, VA 22314
(888) 882-2422
http://www.achca.org

Medical Illustrator

Definition and Nature of the Work

Medical illustrators are artists who work in the field of medicine. They make detailed drawings for textbooks and other publications used by physicians and students. They may illustrate the steps surgeons take during operations or draw pictures of both healthy and diseased body parts to show the effects of illness. Medical illustrators also build models of body parts for use in lectures or seminars. In some cases they help to create artificial parts, such as ears or eyes, for patients who need them. Their work may appear in television programs, films, and exhibits for court cases.

Medical illustrations are important to physicians and students because they show details of structures that are difficult to find in the actual body or in photographs. Artists are selective in what they draw, so their illustrations can be es-

Education and Training
Master's degree

Salary
Median—$59,000 per year

Employment Outlook
Good

Medical illustrators make detailed drawings for textbooks and medical journals that are used by physicians and medical students. (© Martha Tabor/ Working Images Photographs. Reproduced by permission.)

pecially effective in showing the relationship of one body part to another. By studying these illustrations, medical students can learn about the body before they do laboratory work or treat patients.

Medical illustrators choose their techniques and media carefully because each illustration has a specific purpose. Drawings, paintings, and prints, for example, simplify information and show relationships between body systems. Sculptures and models show body parts and systems in three dimensions. For illustrations, artists may use paint, pencil, ink, charcoal, and chalk. For sculpting or making models, they use clay, wax, plaster, wood, plastic, or metal.

The training of medical illustrators, which includes both art and science, is intended to give them a comprehensive knowledge of the human body and medical techniques. However, many illustrators specialize in one branch of medicine, such as neurology, which includes the brain and the nervous system.

Many medical illustrators are employed by commercial art studios that create illustrations for textbooks and other publications. Some work for hospitals, universities, and research institutions, where they sometimes teach. Others work for museums and pharmaceutical companies. Freelance artists are self-employed and receive a fee for each project they complete.

Education and Training Requirements

Most schools of medical illustration require applicants to have bachelor's degrees and to have taken some courses in the biological sciences and in art. They must also show samples of their artwork. Graduate training programs for medical illustrators last two or three years.

Getting the Job

Job seekers can apply directly to hospitals, publishers, or pharmaceutical companies. College placement offices, professional associations and journals, newspaper classified ads, and job banks on the Internet are all sources of employment information, including freelance opportunities.

Advancement Possibilities and Employment Outlook

Medical illustrators usually advance by improving their skills—they may specialize in one particular field, for example. Those who work in hospitals can become senior illustrators and supervise the work of other artists, while those who work for commercial art studios can oversee all illustrations for large-scale projects, such as textbooks. Freelance artists build their reputations through quality work, which gets them more and better assignments. Some medical illustrators move into high-level teaching jobs.

The employment of medical illustrators is expected to grow as fast as the average for all jobs through 2014. Some of their best opportunities should come from new developments in medicine. However, this is a small field, so competition may be stiff.

Working Conditions

Medical illustrators do much of their work in quiet, well-lighted art studios, laboratories, and offices. Sometimes they must sketch in operating rooms. Although they often work alone, medical illustrators must also be able to cooperate and to work closely with medical staffs, scientists, and publishers. In addition to artistic talent, they need the ability to do exact and detailed work.

Medical illustrators who work for hospitals, universities, pharmaceutical companies, or commercial art studios generally work forty-hour weeks. Freelance illustrators set their own schedules. All medical illustrators face deadline pressure at times.

Earnings and Benefits

Earnings vary widely depending on skill, experience, and place of employment. In 2005, according to the Association of Medical Illustrators, the median earnings for salaried medical illustrators were $59,000 per year. Benefits for salaried workers include paid holidays and vacations and health insurance. Self-employed illustrators provide their own benefits.

Where to Go for More Information

The Association of Medical Illustrators
PO Box 1897
Lawrence, KS 66044
(866) 393-4264
http://www.ami.org

Medical Physicist

Definition and Nature of the Work

Medical physicists apply the principles and theories of physics to all aspects of medicine. In hospitals, they help plan radiation treatments for cancer patients using external radiation beams or internal radioactive sources. They provide images of internal organs and determine metabolic rates and blood flow. The images provide physicians with important information that allows them to diagnose illness.

Medical physicists also design radiation installations for hospitals and ensure that the complex equipment functions properly. They are responsible for precautions against the hazards of radiation.

Many medical physicists are involved in the research and design of new medical equipment. They work on new applications for high-energy machines, such as linear accelerators to treat cancer. Diagnostic imaging, such as magnetic resonance imaging, is constantly being improved. Medical physicists are also developing new imaging procedures using infrared and ultrasound sources.

At many teaching hospitals, they are faculty members who instruct future medical physicists, medical students, and radiographic technologists. In colleges and

Education and Training
Advanced degree

Salary
Median—$124,532 per year

Employment Outlook
Good

universities they may teach medical physics, biophysics, and radiobiology to graduate and undergraduate students.

Education and Training Requirements

Graduate training in medical physics is required for all jobs in this field; most medical physicists have doctorates. Knowledge of physics and basic medical sciences, such as anatomy, physiology, genetics, and biochemistry, is essential.

Getting the Job

The best sources for information about job openings are college professors, advisers, and placement offices because they usually have contacts in the medical industry. Graduates can also apply directly to hospitals, universities, and government agencies. Professional associations and journals often list job openings.

Advancement Possibilities and Employment Outlook

Advancement opportunities are good for medical physicists with doctorates. In hospitals and research centers, they can advance by taking on more responsibility and heading project teams. Those in teaching positions can move through the ranks from assistant professor to full professor.

Employment of physicists is expected to grow more slowly than the average for all occupations through 2014. More doctorates are being granted than there are openings for medical physicists, so competition for jobs may be stiff. However, new positions may be created because the aging population may need an increasing number of diagnostic tests. Openings regularly occur when experienced workers retire or leave the field.

Working Conditions

Most medical physicists work in clean, well-lighted laboratories and classrooms in hospitals and universities. They may conduct research independently or as members of teams. They must be able to communicate their ideas to doctors, students, and sometimes patients both orally and in writing. While they generally work forty-hour weeks, overtime may be necessary for emergencies and special projects. They spend additional hours studying the latest developments in the field.

Earnings and Benefits

Salaries for medical physicists are similar to those of other physicists. In 2006 the median salary for experienced medical physicists with advanced degrees was $124,532 per year. Benefits usually include health insurance, paid vacations and sick leave, and retirement plans.

Occupational Therapist

Definition and Nature of the Work

Occupational therapists (OTs) help people who have physical, mental, or emotional impairments improve their ability to perform routine tasks at both home and work. They help patients improve their basic motor functions and reasoning abilities or compensate for permanent loss of function. Their goal is to help patients live independently.

Some patients need exercises that will increase their physical strength, dexterity, visual perception, and ability to distinguish patterns. Others need to relearn basic daily functions: dressing, cooking, eating, and using computers. Patients who have permanent disabilities, such as spinal cord injuries, need training in the use of wheelchairs and aids for eating and dressing. In some cases, OTs may make special equipment that patients need at home or at work.

Most occupational therapists work in hospitals. Government and private agencies, rehabilitation centers, clinics, and nursing homes all hire OTs, often as consultants. In schools, OTs help young patients participate as fully as possible in school programs and activities. In mental health facilities, they may choose activities that help patients learn to engage in and cope with daily life.

Education and Training Requirements

Bachelor's degrees in occupational therapy, which have long been acceptable education for entry into the field, are no longer sufficient. As of 2007, OTs must have at least master's degrees from accredited programs. In addition, they must

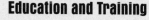

Education and Training
Master's degree

Salary
Median—$54,660 per year

Employment Outlook
Excellent

Occupational therapists plan therapy programs that help patients overcome physical disabilities. These occupational therapists work with a paralyzed patient in the use of a personal computer. (© Bohemian Nomad Picturemakers/Corbis.)

be licensed by passing certification exams. OTs who work in schools or with very young children may need other credentials depending on the state.

Getting the Job

Job seekers can apply directly to hospitals and clinics. School placement offices, professional associations and journals, newspaper classified ads, and job banks on the Internet are other sources of employment leads.

Advancement Possibilities and Employment Outlook

Therapists who work in hospitals or clinics can be promoted to senior therapists and directors of occupational therapy programs after many years of experience. They can also become teachers and consultants.

The employment of occupational therapists is expected to grow much faster than the average for all occupations through 2014. New medical technology is saving more lives, increasing life expectancy, and spurring demand for rehabilitative care. As the baby-boom generation gets older, demand for cardiac rehabilitation programs may increase as well.

Working Conditions

Most occupational therapists work forty-hour weeks. Evening and weekend hours may be required. Part-time jobs are also available.

Occupational therapists should be warm and creative people, for they work closely with patients and other health-care workers. They must be able to use their own initiative in planning and carrying out programs.

Earnings and Benefits

Salaries vary depending on education and experience. In 2004 the median salary of occupational therapists was $54,660 per year. Benefits include paid holidays and vacations, health insurance, and pension plans.

Where to Go for More Information

The American Occupational Therapy
  Association
4720 Montgomery La.
PO Box 31220
Bethesda, MD 20824-1220
(301) 652-2682
http://www.aota.org

National Board for Certification in
  Occupational Therapy
800 S. Frederick Ave., Ste. 200
Gaithersburg, MD 20877-4150
(301) 990-7979
http://www.nbcot.org

Ophthalmologist

Education and Training
College, medical school, and specialized medical training

Salary
Median—$199,423 per year

Employment Outlook
Very good

Definition and Nature of the Work

Ophthalmologists are physicians who diagnose and treat diseases of the eye, including glaucoma and cataracts; vision problems such as nearsightedness; and eye injuries. Optometrists and family doctors often refer patients with serious eye conditions to ophthalmologists. Because of their extensive training, ophthalmologists can often link eye problems to other disorders. For example, they are sometimes the first to detect brain tumors, diabetes, or multiple sclerosis.

Ophthalmologists use a variety of instruments, including ophthalmoscopes, which enable them to see the inner part of the eye. They can prescribe medicine, contact lenses, and eyeglasses. Sometimes they recommend eye exercises. When necessary, they perform surgery, which may involve removing a piece of

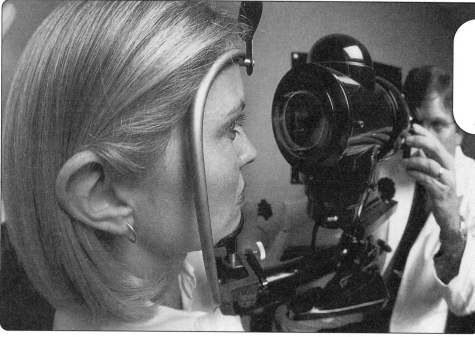

glass embedded in the eye or transplanting a cornea (the transparent covering of the iris and pupil). Because the eye is so small, ophthalmologists usually operate with the help of microscopes and magnifying lenses. They must work with great care.

Most ophthalmologists have private practices, although some work in hospitals, health agencies, and medical colleges. Others are teachers or researchers.

Education and Training Requirements

Ophthalmologists need extensive training after high school: four years of college, four years of medical school, one year of internship, and three years of training as hospital residents in ophthalmology. After their internships, students take a series of exams to become licensed to practice general medicine. After their residencies, ophthalmologists must pass exams and other requirements for certification in their specialty.

Getting the Job

Placement services at medical schools can usually refer graduates to established doctors who are hiring associates; many ophthalmologists begin their careers as associates. Others work as salaried employees of hospitals or government agencies. Professional organizations and journals may also have job information.

Advancement Possibilities and Employment Outlook

Ophthalmologists usually advance by expanding their practices. Some may specialize in one disease or disorder, such as the detachment of the retina, or in one kind of eye care, such as ophthalmology for children or elderly people. Others become teachers or researchers at colleges and universities.

Employment of physicians and surgeons in general is expected to grow faster than the average for all occupations through 2014. The demand for ophthalmologists should increase because of a larger elderly population and extended health-care benefits.

Working Conditions

Most ophthalmologists work in private practice, with regularly scheduled hours in their offices and in operating rooms. Emergencies are rare, so ophthalmologists keep more regular hours than general medical practitioners. Ophthalmologists must keep up with new developments in their field, however, so they often spend extra hours studying, researching, and attending seminars.

Ophthalmology is an important, respected profession. It requires high intelligence, good depth perception, and excellent coordination.

Earnings and Benefits

Earnings vary with experience, skill, and location. In 2006 the median salary for ophthalmologists was $199,423. Those in private practice provided their own benefits. Benefits for salaried ophthalmologists included paid holidays and vacations, health insurance, and pension plans.

Where to Go for More Information

American Academy of Ophthalmology
PO Box 7424
San Francisco, CA 94120-7424
(415) 561-8500
http://www.aao.org

Optometrist

Education and Training
College plus optometry school

Salary
Median—$88,410 per year

Employment Outlook
Good

Definition and Nature of the Work

Optometrists examine eyes and treat vision problems, usually by prescribing eyeglasses or contact lenses, vision therapy, or rehabilitation programs. They also prescribe medicines to treat some eye diseases and allergies.

Optometrists examine patients' eyes with several instruments. Retinoscopes, for example, help them see how patients react to lenses of different strengths. Ophthalmoscopes allow them to see the inside of the eye. Based on their examinations, they make diagnoses, such as nearsightedness or farsightedness, and prescribe lenses or other treatments. If they diagnose eye diseases that need surgery, they refer patients to ophthalmologists (physicians who perform eye surgery). Sometimes optometrists discover eye conditions caused by systemic problems, such as diabetes or high blood pressure, and refer their patients to other medical doctors.

Most optometrists have their own practices or are associates in group practices. Others are employed in hospitals, clinics, and health or government agencies. Still others work for insurance companies; for manufacturers of eyeglasses, contact lenses, and other optical equipment; or for large eyewear chains. Some jobs involve the designing and testing of new products.

Education and Training Requirements

Most future optometrists complete fours years of college before enrolling in optometry schools, which offer four-year programs leading to doctor of optometry degrees. Some optometrists may want to specialize in work with the elderly, with children, with the partially sighted, or in vision therapy. They can study for master's degrees or doctorates, or they may enter one-year residency programs offered for certain optometric specialties.

Optometrists must be licensed. They must pass both a written National Board of Examiners in Optometry examination and a clinical board examination at the

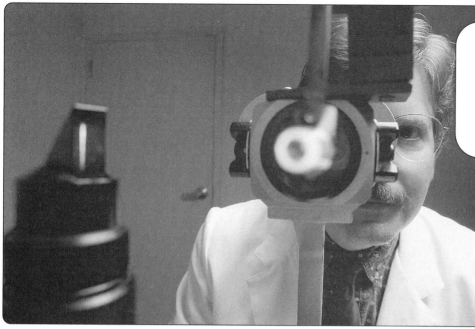

national, regional, or state level. Many states also require applicants to pass examinations on relevant state laws.

Getting the Job

Optometrists set up their own practices or begin by working with established optometrists. Jobs are also available in clinics, in private industry, and in health or government agencies. School placement offices and the American Optometric Association can offer career advice.

Advancement Possibilities and Employment Outlook

Many optometrists become self-employed after some years as salaried workers or as associates in group practices. Other optometrists specialize. Optometrists who have additional education and experience can move into jobs in teaching, research, or administration.

Employment for optometrists is expected to grow faster than the average for all occupations through 2014. The maturing of the large baby-boom generation, together with rapid growth in the elderly population, should increase the demand for qualified optometrists. The growth of large eyewear chains will provide additional jobs. However, increased use of optometric assistants and more sophisticated equipment may affect employment is some geographic areas.

Working Conditions

Optometrists usually work in pleasant surroundings. Those in private practice may supervise assistants. In large offices, clinics, and health and government agencies, optometrists work as members of professional health-care teams. Most optometrists work forty-hour weeks, often including some evening and Saturday hours.

Optometrists have responsible jobs that require close contact with the public. They need manual dexterity and—especially if they are in private practice— business skills.

Where to Go for More Information

Earnings and Benefits

Earnings depend on experience, location, and area of specialization. In 2004 the median earnings of salaried optometrists were $88,410 per year. Benefits usually included paid holidays, sick days, and vacations and health insurance. Optometrists in private practice provided their own benefits.

Orthoptist

Education and Training
Bachelor's degree plus training

Salary
Average—$45,000 to $50,000 per year

Employment Outlook
Excellent

Definition and Nature of the Work

Orthoptists treat imbalances of the muscles of the eye or the nerves that serve those muscles. Many of their patients have amblyopia—commonly called lazy eye—or strabismus—known as cross-eye. Orthoptists also treat vision problems that arise from strokes or head injuries.

Patients with such disorders do not have proper binocular vision; that is, their eyes do not work together as they should. Using diagnostic instruments and procedures, orthoptists determine appropriate treatments, which often include exercising eye muscles or temporarily covering one eye with a patch so the other eye works more effectively. Orthoptists work mainly with children because these vision problems are usually present and noticed in childhood.

Orthoptists usually work under the supervision of ophthalmologists, who are medical doctors specializing in diseases of the eye. Orthoptists work in hospitals, clinics, private doctors' offices, and medical centers.

Education and Training Requirements

To enter orthoptist training programs, applicants must have bachelor's degrees from accredited colleges or universities. Degrees in science are preferred. Training programs usually last about twenty-four months and include both classroom and clinical work. Orthoptists who complete approved programs must pass exams to become certified.

Getting the Job

Graduates of training programs can apply directly to ophthalmologists for employment. School placement offices and the American Association of Certified Orthoptists usually have information about job openings. Professional journals, newspaper classified ads, and job banks on the Internet may also provide employment leads.

Advancement Possibilities and Employment Outlook

Orthoptists advance by taking on more responsibility in the care of patients with cross-eye and related vision problems. Sometimes they also help in the training of new orthoptists.

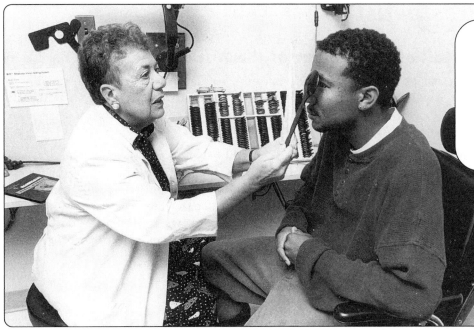

Orthoptists use diagnostic instruments and procedures to test patients. They treat patients who have eye muscle imbalance problems. (© Martha Tabor/Working Images Photographs. Reproduced by permission.)

Employment opportunities should be good over the next decade because more openings exist than there are qualified orthoptists. Demand should also grow as more ophthalmologists make use of the special training of orthoptists.

Working Conditions

Because this is a very specialized field, most jobs are located in or near major cities. Orthoptists often work in ophthalmologists' offices and keep the same hours, usually forty hours per week. Some evening or Saturday work may be required. Part-time work is sometimes available.

Because they treat patients who have handicaps that can be emotionally upsetting, orthoptists have to be understanding, enthusiastic, and encouraging. They should be good teachers who can explain eye exercises clearly, especially to children.

Earnings and Benefits

Salaries vary depending on experience, position, and location. The American Medical Association reported that in 2000 the average salary of orthoptists in the United States ranged from $45,000 to $50,000 per year. Some orthoptists earned more than $80,000 per year. Benefits generally included paid holidays and vacations and health insurance.

Where to Go for More Information

American Association of Certified Orthoptists and American Orthoptic Council
3914 Nakoma Rd.
Madison, WI 53711
(608) 233-5383
http://www.orthoptics.org

Orthotist and Prosthetist

Education and Training
Bachelor's degree

Salary
Median—$59,540 per year

Employment Outlook
Good

Definition and Nature of the Work

Orthotists and prosthetists help patients use damaged parts of their bodies or replace parts that patients have lost to accidents or illnesses. Orthotists fit braces to help support parts of the body or to correct malformations. Prosthetists fit artificial limbs.

Working with doctors' prescriptions, orthotists and prosthetists carefully measure their patients and design braces or artificial limbs that suit the patients' specific needs. Braces and artificial limbs are crafted from wood, steel, aluminum, leather, cloth, rubber, and plastic. Once the devices are made, orthotists or prosthetists fit them on their patients, often with the help of doctors and physical therapists. The team makes sure the devices work properly. Adjustments are made, if necessary.

Education and Training Requirements

Bachelor's degrees in orthotics or prosthetics are usually required. After a period of supervised clinical practice, college graduates are eligible for exams given by the American Board for Certification in Orthotics and Prosthetics. Others become certified by earning associate degrees in any field; completing certificate programs in orthotics and prosthetics; working for four years in the field; and taking exams.

Getting the Job

Job seekers can apply directly to hospitals, clinics, government agencies, and private companies. School placement offices, professional journals, newspaper classified ads, and job banks on the Internet may offer employment information.

Orthotists make and fit braces to help support parts of the body or to correct malformations. They must design each device to suit the unique needs of its wearer. (© Bob Rowan; Progressive Image/Corbis.)

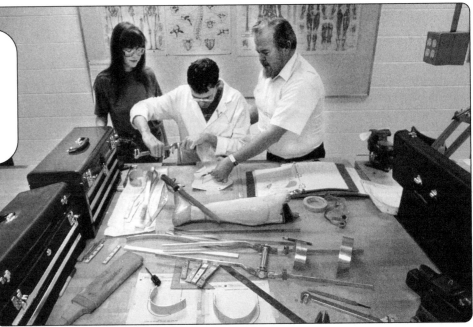

Advancement Possibilities and Employment Outlook

The possibilities for advancement depend on education, experience, and skill. In large hospitals or clinics, orthotists and prosthetists can become department heads. Some start their own practices or become researchers, salespeople, or teachers.

Employment of orthotists and prosthetists is expected to grow faster than the average for all occupations through 2014. The field is growing because an aging population needs more rehabilitative care and insurance companies are providing greater access to orthotic and prosthetic devices. Also, advancements in technology are allowing more people to have new devices designed for them.

Working Conditions

Most orthotists and prosthetists work in combination shop-laboratories, which are usually inspected by the American Board for Certification in Orthotics and Prosthetics.

Orthotists and prosthetists must work well with their hands and machinery. They must also be able to communicative compassionately with their patients.

Earnings and Benefits

Salaries vary with education, experience, and place of employment. In 2006 the median salary for experienced, certified orthotists and prosthetists was $59,540 per year. Beginning workers with bachelor's degrees earned about $27,500 per year. Benefits generally included paid holidays and vacations, health insurance, and retirement plans. Self-employed orthotists and prosthetists provided their own benefits.

Where to Go for More Information

American Academy of Orthotists and
  Prosthetists
526 King St., Ste. 201
Alexandria, VA 22314
(703) 836-0788
http://www.oandp.org

The American Board for Certification in
  Orthotics and Prosthetics
330 John Carlyle St., Ste. 210
Alexandria, VA 22314
(703) 836-7114
http://www.abcop.org

Osteopathic Physician

Definition and Nature of the Work

Osteopathic physicians practice a system of health care known as osteopathy, which is based on the idea that health is closely related to the structure of the body. They specialize in a treatment called manipulative therapy in which they use their hands to move parts of the patient's body, especially the muscles and bones, into the proper positions. This therapy continues until the patient's body systems are brought back to their correct relationship.

Osteopathic physicians use the same methods that medical doctors use to diagnose and treat illness and injury. They prescribe medicines, perform surgery, and recommend diets and other kinds of therapy. More than forty-five percent of all osteopathic physicians are general practitioners or family doctors. As with medical doctors, osteopaths have office practices and work in hospitals. About fifteen percent of all osteopathic physicians are specialists in such fields as surgery, obstetrics and gynecology, pediatrics, psychiatry, neurology, and internal medicine. A small number of osteopathic physicians have salaried positions in osteopathic hospitals and colleges, private industry, and government agencies.

Education and Training
College, osteopathic medical college, and specialized training

Salary
Median—$156,010 per year

Employment Outlook
Very good

Osteopathic physicians manipulate patients' bones and muscles until all the body systems are brought back into alignment with one another. (© Martha Tabor/Working Images Photographs. Reproduced by permission.)

Education and Training Requirements

A few students start osteopathic college after only three years at preprofessional colleges, but most students earn bachelor's degrees first. The four-year programs at osteopathic colleges are similar to the training at other medical schools. However, osteopathy puts more emphasis on anatomy and the relationship between the structure of the body and its functions. Nearly all new graduates of osteopathic colleges spend a year as interns in osteopathic hospitals before residencies of two to six years of specialized training.

Osteopathic physicians must be licensed. Requirements vary, but in all states osteopathic physicians must graduate from accredited osteopathic colleges, pass licensing examinations, and complete one to seven years of graduate medical education.

Getting the Job

Nearly all osteopathic physicians go into private practice. Many start as assistants in the offices of established osteopathic physicians. Others take jobs on the staffs of osteopathic hospitals. Professional associations and colleges or hospitals of osteopathy can provide information about developing private practices or finding salaried positions.

Advancement Possibilities and Employment Outlook

Most osteopathic physicians advance by building their practices. Some become specialists. A small number become teachers, researchers, or administrators. Others write or edit scientific books or journals.

The federal government and most states grant osteopathic physicians the same privileges as medical doctors. Some osteopathic physicians practice with medical doctors. Most set up their practices in areas where there are osteopathic hospitals or clinics.

Employment of both medical and osteopathic physicians and surgeons is projected to grow faster than the average for all occupations through 2014 because all health-care industries are expanding. The growing and aging population should drive overall growth in the number of physicians. New technologies permit more tests and more procedures, allowing physicians to treat more conditions. General and primary care practitioners should have the best prospects; competition may be stiff for specialists because of the limits set by managed health care organizations.

Working Conditions

Most osteopathic physicians have their own practices and are able to set their own working conditions. Many work more than fifty hours per week. Some of this time is spent studying the latest advances in the field. Family doctors usually work longer and more irregular hours than specialists.

Osteopathic physicians need good health, stamina, self-discipline, and business skills.

Earnings and Benefits

Osteopathic physicians earn salaries comparable to medical doctors in general practice. In 2004 the median salary of osteopathic physicians in family practice was $156,010 per year. Osteopathic physicians in private practice must provide their own benefits, such as health insurance and pensions.

Where to Go for More Information

American Academy of Osteopathy
3500 DePauw Blvd., Ste. 1080
Indianapolis, IN 46268
(317) 879-1881
http://www.academyofosteopathy.org

American Osteopathic Association
142 E. Ontario St.
Chicago, IL 60611
(800) 621-1773
http://www.do-online.osteotech.org

Pharmacist

Definition and Nature of the Work

Pharmacists are health practitioners who specialize in dispensing drugs prescribed by physicians and providing information to patients about their side effects and use. Pharmacists must understand the composition of medicines, as well as the laws that regulate their manufacture and sale. They order and store medicines, keeping them safe, pure, and effective. They are required by law to maintain records of the drugs they handle.

Most pharmacists work in community pharmacies. Some of these retail stores, which are owned either by the pharmacists themselves or by drugstore chains, sell only medical and sickroom supplies; others carry a wide range of items, from health supplies to laundry detergent and stationery. Some pharmacists concentrate on the dispensing of drugs, while others manage entire stores, creating combined pharmacy and business careers.

Some pharmacists work in hospital or nursing home pharmacies. They buy, inspect, store, and distribute drugs. They often keep drug information libraries and advise the medical and nursing staffs about new drugs.

Other pharmacists work in the pharmaceutical industry, which includes companies that research, manufacture, or sell medicines. Pharmacists are also em-

Education and Training
Advanced degree

Salary
Median—$84,900 per year

Employment Outlook
Very good

Pharmacists work in pharmacies, hospitals, or nursing homes, dispensing drugs that require a doctor's prescription. (© Martha Tabor/Working Images Photographs. Reproduced by permission.)

ployed by government agencies and as teachers in colleges and universities. A small number work in specialized areas, such as writing or editing books, articles, or advertisements about drugs.

Education and Training Requirements

Pharmacists must have at least six years of education beyond high school. After two or three years of college, students enter four-year programs that result in pharmacy degrees. Entry requirements usually include courses in mathematics, natural sciences, humanities, and social sciences. About two-thirds of all colleges of pharmacy require applicants to take the Pharmacy College Admissions Test. Students may go on to earn master's degrees or doctorates in specialty areas of pharmacy.

All states expect pharmacists to be licensed. Requirements include degrees from colleges of pharmacy accredited by the Accreditation Council for Pharmacy Education and examinations.

Getting the Job

Most pharmacists begin their careers as employees in community or hospital pharmacies. Placement services of colleges of pharmacy usually have information about job openings. Graduates can also apply directly to pharmacies or to firms that make medicines. Professional associations can help graduates get jobs or open pharmacies of their own.

Advancement Possibilities and Employment Outlook

Advancement depends on many factors, including location, type of work, business skill, and ambition. About sixty percent of all pharmacists work in community pharmacies. Some open their own pharmacies. Those who work for chain-owned drugstores can become managers, while those employed by hospitals can become directors of pharmacy services. Pharmacists working for drug manufacturers can move into executive positions. Some pharmacists become administrators in government agencies, teachers, or researchers.

The employment of pharmacists is expected to grow faster than the average for all occupations through 2014. The demand for pharmacists—because of general employment growth or because of retirements—should exceed the number of new graduates.

Working Conditions

Pharmacists work in clean, pleasant surroundings. Most salaried employees work about forty hours per week, while self-employed pharmacists work about fifty hours per week. They often work evening and weekend hours. Some pharmacists work part time.

Pharmacists are usually on their feet for long hours. They should be in good health and be able to communicate with other professionals as well as with the public. They must be responsible people who can do careful, detailed, and confidential work. Management skills are also an asset.

Earnings and Benefits

Earnings vary depending on experience, skill, and place of employment. In 2004 the median annual salary of pharmacists was $84,900 per year. Owners of pharmacies, managers of chain drugstores, and high-level administrators often earned much more.

Self-employed pharmacists must provide their own benefits. Benefits for salaried pharmacists generally include paid holidays and vacations, health insurance, and retirement plans.

Where to Go for More Information

American Pharmacists Association
2215 Constitution Ave. NW
Washington, DC 20037-2985
(800) 237-2742
http://www.aphanet.org

National Association of Chain Drug Stores
413 N. Lee St.
PO Box 1417-D49
Alexandria, VA 22313-1480
(703) 549-3001
http://www.nacds.org

Pharmacologist

Definition and Nature of the Work

Pharmacologists are research scientists who develop, identify, and test drugs to cure, treat, and prevent disease. They also test substances, such as gases, dusts, or food colorings, to determine if they are harmful. They often study the effects of drugs and other substances on laboratory animals, such as guinea pigs and monkeys.

Among the many areas of specialization are clinical pharmacology, which involves testing drugs on human beings; neuropharmacology, which analyzes the effect of drugs on the nervous system; and chemotherapy, the development and study of drugs that kill cancer cells, germs, or viruses without destroying healthy cells. Toxicologists study poisonous drugs and other substances, such as chemicals and air pollutants, that have harmful effects.

The majority of pharmacologists spend their time in laboratories, although many also teach. Pharmacologists work in private industry, hospitals, universities, and government agencies.

Education and Training Requirements

Bachelor's degrees, including courses in sciences and mathematics, are required to enter pharmacology programs. Graduate study includes theoretical courses

Education and Training
Advanced degrees

Salary
Average—$91,407 to $118,828 per year

Employment Outlook
Very good

and laboratory research, resulting in doctorates in pharmacology. Pharmacologists must have both doctorates and medical degrees to conduct clinical testing on humans. Some medical schools have special programs that offer both degrees.

Getting the Job

Graduates can apply directly to drug companies, universities, hospitals, or government agencies. School placement offices and professional associations usually have lists of job openings.

Advancement Possibilities and Employment Outlook

Most pharmacologists advance by continuing their education. They often become experts in one area of pharmacology or lead research teams or university departments.

The employment outlook for pharmacologists is very good through the year 2010. The projected increase in the middle-aged and elderly populations should increase the demand for trained professionals in all of the life sciences. Scientific advances that make more drug products available—and require more testing—should create many new jobs for pharmacologists.

Working Conditions

Pharmacologists usually spend long hours in laboratories and research libraries. Their meticulous work usually gives them great personal satisfaction.

Earnings and Benefits

Salaries vary depending on education, experience, and type of employment. In 2006 average earnings of experienced pharmacologists ranged from $91,407 to $118,828 per year. Benefits included paid vacations and holidays, health insurance, and retirement plans.

Where to Go for More Information

American Society for Pharmacology and
   Experimental Therapeutics
9650 Rockville Pike
Bethesda, MD 20814-3995
(301) 634-7060
http://www.aspet.org

American Board of Clinical Pharmacology
PO Box 40278
San Antonio, TX 78229-1278
(210) 567-8505
http://www.abcp.net

Physical Therapist

Education and Training
Advanced degree

Salary
Median—$60,180 per year

Employment Outlook
Very good

Definition and Nature of the Work

Physical therapists help patients suffering from injury or disease to restore function, improve mobility, relieve pain, and prevent or limit permanent physical disabilities. In addition, they promote patients' overall fitness and health. Physical therapists work with health-care teams that include physicians, occupational therapists, and psychologists. They are employed by hospitals, nursing homes, or rehabilitation centers.

Physical therapists test each patient and design individual programs of treatment. They may use massage to improve muscle condition; apply ice to reduce swelling or heat to relieve pain; and utilize therapeutic equipment, such as whirlpool baths, ultrasonic machines, and ultraviolet and infrared lamps. They teach patients how to do exercises with such equipment as pulleys and weights, stationary bicycles, and parallel bars. They also teach patients and their families how to use and care for wheelchairs, braces, canes and crutches, and artificial limbs.

A physical therapist monitors the progress of a patient on a treadmill. (© Wolfgang Flamisch/zefa/Corbis.)

Physical therapists often supervise and instruct aides and assistants who help carry out programs of treatment. Therapists also keep records and write reports on the progress of each patient.

Education and Training Requirements

Accredited physical therapy programs offer both master's degrees or doctorates in physical therapy. Applicants need bachelor's degrees that include prerequisite courses, which are set by each graduate program. To be licensed, graduates of accredited programs must pass state examinations. Many states require continuing education to remain licensed in the field.

Getting the Job

Job seekers can apply directly to hospitals and rehabilitation centers. College placement offices, the American Physical Therapy Association, professional journals, newspaper classified ads, and job banks on the Internet are all sources of employment openings. High school or college students can gain useful experience through volunteer or part-time work in physical therapy departments of hospitals.

Advancement Possibilities and Employment Outlook

Experienced therapists can become supervisors of hospital departments. With additional education, they may teach physical therapy.

Employment of physical therapists is expected to grow much faster than the average for all occupations through 2014, largely because the population is growing older and likely to need rehabilitation and long-term care. Advances in therapeutic techniques, especially for trauma victims and newborns with birth defects, should create additional demand for rehabilitative care.

Although many people are training to become physical therapists, the supply of these workers is expected to fall short of demand. However, employment growth may be restricted by controls on health-care costs.

Working Conditions

Physical therapists usually work in clean, pleasant, and spacious areas. Some therapists treat patients who are confined to hospital beds or their homes. Because they treat patients who may be depressed by their disabilities, physical therapists should be patient and encouraging. They need to be in good health and should be able to work well with their hands.

Most physical therapists work forty hours per week. Those who prefer flexible hours can usually find part-time or consulting work.

Earnings and Benefits

Salaries vary with education, experience, and place of employment. In 2004 the median salary of physical therapists was $60,180 per year. Benefits for salaried physical therapists included paid holidays and vacations, health insurance, and retirement plans. Self-employed therapists had to provide their own benefits.

Where to Go for More Information

American Physical Therapy Association
1111 N. Fairfax St.
Alexandria, VA 22314-1488
(800) 999-2782
http://www.apta.org

The Federation of State Boards of Physical
   Therapy
509 Wythe St.
Alexandria, VA 22314
(703) 229-3100
http://www.fsbpt.org

Physician

Education and Training
College and medical school, possibly with specialty training

Salary
Varies—see profile

Employment Outlook
Good

Definition and Nature of the Work

Physicians, or medical doctors (MDs), diagnose and treat diseases, injuries, and other disorders. They also work to promote good health and prevent illness. Physicians often supervise other health-care workers, such as physician assistants, nurses, and technicians.

Most American physicians are involved directly in patient care. Only about a tenth of all physicians in the United States work in areas other than patient care, such as administration or research. The majority of the physicians who provide patient care have their own practices or are partners in group practices. Others work full time in hospitals.

About a third of the physicians providing patient care are general practitioners. They treat a wide variety of common health problems. When general practitioners discover illnesses or injuries that need special care, they refer patients to specialists. Family practitioners, who are general practitioners, concentrate on primary health care for the entire family.

The other two-thirds of the physicians providing patient care are specialists who work in one particular branch of medicine. There are about thirty-five major fields of specialization with more than fifty different subspecialties. Physician specialties described in this book include anesthesiologist, dermatologist, gerontologist, ophthalmologist, psychiatrist, and surgeon. Specialties in primary care, which are described in brief in the following paragraphs, are internal medicine, obstetrics/gynecology, and pediatrics.

Physicians who specialize in internal medicine are called internists. They diagnose and treat problems of the internal organs, such as the liver, heart, and lungs. They do not perform surgery. Internists manage and treat common health problems, such as infections, influenza and pneumonia, as well as more

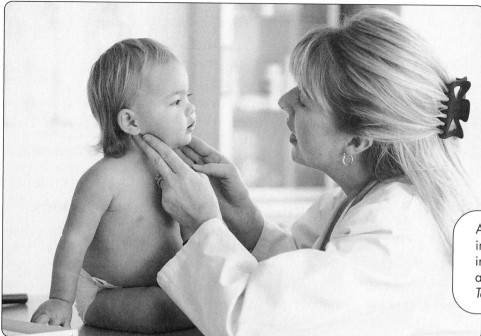

A physician who specializes in providing health care for infants and children is called a pediatrician. (© LWA-Dann Tardif/zefa/Corbis.)

serious, chronic, and complex illnesses. Their patients range in age from adolescents to the elderly.

Obstetrician/gynecologists (ob/gyns) focus on women's health. Along with general medical care of women, ob/gyns care for women before, during, and after pregnancy. They monitor not only women's state of health, but also that of their developing fetuses. They deliver the babies and care for the mothers after they have given birth. Ob/gyns also diagnose and treat diseases of the female reproductive, urinary, and rectal organs and breasts. They may prescribe medications, suggest exercise regimens, or perform surgery.

Pediatricians provide health care for children from birth through adolescence. They chart the growth and development of children, provide immunizations, and diagnose and treat illnesses, injuries, and behavioral problems. Pediatricians may refer children to specialists.

Education and Training Requirements

Students who want to be physicians usually get bachelor's degrees in sciences, such as chemistry or biology. Medical schools look for students who are well rounded, so other courses and activities are important. Most medical colleges have four-year programs that lead to doctor of medicine (MD) degrees. A few medical schools offer combined undergraduate and medical school programs that last six rather than eight years. Internship and residency—on-the-job medical training at hospitals—last from three to eight years.

In every state, physicians must be licensed. Requirements vary, although all states require degrees from approved medical colleges and licensing examinations. In most states MDs must also serve one or two years of residency in hospitals before they can be licensed.

Physicians who want to work as general practitioners usually serve three-year residencies in general internal medicine. Those who want to become specialists serve three-year residencies in their chosen fields. Specialists also need additional practice in their fields before they can be certified by the appropriate specialty boards. Physicians who want to go into teaching or research earn master's degrees or doctorates in particular sciences, such as biochemistry or microbiology.

Getting the Job

Some newly licensed physicians start their own practices and work alone. Others share offices in group practices or join health maintenance organizations (HMOs). A small percentage of physicians take salaried jobs in hospitals, clinics, government agencies, or private industry. Professional associations and medical colleges can provide information about going into private practice or finding salaried positions.

Advancement Possibilities and Employment Outlook

Most physicians advance by expanding their practices. They can improve their skills in general medicine or in special fields. Some physicians advance by teaching or doing research. Others study business administration and become hospital administrators.

Employment of physicians and surgeons is projected to grow faster than the average for all occupations through 2014, largely because health-care industries are continuing to expand. New technologies permit more tests, more procedures, and new treatments for patients with conditions that were previously untreatable. The growing and aging population should generate demand for physicians as well. The greatest needs may be in the fields of family practice, geriatrics, internal medicine, pediatrics, and preventive care. Job opportunities should be good in rural and low-income areas; earnings potential may be lower.

Working Conditions

Physicians generally work in clean, comfortable offices, clinics, or hospitals. Those who have their own practices can control some of their working conditions. Many physicians work long and irregular hours. They must be available to handle emergencies. Some physicians limit their hours or work in specialties that have few emergencies.

Physicians need high intelligence, good health, and self-discipline. They should be able to communicate with many kinds of people. They must have good business sense and the ability to organize the work of others. Their profession demands that they continue to study new developments in medicine throughout their careers.

Where to Go for More Information

American College of Physicians
190 N. Independence Mall W.
Philadelphia, PA 19106-1572
(800) 523-1546
http://www.acponline.org

The American Medical Association
515 N. State St.
Chicago, IL 60610
(800) 621-8335
http://www.ama-assn.org

Earnings and Benefits

Earnings vary widely depending on experience, skill, location, field of specialization, and other factors. In 2004 physicians who had been in practice for more than one year earned the following median incomes: general practitioners, $156,010 per year; internists, $166,420; ob/gyns, $247,348; and pediatricians $161,331. Physicians who had their own practices tended to earn more than salaried physicians.

Self-employed physicians arrange their own benefits. For those who are salaried, benefits generally include paid holidays and vacations, health insurance, and retirement plans.

Physician Assistant

Definition and Nature of the Work

Physician assistants (PAs) relieve doctors of routine chores, allowing them to devote more of their time to patient care that requires highly specialized training. Although they are not doctors, physician assistants practice medicine and do many of the jobs doctors do. Physician assistants can take medical histories, examine and treat patients, order and interpret laboratory tests and X-rays, make diagnoses, treat minor injuries, instruct and counsel patients, and order or carry out therapy. In most states, PAs can also prescribe medicines.

Physician assistants, who work only under the supervision of doctors, are employed in hospitals, clinics, and private offices. In rural areas, PAs may provide most of the medical care, with a physician available only one or two days each week.

Education and Training Requirements

Two years of college and health care experience are common requirements for admission to physician assistant training programs. Many applicants have bachelor's or master's degrees. Medical schools, colleges, community colleges, and teaching hospitals offer training programs, which combine classroom and clinical study and last about two years.

Physician assistants' activities are regulated in almost all states. Many states require certification. Most states require registration with the state medical board.

Getting the Job

Graduates can apply directly to hospitals, clinics, and doctors' offices. School placement offices usually have lists of job openings.

> ### Education and Training
> Some college and additional training

> ### Salary
> Median—$69,410 per year

> ### Employment Outlook
> Excellent

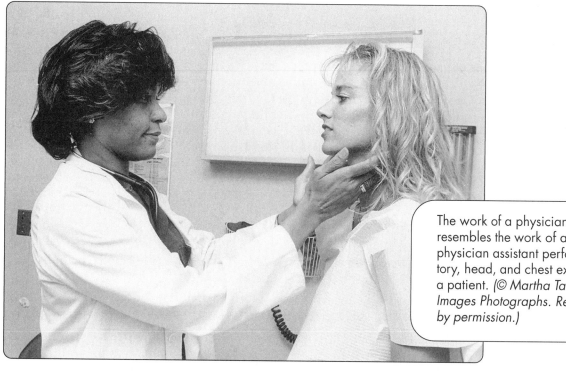

The work of a physician assistant often resembles the work of a doctor. This physician assistant performs a respiratory, head, and chest examination on a patient. (© Martha Tabor/Working Images Photographs. Reproduced by permission.)

Advancement Possibilities and Employment Outlook

Physician assistants advance by accepting more responsibility or by moving into jobs that present greater challenges. Some become specialists.

Employment of physician assistants is expected to grow much faster than the average for all occupations through 2014. It is among the fastest growing occupations, largely because of expansion of the health-care industry. Physicians and institutions are employing more PAs to provide primary care and assist with medical and surgical procedures. Job prospects should be particularly good in areas that have difficulty attracting physicians, such as inner-city and rural clinics. In addition to office-based settings, there should be a growing number of jobs in hospitals, academic medical centers, public clinics, and prisons.

Working Conditions

The job is demanding and requires a high degree of commitment. Physician assistants, like doctors, are always on call and generally work forty to sixty hours per week. Physician assistants must be able to communicate well with patients and other health-care workers.

Earnings and Benefits

Salaries depend on education, experience, and location. In 2004 the median earnings of physician assistants were $69,410 per year. Benefits generally included paid holidays and vacations, health insurance, and retirement plans.

Where to Go for More Information

American Academy of Physician Assistants
950 N. Washington St.
Alexandria, VA 22314-1552
(703) 836-2272
http://www.aapa.org

Physician Assistant Education Association
300 N. Washington St., Ste. 505
Alexandria, VA 22314-2544
(703) 548-5538
http://www.paeaonline.org

Podiatrist

Education and Training
Advanced degree

Salary
Median—$94,400 per year

Employment Outlook
Good

Definition and Nature of the Work

Podiatrists are medical practitioners who specialize in the treatment of sore, badly shaped, diseased, or injured feet and ankles. Podiatrists were formerly called chiropodists. They order X-rays and laboratory tests to diagnose patients' problems, which they treat by manipulation, massage, physical therapy, and surgery. Sometimes they provide patients with bandages, pads, braces, splints, or other supports. They may prescribe drugs, exercise, or special shoes. Because foot problems may be signs of general illnesses, such as diabetes or heart trouble, podiatrists may refer patients to physicians for treatment.

Some podiatrists specialize in foot surgery and orthopedics. They treat deformities of foot muscles, joints, or bones. Others specialize in podopediatrics, the care of children's feet, or podogeriatrics, the treatment of foot problems of the elderly.

Most podiatrists have private practices. Others work in hospitals, podiatric colleges, government agencies, or private clinics.

Education and Training Requirements

Admission to a school of podiatry requires at least three years of college, although most applicants have bachelor's degrees. The four-year programs lead to the degree of doctor of podiatric medicine (DPM). All states require that podiatrists be licensed. Requirements vary, but in all states podiatrists must graduate from accredited colleges of podiatry and pass state board examinations. A few states also require one-year residencies.

Getting the Job

Most podiatrists go into private practice—they either set up their own practices or buy established ones. Others start by working as assistants in the offices of established podiatrists. Still others take salaried positions until they have the money and experience to open their own practices. Professional associations and colleges of podiatry can provide information about getting started in this field.

Advancement Possibilities and Employment Outlook

Most podiatrists advance by expanding their practices; others may specialize. A small number of podiatrists move into teaching, research, or administrative positions in hospitals or colleges of podiatry.

Employment of podiatrists is expected to grow about as fast as the average for all occupations through 2014. A growing elderly population may require more treatment of foot problems, which should create openings for qualified podiatrists. Also, the popularity of fast-moving sports, such as jogging, tennis, and racquetball, may increase demand in the specialty of podiatric sports medicine. However, employment may be affected by insurers, who control payments for specialty health care.

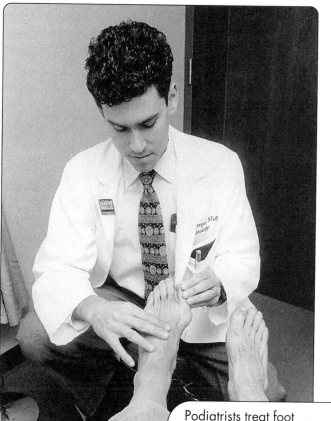

Podiatrists treat foot problems by manipulating or massaging the foot and by using forms of physical therapy. (© Martha Tabor/Working Images Photographs. Reproduced by permission.)

Working Conditions

Podiatrists generally set their own working conditions. Most work about forty hours per week, often including some evening and Saturday hours. Some podiatrists work part time.

Podiatrists need good vision and must work well with their hands. They should communicate well with all kinds of people and have good business sense.

Earnings and Benefits

Earnings vary with experience, skill, and place of work. In 2004 the median earnings of podiatrists were $94,400 per year. Because most podiatrists are self-employed, they must provide their own health insurance and other benefits.

Where to Go for More Information

American Association of Colleges of
   Podiatric Medicine
15850 Crabbs Branch Way, Ste. 320
Rockville, MD 20855
(800) 922-9266
http://www.aacpm.org

American Podiatric Medical Association
9312 Old Georgetown Rd.
Bethesda, MD 20814-1621
(800) 366-8227
http://www.apma.org

Psychiatrist

Education and Training
College, medical school, and specialized training

Salary
Median—$180,000 per year

Employment Outlook
Very good

Definition and Nature of the Work

Psychiatrists are physicians who specialize in the prevention, diagnosis, and treatment of mental disorders. They treat patients with mild cases of anxiety as well as those with severe disorders that can cause dangerous and bizarre behavior. Psychiatrists may also diagnose mental retardation and treat alcoholism. They often work with other mental health workers, such as psychologists, psychiatric nurses, and psychiatric social workers.

Psychiatrists talk with patients to learn about their mental health problems. They may also use information provided by patients' families or by other mental health workers. They are trained to recognize the connection between mental and physical disorders, so they may order laboratory or other diagnostic tests.

For treatment, psychiatrists can prescribe drugs and use shock therapy and psychotherapy. In psychotherapy, psychiatrists use their special training to talk with one or more patients to help them understand and cope with their problems.

Psychiatrists may work with patients in private offices or in hospitals or clinics. They may also do research, studying the causes and treatment of mental illness. Some psychiatrists teach in medical schools or in special psychiatric institutes. Others write or edit psychiatric books or journals.

Psychiatrists are often confused with psychologists and psychoanalysts. Psychiatrists are physicians who have advanced training in psychiatry. As physicians, they can prescribe medication. Psychologists have either master's degrees or doctorates in psychology. They are not physicians and cannot prescribe drugs or perform surgery. Psychologists are basically scientists who study the reactions of people to their environment. Psychoanalysts are specially trained to practice long-term therapy that investigates the subconscious or hidden causes of emotional disturbances. Most psychoanalysts are psychiatrists, while those known as lay analysts are not.

Education and Training Requirements

Psychiatrists need extensive training after high school. They get bachelor's degrees, followed by four years of medical school. After one-year internships, they must also have three years of psychiatric training as residents in hospitals. Usually after one or two years of residency, psychiatrists must take examinations to be licensed, which is required in all states. They need additional experience before they are eligible to take examinations for certification as psychiatrists.

Getting the Job

Psychiatrists work in institutions or in private practice. Some combine the two types of work. Building a successful private practice can take a while, so many beginning psychiatrists start their careers in established psychiatric offices. Professional associations can provide information about setting up a practice or getting salaried positions.

Advancement Possibilities and Employment Outlook

Psychiatrists usually advance by building their practices. Some specialize in fields such as child, educational, or legal psychiatry. Others become teachers, researchers, or administrators in colleges, hospitals, or other institutions.

Employment of physicians in general is expected to grow faster than average for all occupations through 2014. Expansion of the health-care industry, a growing population, and increasing life spans, as well as higher incomes and educational levels, are spurring the demand. Shortages of psychiatrists exist, especially in rural areas and in public facilities.

Working Conditions

Psychiatrists in private practice work in quiet, peaceful settings so their patients can feel at ease. However, the work can be stressful because of the suffering they see every day. In addition, psychiatrists in private practice must be available to their patients whenever they need help, so their working hours can be irregular. Psychiatrists who work in hospitals and clinics often have more regular hours than private practitioners do because the staff divides the hours they must be on call. To do their work well, psychiatrists must be well balanced, disciplined, and enjoy working with all kinds of people.

Earnings and Benefits

Psychiatrists' earnings are similar to those of other physicians. In 2004 psychiatrists who had been in practice more than one year earned a median income of $180,000 per year. Psychiatrists in private practice provided their own benefits. Salaried psychiatrists received paid holidays and vacations, health insurance, and retirement plans.

Where to Go for More Information

American College of Psychiatrists
122 S. Michigan Ave., Ste. 1360
Chicago, IL 60603
(312) 622-1020
http://www.acpsych.org

American Psychiatric Association
1000 Wilson Blvd., Ste. 1825
Arlington, VA 22209-3901
(703) 907-7300
http://www.psych.org

Psychologist

Definition and Nature of the Work

Psychologists are scientists who study behavior. Their work usually involves teaching, research, or social service in schools, clinics, government agencies, and private industry. About forty percent are in private practice.

To learn about behavior, they may conduct tests and laboratory experiments, record case histories, or take surveys. Using their research, they develop theories to explain the reactions of people to their environment. They also use their knowledge to help emotionally or mentally disturbed people adjust to life. Some psychologists work with medical and surgical patients who must cope with illness and injury.

Psychology is a broad field with several areas of specialization. In experimental psychology, for example, psychologists carry out research projects to develop theories about learning, motivation, and other aspects of behavior. Developmental psychologists study the growth and change that takes place throughout life. They may concentrate on one particular stage of development, such as adolescence or old age. Other specialties include educational psychology, comparative psychology, social psychology, and psychometrics.

Just as there are many areas of specialization, there are also many kinds of psychologists. The largest group is made up of clinical psychologists, who often provide individual, family, or group psychotherapy for people with emotional prob-

Education and Training
Master's degree or doctorate

Salary
Median—$54,950 per year

Employment Outlook
Good

Clinical psychologists help emotionally or mentally unstable people understand and cope with their problems. They constitute the largest area of specialization within the field of psychology. (© Martha Tabor/Working Images Photographs. Reproduced by permission.)

lems. They may implement behavior modification programs. School psychologists work with teachers and parents to create supportive learning environments for all types of students. They often give tests to identify gifted, handicapped, and emotionally disturbed students. Industrial and organizational psychologists study problems of motivation and morale in offices and factories. They may advise companies on personnel, management, or marketing methods. Other kinds of psychologists include engineering psychologists, counseling psychologists, and environmental psychologists.

Education and Training Requirements

Competition for graduate programs in psychology is stiff. All applicants must have bachelor's degrees in psychology or related fields. Those who want to work as school psychologists must earn specialist degrees, which require three years of graduate study and a one-year internship. Master's degrees may be sufficient in some areas. Clinical or counseling psychologists in private practice and those in teaching and research positions usually need doctorates, which require from five to seven years of graduate study. Clinical and counseling psychologists must spend at least a year in internships. Unlike psychiatrists, psychologists are not physicians.

All states require that psychologists be certified or licensed to start private practices. Candidates for licenses usually need doctorates plus two years of experience. The American Board of Professional Psychology recognizes professional achievement by awarding specialty certification in areas such as clinical, counseling, school, and industrial and organizational psychology. Candidates for certification must have doctorates, five years of experience, and professional endorsements.

Getting the Job

Job seekers can apply directly to agencies or get help from school placement offices. Professional associations can provide information about opening private practices. Professional journals, newspaper classified ads, and job banks on the Internet list openings for psychologists.

Advancement Possibilities and Employment Outlook

Advancement depends on many factors, including education, experience, and other personal qualities. Psychologists can expand their private practices or move into high-level jobs in research, teaching, counseling, or administration. Some psychologists advance by serving as consultants to government or industry or by writing about their special fields.

The employment of psychologists is expected to grow faster than the average for all occupations through 2014. Job opportunities should increase slightly in health maintenance and preferred provider organizations, in nursing homes, and in alcohol and drug abuse programs. More opportunities will arise in businesses, nonprofit organizations, and research firms, especially for psychologists who work as consultants. Companies will employ psychologists to design and analyze surveys and to help employees with personal problems.

Working Conditions

Working conditions vary widely. Psychologists in private practice usually have comfortable offices. Most work forty hours per week. However, their schedules vary according to the type of work and may include some evening and Saturday hours. They spend additional time studying the latest developments in the field. Psychologists must be emotionally stable, intelligent, and able to communicate with a wide variety of people. Those involved in research must be suited for detailed work.

Earnings and Benefits

Salaries vary with education, experience, and type of work. In 2004 the median earnings of clinical, counseling, and school psychologists were $54,950 per year.

Benefits for salaried psychologists usually include paid holidays and vacations, health insurance, and retirement plans. Psychologists in private practice must provide their own benefits.

Where to Go for More Information

American Psychological Association
750 First St. NE
Washington, DC 20002-4242
(800) 374-2721
http://www.apa.org

Association of State and Provincial
  Psychology Boards
PO Box 241245
Montgomery, AL 36124-1245
(334) 832-4580
http://www.asppb.org

American Board of Professional Psychology
300 Drayton St., 3rd Fl.
Savannah, GA 31401
(800) 255-7792
http://www.abpp.org

Recreational Therapist

Definition and Nature of the Work

Recreational therapists devise programs in art, music, dance, sports, games, and crafts for individuals with disabilities or illnesses. These activities help to prevent or to alleviate physical, mental, and social problems. They improve self-confidence and self-control and relieve depression and anger.

With the help of recreational therapists, for example, children may be able to channel their aggression into painting rather than expressing it through negative behavior. Patients who have difficulty relating to other people can improve their social skills by playing and moving to music in groups.

Recreational therapists who specialize in art therapy often use art as a diagnostic tool in cases of mental illness, particularly in children. Shapes, colors, de-

Education and Training
Bachelor's degree, additional training

Salary
Median—$32,900 per year

Employment Outlook
Fair

Recreational therapists plan and participate in specialized games, sports, crafts, and other leisure activities to help people overcome mental, emotional, and physical disabilities. (© Michael Heron/ Corbis.)

tails, or the lack of fine points in a drawing or painting can reveal emotions and underlying problems.

Recreational therapists often work as members of health care teams serving a number of patients. Together, they discuss their cases and decide on the best forms of treatment. Recreational therapists may work with individual patients or groups.

Education and Training Requirements

Recreational therapists need bachelor's degrees in therapeutic recreation or in recreation with a concentration in therapeutic recreation. Those who already hold bachelor's degrees can enter two- to five-year programs leading to graduate degrees or graduate certificates in recreational therapy. Alternatively, students can get associate degrees in recreational therapy. The two-year program, plus experience or training in art, drama, or music therapy, may qualify them to be activity directors at nursing homes.

Certification in recreational therapy is usually voluntary, but most employers prefer to hire applicants certified by the National Council for Therapeutic Recreation Certification. Applicants must have bachelor's degrees, pass written tests, and complete internships. Some states require licenses or certification to practice.

Getting the Job

College placement offices are probably the best sources of job information. Recreational therapists can also apply directly to local, state, and federal agencies, hospitals, and clinics.

Advancement Possibilities and Employment Outlook

Recreational therapists who work in government-supported institutions advance with increases in pay and rank. Those who work in hospitals and clinics may advance to supervisory positions, while those in private practice can expand their number of clients.

Employment is expected to grow more slowly than the average for all occupations through 2014. Demand should be greatest in residential and outpatient settings that serve disabled persons, the elderly, or those diagnosed with mental retardation, mental illness, or substance abuse problems.

Working Conditions

Recreational therapists work in hospitals and mental health facilities, schools, and private offices. Their surroundings are generally cheerful and pleasant. Most therapists work forty-hour weeks, although their schedules may vary to accommodate their patients' needs.

Earnings and Benefits

In 2004 the median salary for recreational therapists was $32,900 per year. Those with doctorates who taught at universities earned $50,000 per year or more.

Benefits usually include paid holidays and vacations, health insurance, and retirement plans. Some therapists receive tuition assistance for additional study. Recreational therapists in private practice must provide their own benefits.

Where to Go for More Information

American Therapeutic Recreation
    Association
1414 Prince St., Ste. 204
Alexandria, VA 22314-2853
(703) 683-9420
http://www.atra-tr.org

The National Council for Therapeutic
    Recreation Certification
7 Elmwood Dr.
New City, NY 10956
(845) 639-1439
http://www.nctrc.org

National Therapeutic Recreation Society
22377 Belmont Ridge Rd.
Ashburn, VA 20148-4501
(703) 858-0784
http://www.nrpa.org/content/
    default.aspx?documentid=530

Registered Nurse

Definition and Nature of the Work

Registered nurses (RNs) work to promote good health and prevent illness. They educate patients and the public about various medical conditions; treat patients and help in their rehabilitation; and provide advice and emotional support to patients' families. RNs use considerable judgment in providing a wide variety of services.

Many registered nurses are general-duty nurses who focus on the overall care of patients. They administer medications under the supervision of doctors and keep records of symptoms and progress. General-duty nurses also supervise licensed practical nurses (LPNs), nursing aides, and orderlies.

RNs can specialize: (1) by work setting or type of treatment—critical-care nurses work in intensive care units, and psychiatric nurses treat patients with mental health disorders; (2) by disease, ailment, or condition—HIV/AIDS nurses care for patients with HIV infection and AIDS, and addictions nurses treat patients with substance abuse problems; (3) by organ or body system—nephrology nurses care for patients with kidney disease, and respiratory nurses treat patients with disorders such as asthma; and (4) by population—school nurses provide care for children and adolescents in school, while geriatric nurses provide care for the elderly. RNs may also work in combined specialties, such as pediatric oncology (the care of children and adolescents with cancer) or cardiac emergency (the care of patients with heart problems in emergency rooms).

Some RNs choose to become advanced-practice nurses and get special training beyond their RN education. They are often considered primary health care practitioners and work independently or in collaboration with physicians. There are

Education and Training
College and possibly advanced degree

Salary
Median—$52,330 per year

Employment Outlook
Excellent

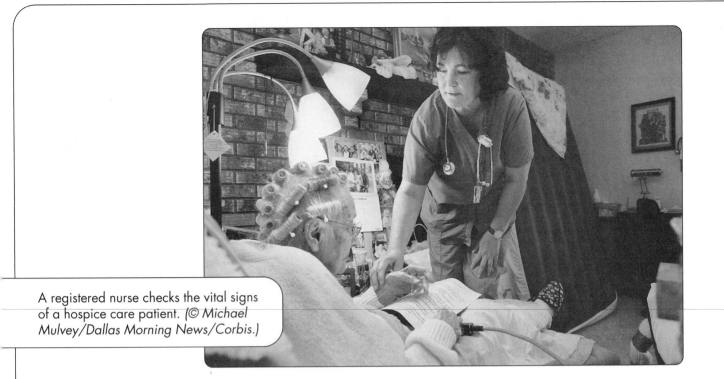

four categories of advanced-practice nurses: nurse-practitioners, clinical nurse specialists, Certified Nurse-Midwives, and Certified Registered Nurse Anesthetists.

The duties of nurse-practitioners include conducting physical exams; diagnosing and treating common illnesses and injuries; providing immunizations; managing high blood pressure, diabetes, and other chronic problems; ordering and interpreting X-rays and other lab tests; and counseling patients on healthy lifestyles. They practice in hospitals and clinics and often deliver care in rural or inner-city locations not well served by physicians. Some have private practices. Nurse-practitioners can prescribe medications in all states, and in many states they can practice without the supervision of physicians.

Clinical nurse specialists provide care in specialty areas, such as cardiac, oncology (cancer), pediatrics, and psychiatric/mental health. They work in hospitals and clinics, providing medical care and mental health services, developing quality assurance procedures, and serving as educators and consultants.

Certified Nurse-Midwives provide routine health care for women, but their practices are focused on pregnancy and delivery of babies. They lead classes in childbirth, sibling preparation, and care of newborns. If pregnancies continue without complications, nurse-midwives provide all prenatal care, assist mothers during labor, and deliver the babies. Following the births, they make sure that mothers and newborns are well and provide follow-up care. If emergencies occur, nurse-midwives are trained to provide assistance until doctors arrive.

Certified Registered Nurse Anesthetists receive special training in the use of anesthetics, which produce a state of painlessness or unconsciousness. They work under the supervision of anesthesiologists (physicians who specialize in anesthesia) or other physicians. Most work in operating rooms during surgery, but others administer anesthetics in delivery rooms, emergency rooms, and dental offices. Sometimes nurse anesthetists help to care for patients during recovery from anesthesia.

Some experienced hospital nurses are head nurses or directors of nursing services. RNs also work as nurse educators or as researchers in hospitals. They may become forensics nurses, combining their nursing knowledge with law enforcement. They often work with victims who have been assaulted. Many registered nurses work in private doctors' offices or clinics. They may assist such physicians as obstetricians and dental surgeons.

Education and Training Requirements

To become registered nurses, high school graduates can earn associate degrees in two-year nursing programs at community colleges; earn diplomas in three-year programs offered by hospitals or independent schools of nursing; or earn bachelor of science in nursing degrees (BSN). BSN programs usually take four or five years to complete and combine liberal arts courses with scientific and technical training. All programs include practical experience.

Those who have completed an approved program are eligible to take the national written licensing exam, which is administered by each state. All states require licensing.

The profession is moving toward two levels of nursing: technical nursing, which requires associate degrees, and professional nursing, which requires bachelor's degrees. Under this system, only nurses with bachelor's degrees would be eligible for RN licensing. The American Association of Colleges of Nursing (AACN) and other leading nursing organizations recognize the BSN as the minimum educational requirement for professional nursing. While graduates can begin practice as RNs with associate degrees or hospital diplomas, the BSN is essential for nurses seeking to perform at the case-manager or supervisory level. Students desiring to become advanced-practice nurses must obtain master of science in nursing degrees (MSN). Some nurses go on to earn doctorates.

Getting the Job

Nursing school and college placement services can help graduates find jobs. Graduates can also apply directly to hospitals, clinics, nursing homes, and doctors' offices. Those interested in community health jobs can contact public health departments, home health agencies, and visiting nurse associations. The armed services also have openings for nurses. In addition, professional nurse registries list openings for private-duty nurses.

Advancement Possibilities and Employment Outlook

Advancement in nursing depends on education, experience, and place of employment. Registered nurses can become supervisors of departments or specialists in particular fields of nursing. Those with bachelor's or master's degrees are more likely to move into higher-level jobs. Many positions in research, teaching, and administration require master's degrees or even doctorates in nursing.

According to the U.S. Department of Labor's Bureau of Labor Statistics, "Registered nurses are projected to create the second largest number of new jobs among all occupations; job opportunities in most specialties and employment settings are expected to be excellent, with some employers reporting difficulty in attracting and retaining enough RNs." Employment of registered nurses is expected to grow much faster than the average for all occupations through 2014. In part, increases in demand are due to technological advances in patient care, which permit a greater number of medical problems to be treated. In addition, the number of elderly people is projected to grow rapidly, which should spur demand for RNs in nursing homes and long-term care facilities. Employment in home health care is expected to increase the fastest; employment in hospitals is expected to increase the least, largely because patients are being released earlier to reduce costs. Also, technological progress is making it possible to bring complex treatments to patients' homes.

Where to Go for More Information

The American Assembly for Men in Nursing
PO Box 130220
Birmingham, AL 35213
(205) 802-7551
http://www.aamn.org

American Association of Colleges of
   Nursing
1 Dupont Circle NW, Ste. 530
Washington, DC 20036-1110
(202) 463-6930
http://www.aacn.nche.edu

National League for Nursing
61 Broadway, 33rd Fl.
New York, NY 10006
(800) 669-1656
http://www.nln.org

Working Conditions

Although working conditions vary with the place of employment, nearly all nursing jobs involve close contact with people. Good health and emotional stability are valuable assets. Nurses must be careful workers who take their responsibilities seriously. They must follow rigid guidelines to ensure the health and safety of themselves and their patients.

Registered nurses generally work forty hours per week. They may have to work some night and weekend shifts, especially if they work in hospitals. Many nurses work part time.

Earnings and Benefits

Salaries for nurses vary with education, experience, and area of specialization. In 2004 the median annual salary of registered nurses was $52,330 per year.

Benefits include paid holidays and vacations, health insurance, and retirement plans. Private-duty nurses generally charge a daily fee and must provide their own benefits.

Speech-Language Pathologist

Education and Training
Master's degree

Salary
Median—$52,410 per year

Employment Outlook
Good

Definition and Nature of the Work

Speech pathologists, sometimes called speech therapists, work with people who cannot speak or cannot speak clearly; have speech problems, such as stuttering, an unwanted accent, or an inappropriate pitch; have problems understanding language; or have communication impairments, such as attention, memory, and problem-solving disorders. They also work with people who have trouble swallowing.

Speech and language problems result from injury, illness, cognitive deficits, developmental delays, or emotional difficulties. Many patients are children who lisp or stutter. Adult patients may be victims of strokes or of cerebral palsy. Speech pathologists often work closely with doctors, psychologists, physical therapists, or classroom teachers. They plan and carry out treatments that take into account the specific needs of each patient.

About half of all speech-language pathologists work in public schools. The remaining fifty percent have private practices or work in colleges and universities, clinics, hospitals, special speech and hearing centers, government agencies, and private industry. Some speech pathologists work on research projects to design and develop new equipment or methods for treating speech and hearing problems.

Education and Training Requirements

Master's degrees in speech-language pathology are the standard requirement for licensing in most states. Some states require teaching certificates to work in

A speech-language pathologist works with children who have speech problems that result from injury, illness, or emotional difficulties. (© Martha Tabor/Working Images Photographs. Reproduced by permission.)

public schools and licenses to work in private practice, clinics, or other non-school settings. Certification and licensing requirements vary from state to state.

Certification by the American Speech-Language-Hearing Association is recommended for those who want to advance. Applicants for certification must have master's degrees or their equivalent and work experience.

Getting the Job

Job seekers can apply directly to schools, clinics, or other institutions. School placement offices or the American Speech-Language-Hearing Association can provide information about job openings. State employment services, newspaper classified ads, and job banks on the Internet may also provide employment leads.

Advancement Possibilities and Employment Outlook

Advancement depends on education and experience. Speech-language pathologists can become supervisors or heads of clinics. They can set up private practices. Those with the necessary training can work as consultants, do research, and write books or articles on speech problems. Opportunities should be particularly favorable for those who are fluent in second languages, especially Spanish.

Employment of speech-language pathologists is expected to grow about as fast as the average for all occupations through 2014. Openings in health and rehabilitation services will increase because of advances in medical technology and growth in the elderly population. In addition, demand for speech-language pathologists in schools should increase as people become more aware of the importance of early recognition and treatment of speech problems. Other job opportunities will occur when experienced workers retire or leave the field.

Working Conditions

Working conditions are usually pleasant. Speech pathologists are members of health-care teams and interact with a wide variety of people. They should be patient and able to work well with others.

Many speech pathologists work more than forty hours per week. Their hours are often flexible, and part-time jobs are available. Speech pathologists working in public schools usually have the same schedule that classroom teachers have.

Earnings and Benefits

Salaries vary widely with education, experience, and location. In 2004 the median earnings of speech-language pathologists were $52,410 per year. Benefits usually include paid holidays and vacations, health insurance, and retirement plans.

Surgeon

Education and Training
College, medical school, and specialized training

Salary
Median—$282,504 per year

Employment Outlook
Very good

Definition and Nature of the Work

Surgeons are physicians who operate to repair injuries, correct deformities, prevent diseases, and generally improve the health of patients. They examine patients to determine if surgery is necessary, evaluate the risks involved, and select the appropriate surgical procedure.

General surgeons perform many kinds of operations. Others specialize in one type of operation or one system or area of the body. Neurosurgeons, for example, operate on the brain, spinal cord, and nervous system, while thoracic surgeons operate on lungs and other organs in the chest cavity. Diseases of bones and joints, such as arthritis, as well as the treatment of broken bones, are the focus of orthopedic surgeons.

Education and Training Requirements

Medical schools require applicants to have bachelor's degrees, usually with majors in a science, such as chemistry or biology. They look for well-rounded students, so other courses and activities are important. Most medical colleges have four-year programs that lead to doctor of medicine (MD) degrees. A few medical schools offer combined undergraduate and medical school programs that last six rather than eight years. In all cases, medical school is followed by internships and residencies—on-the-job training at hospitals. Surgical residency programs generally last five years. Surgeons must also take licensing examinations and earn board certification in their areas of specialization.

Individuals who want to be surgeons must be self-motivated and have the physical and mental stamina to handle the pressure and long hours of medical education. Surgeons continue studying throughout their careers to keep current in their fields.

Getting the Job

Beginning surgeons may enter private practice or group practice, with affiliations with one or more hospitals. Some surgeons choose to work for the federal government in veterans' hospitals or the military. College placement offices can be helpful in finding positions. Surgeons also make contacts during their internships and residencies that may lead to employment.

Advancement Possibilities and Employment Outlook

Surgeons advance by gaining more skill and knowledge and by increasing their number of patients. General surgeons may move into areas of specialty. In some large urban hospitals, surgeons become heads of surgery departments. With additional education and training, surgeons may also teach or do research.

Employment of surgeons is projected to grow faster than the average for all occupations through 2014, largely because the health-care industry is expected to expand. The growing and aging population should spur overall growth. Also, new technologies permit more tests and more procedures for conditions that were once untreatable. Competition may be stiff for specialists in urban and suburban areas, which are attractive to surgeons because of higher earning potential and continued contact with colleagues.

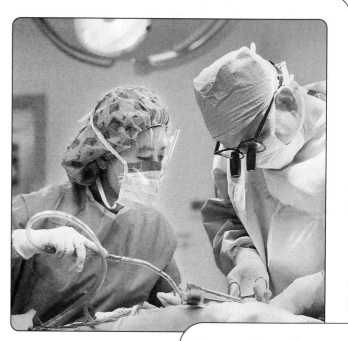

Surgeons are medical specialists who operate on patients to repair injuries, correct deformities, prevent diseases, and generally improve the health of patients. (© Helen King/Corbis.)

Working Conditions

Surgeons work long hours, mostly at hospitals where they operate on patients or visit pre- or postsurgery patients. Surgeons frequently perform emergency operations. Most surgeons maintain offices outside hospitals where they explain procedures to their patients.

Earnings and Benefits

The income of surgeons varies according to specialty, geographic location, years in practice, and reputation. In 2004 the median salary for general surgeons was $282,504 per year.

Self-employed surgeons arrange their own benefits. For those who are not self-employed, benefits generally include paid holidays and vacations, health insurance, and retirement plans.

Where to Go for More Information

Association of American Physicians and
  Surgeons
1601 N. Tucson Blvd., Ste. 9
Tucson, AZ 85716
(800) 635-1196
http://www.aapsonline.org

American College of Surgeons
Division of Education
633 N. Saint Clair St.
Chicago, IL 60611-3211
(800) 621-4111
http://www.facs.org

Books

Exploring the Working World

American Salaries and Wages Survey, 8th ed., Helen S. Fisher. Farmington Hills, MI: Thomson Gale, 2005.

America's Fastest Growing Jobs: Detailed Information on the 140 Fastest Growing Jobs in Our Economy, 8th ed., Michael Farr. Indianapolis, IN: JIST Publishing, 2004.

America's Top 101 Jobs for College Graduates, 6th ed., Michael Farr. Indianapolis, IN: JIST Publishing, 2005.

America's Top 101 Jobs for People without a Four-Year Degree, 7th ed., Michael Farr. Indianapolis, IN: JIST Publishing, 2004.

America's Top 300 Jobs, 9th ed., U.S. Department of Labor. Indianapolis, IN: JIST Publishing, 2004.

Best Career and Education Web Sites: A Quick Guide to Online Job Search, 4th ed., Rachel Singer Gordon and Anne Wolfinger. Indianapolis, IN: JIST Publishing, 2004.

Best Entry-Level Jobs, Ron Lieber and Tom Meltzer. New York: Princeton Review, 2006.

Best Jobs for the 21st Century, 4th ed., Michael Farr and Laurence Shatkin. Indianapolis, IN: JIST Publishing, 2006.

Big Book of Jobs, 2003–2004, U.S. Department of Labor. New York: McGraw-Hill, 2003.

Career Discovery Encyclopedia, 5th ed., 8 vols. Chicago: Ferguson, 2003.

Enhanced Occupational Outlook Handbook, 5th ed., Indianapolis, IN: JIST Publishing, 2005.

Job Hunter's Sourcebook: A Thomson Gale Career Information Guide. Farmington Hills, MI: Thomson Gale, biennial.

Jobs Rated Almanac, 6th ed., Les Krantz. Fort Lee, NJ: Barricade, 2002.

The National JobBank, 2006. Avon, MA: Adams Media, 2006.

Occupational Outlook Handbook series. Washington, DC: United States Government Printing Office, biennial. Briefs, separately published.

Occupational Outlook Quarterly. Washington, DC: United States Government Printing Office. Quarterly publication.

Professional Careers Sourcebook, 7th ed. Farmington Hills, MI: Thomson Gale, 2002.

200 Best Jobs for College Graduates, 3rd ed., Michael Farr and Laurence Shatkin. Indianapolis, IN: JIST Publishing, 2006.

Recommended

Best Jobs for the 21st Century, 4th ed., Michael Farr and Laurence Shatkin. Indianapolis, IN: JIST Publishing, 2006. Lists five hundred jobs and categorizes them into sixty-five "Best Jobs for..." lists. Organizes jobs by category, education required, best growth potential.

Jobs Rated Almanac, 6th ed., Les Krantz. Fort Lee, NJ: Barricade, 2002. Rates 250 jobs and sorts into "best for" and "worst for" rankings. Factors include salary, benefits, and stress level.

300 Best Jobs without a Four-Year Degree, 2nd ed., Michael Farr and Laurence Shatkin. Indianapolis, IN: JIST Publishing, 2006.

VGM's Career Encyclopedia, 5th ed., New York: McGraw-Hill, 2002.

Vocational Careers Sourcebook, 5th ed., Farmington Hills, MI: Thomson Gale, 2002.

Education and Training Opportunities

Acing the College Application: How to Maximize Your Chances for Admission to the College of Your Choice, Michele Hernandez. New York: Ballantine, 2002.

Admission Matters: What Students and Parents Need to Know about Getting Into College, Sally P. Springer and Marion R. Franck. San Francisco: Jossey-Bass, 2005.

Barron's Guide to Graduate Business Schools, Eugene Miller and Neuman F. Pollack. Hauppauge, NY: Barron's Educational Series, revised regularly.

Barron's Guide to Law Schools. Hauppauge, NY: Barron's Educational Series, revised regularly.

Barron's Guide to Medical and Dental Schools, Sol Wischnitzer and Edith Wischnitzer. Hauppauge, NY: Barron's Educational Series, revised regularly.

Barron's Profiles of American Colleges. Hauppauge, NY: Barron's Educational Series, annual.

Bear's Guide to College Degrees by Mail and Internet, 10th ed., John Bear. Berkeley, CA: Ten Speed Press, 2005.

Best 109 Internships, 9th ed., Mark Oldman and Samer Hamadah. New York: Princeton Review, 2003.

The Best 361 Colleges. New York: Princeton Review, annual.

Chronicle Vocational School Manual. Moravia, NY: Chronicle Guidance Publications, annual.

The College Application Essay, Sarah Myers McGinty. New York: The College Board, 2004.

The College Board Book of Majors, 2nd ed. New York: The College Board, 2006.

The College Board Scholarship Handbook. New York: The College Board, annual.

The College Cost and Financial Aid Handbook. New York: The College Board, annual.

College Financial Aid: How to Get Your Fair Share, 6th ed., Peter V. Laurenzo. Albany, NY: Hudson Financial Press, 2002.

The College Handbook. New York: The College Board, annual.

College Majors Handbook with Real Career Paths and Payoffs, 2nd ed., Neeta P. Fogg. Indianapolis, IN: JIST Publishing, 2004.

College Planning for Gifted Students, 3rd ed., Sandra L. Berger. Waco, TX: Prufrock Press, 2006.

College Success Guide: Top 12 Secrets for Student Success, Karine Blackett and Patricia Weiss. Indianapolis, IN: JIST Publishing, 2005.

Complete Book of Colleges. New York: Princeton Review, annual.

Recommended

Acing the College Application: How to Maximize Your Chances for Admission to the College of Your Choice, Michele Hernandez. New York: Ballantine, 2002. Written by former Dartmouth College admissions officer. Frank but reassuring advice on application, essay, and personal interview.

The Insider's Guide to Colleges. New York: St. Martin's Griffin, annual. Surveys students at 320 U.S. and Canadian schools on dorm life, class size, and other campus-related topics.

Vault Guide to Top Internships, Samer Hamadah. New York: Vault, 2005. Provides information on internships offered by 700-plus companies, including Fortune 500 corporations. Nonprofit and government programs also listed.

Fiske Guide to Colleges, Edmund Fiske. Naperville, IL: Sourcebooks, annual.

The Gourman Report: A Rating of Undergraduate Programs in American and International Universities, Jack Gourman. Los Angeles: National Educational Standards, revised regularly.

Guide to College Majors. New York: Princeton Review, 2006.

Guide to the Most Competitive Colleges. Hauppauge, NY: Barron's Educational Series, revised regularly.

How to Choose a College Major, Linda Landis Andrews. New York: McGraw-Hill, 2006.

How to Write Your College Application Essay, Kenneth Nourse. New York: McGraw-Hill, 2001.

The Insider's Guide to Colleges. New York: St. Martin's Griffin, annual.

The Internship Bible, 10th ed. New York: Princeton Review, 2005.

The National Guide to Educational Credit for Training Programs. Washington, DC: American Council on Education, revised regularly.

100 Successful College Application Essays, 2nd ed. New York: New American Library, 2002.

Peterson's Best College Admission Essays, 3rd ed. Princeton, NJ: Thomson Peterson's, 2004.

Peterson's College Money Handbook. Princeton, NJ: Thomson Peterson's, annual.

Peterson's College and University Almanac. Princeton, NJ: Thomson Peterson's, annual.

Peterson's Competitive Colleges. Princeton, NJ: Thomson Peterson's, annual.

Peterson's Financial Aid Answer Book. Princeton, NJ: Thomson Peterson's, annual.

Peterson's Guide to Four-Year Colleges. Princeton, NJ: Thomson Peterson's, annual.

Peterson's Guide to Two-Year Colleges. Princeton, NJ: Thomson Peterson's, annual.

Peterson's Internships. Princeton, NJ: Thomson Peterson's, annual.

Quick Guide to College Majors and Careers, Laurence Shatkin. Indianapolis, IN: JIST Publishing, 2002.

Rugg's Recommendations on the Colleges, Frederick Rugg. Fallbrook, CA: Rugg's Recommendations, annual.

Students' Guide to Colleges: The Definitive Guide to America's Top 100 Schools Written by the Real Experts—the Students Who Attend Them, Jordan Goldman and Colleen Buyers. New York: Penguin, 2005.

The Truth about Getting In: A Top College Advisor Tells You Everything You Need to Know, Katherine Cohen. New York: Hyperion, 2002.

US News Ultimate College Guide. Naperville, IL: Sourcebooks, annual.

Vault Guide to Top Internships, Samer Hamadah. New York, Vault, 2005.

Career Goals

The Career Adventure: Your Guide to Personal Assessment, Career Exploration, and Decision Making, 4th ed., Susan M. Johnston. Upper Saddle, NJ: Prentice-Hall, 2005.

Career Guide to America's Top Industries, 6th ed., U.S. Department of Labor. Indianapolis, IN: JIST Publishing, 2004.

Career Warfare: 10 Rules for Building a Successful Personal Brand and Fighting to Keep It, David F. D'Alessandro and Michele Owens. New York: McGraw-Hill, 2003.

College Majors and Careers: A Resource Guide for Effective Life Planning, 5th ed., Paul Phifer. Chicago: Ferguson, 2003.

Cool Careers for Dummies, Marty Nemko, Paul Edwards, and Sarah Edwards. Foster City, CA: IDG Books, 2001.

Customize Your Career, Roz Usheroff. New York: McGraw-Hill, 2004.

Do What You Are: Discover the Perfect Career for You through the Secrets of Personality Type, 3rd ed., Paul D. Tieger and Barbara Barron-Tieger. New York: Little, Brown, 2001.

50 Best Jobs for Your Personality, Michael Farr and Laurence Shatkin. Indianapolis, IN: JIST Publishing, 2005.

Finding a Career That Works for You: A Step-by-Step Guide to Choosing a Career and Finding a Job, Wilma Fellman. Plantation, FL: Specialty Press, 2000.

Finding Your Perfect Work: The New Career Guide to Making a Living, Creating a Life, 2nd ed., Paul Edwards and Susan Edwards. New York: Penguin, 2003.

The 5 Patterns of Extraordinary Careers: The Guide for Achieving Success and Satisfaction, James M. Citrin and Richard Smith. New York: Crown Business, 2003.

The Global Citizen: A Guide to Creating an International Life and Career, Elizabeth Kruempelmann. Berkeley, CA: Ten Speed Press, 2002.

Guide to Your Career, 5th ed., Alan B. Bernstein. New York: Princeton Review, 2004.

How Hard Are You Knocking? The Job Seeker's Guide to Opening Career Doors, Timothy J. Augustine and Rona Curcio. Winchester, VA: Oakhill Press, 2005.

Job Search and Career Checklists: 101 Proven Time-Saving Checklists to Organize and Plan Your Career Search, Arlene S. Hirsch. Indianapolis, IN: JIST Publishing, 2005.

Monster Careers: How to Land the Job of Your Life, Jeffrey Taylor and Douglas Hardy. New York: Penguin, 2004.

New Guide for Occupational Exploration: Linking Interests, Learning and Careers, 4th ed., Michael Farr and Laurence Shatkin. Indianapolis, IN: JIST Publishing, 2006.

The Play of Your Life: Your Program for Finding the Career of Your Dreams—And a Step-by-Step Guide to Making It a Reality, Colleen A. Sabatino. New York: Rodale, 2004.

What Color Is Your Parachute? A Practical Manual for Job-Hunters and Career-Changers, Richard Nelson Bolles. Berkeley, CA: Ten Speed Press, revised annually.

What Should I Do with My Life? The True Story of People Who Answered the Ultimate Question, Po Brosnan. New York: Random House, 2002.

Where's My Oasis? The Essential Handbook for Everyone Wanting the Perfect Job, Rowan Manahan. New York: Vermillion, 2004.

Recommended

Finding Your Perfect Work: The New Career Guide to Making a Living, Creating a Life, 2nd ed., Paul Edwards and Susan Edwards. New York: Penguin, 2003. Lists types of careers, with emphasis on self-employment opportunities.

What Color Is Your Parachute? A Practical Manual for Job-Hunters and Career-Changers, Richard Nelson Bolles. Berkeley, CA: Ten Speed Press, revised annually. The classic in the genre, and the top-selling career-advice book consistently since the mid-1970s. Updated to reflect twenty-first-century concerns.

Getting the Job and Getting Ahead

Almanac of American Employers, Jack W. Plunkett. Galveston, TX: Plunkett Research Ltd., biennial.

e-Resumes: A Guide to Successful Online Job Hunting, Pat Criscito. Hauppauge, NY: Barron's Educational Series, 2004.

Guide to Internet Job Searching, Margaret Riley Dikel. New York: McGraw-Hill, 2004.

How to Earn What You're Worth: Leveraging Your Goals and Talents to Land Your Dream Job, Sunny Bates. New York: McGraw-Hill, 2004.

How to Get Any Job with Any Major: Career Launch & Re-launch for Everyone Under 30 (or How to Avoid Living in Your Parents' Basement), Donald Asher. Berkeley, CA: Ten Speed Press, 2004.

How to Get Your First Job and Keep It, 2nd ed., Deborah Perlmutter Bloch. New York: McGraw-Hill, 2002.

Insider's Guide to Finding a Job: Expert Advice from America's Top Employers and Recruiters, Wendy S. Enelow and Shelly Goldman. Indianapolis, IN: JIST Publishing, 2004.

International Job Finder: Where the Jobs Are Worldwide, Daniel Lauber and Kraig Rice. River Forest, IL: Planning/Communications, 2002.

International Jobs: Where They Are and How to Get Them, 6th ed., Nina Segal and Eric Kocher. New York: Basic Books, 2003.

Job-Hunting on the Internet, 4th ed., Richard Nelson Bolles and Mark Emery Bolles. Berkeley, CA: Ten Speed Press, 2005.

Job Savvy: How to Be a Success at Work, 3rd ed., LaVerne L. Ludden. Indianapolis, IN: JIST Publishing, 2002.

Job Search Magic: Insider Secrets from America's Career and Life Coach, Susan Britton Whitcomb. Indianapolis, IN: JIST Publishing, 2006.

The Job Search Solution: The Ultimate System for Finding a Great Job Now!, Tony Bashara. New York: AMACOM, 2005.

Job Seeker's Online Goldmine: A Step-by-Step Guidebook to Government and No-Cost Web Tools, Janet E. Wall. Indianapolis, IN: JIST Publishing, 2006.

Knock 'Em Dead 2006: The Ultimate Job Seekers Guide, Martin Yate. Avon, MA: Adams Media, 2006.

National Job Hotline Directory: The Job Finder's Hot List, 3rd ed., Sue Cubbage and Marcia Williams. River Forest, IL: Planning/Communications, 2003.

1000 Best Job Hunting Secrets, Diane Stafford and Moritza Day. Naperville, IL: Sourcebooks, 2004.

Super Job Search: The Complete Manual for Job-Seekers & Career-Changers, 3rd ed., Peter Studner. Los Angeles: Jamenair Ltd., 2003.

10 Insider Secrets to a Winning Job Search: Everything You Need to Get the Job You Want in 24 Hours—Or Less, Todd Bermont. Franklin Lakes, NJ: Career Press, 2004.

Very Quick Job Search: Get a Better Job in Half the Time, 3rd ed., Michael Farr. Indianapolis, IN: JIST Publishing, 2003.

Resumes and Interviews

Adams Job Interview Almanac, 2nd ed., Richard Wallace. Avon, MA: Adams Media Corp., 2005.

Recommended

How to Get Any Job with Any Major: Career Launch & Re-launch for Everyone Under 30 (or How to Avoid Living in Your Parents' Basement), Donald Asher. Berkeley, CA: Ten Speed Press, 2004. Counsels liberal arts degree-holders on how to package their education and strengths to land a high-paying position.

Knock 'Em Dead 2006: The Ultimate Job Seekers Guide, Martin Yate. Avon, MA: Adams Media, 2006. Offers range of advice for job-hunters at all levels, including resume-building, interview strategies, and salary negotiation tips.

Adams Resume Almanac, 2nd ed., Richard Wallace. Avon, MA: Adams Media Corp., 2005.

Amazing Resumes: What Employers Want to See—and How to Say It, Jim Bright and Joanne Earl. Indianapolis, IN: JIST Publishing, 2005.

Competency-Based Resumes: How to Bring Your Resume to the Top of the Pile, Robin Kessler and Linda A. Strasburg. Franklin Lakes, NJ: Career Press, 2004.

Cover Letter Magic, 2nd ed., Wendy S. Enelow and Louise Kursmark. Indianapolis, IN: JIST Publishing, 2004.

Cover Letters That Knock 'Em Dead, 6th ed., Martin Yate. Avon, MA: Adams Media, 2004.

The Elements of Resume Style: Essential Rules and Eye-opening Advice for Writing Resumes and Cover Letters That Work, Scott Bennett. New York: AMACOM, 2005.

Expert Resumes for Career Changers, Wendy S. Enelow and Louise M. Kursmark. Indianapolis, IN: JIST Publishing, 2005.

Fearless Interviewing: How to Win the Job by Communicating with Confidence, Marky Stein. New York: McGraw-Hill, 2002.

Ferguson Guide to Resumes and Job-Hunting Skills, Maurene J. Hinds. Chicago: Ferguson, 2005.

Gallery of Best Resumes: A Collection of Quality Resumes by Professional Resume Writers, 3rd ed., David F. Noble, Ph.D. Indianapolis, IN: JIST Publishing, 2004.

Get the Interview Every Time: Fortune 500 Hiring Professionals' Tips for Writing Winning Resumes and Cover Letters, Brenda Greene. Chicago: Dearborn Trade Publishing, 2004.

How to Interview Like a Top MBA: Job-Winning Strategies from Headhunters, Fortune 100 Recruiters, and Career Counselors, Shel Leanne. New York: McGraw-Hill, 2003.

How to Turn an Interview into a Job, Jeffrey G. Allen. New York: Simon and Schuster, 2004.

McGraw-Hill's Big Red Book of Resumes. New York: McGraw-Hill, 2002.

Monster Careers: Interviewing—Master the Moment That Gets You the Job, Jeffrey Taylor and Doug Hardy. New York: Penguin Books, 2005.

The Resume.com Guide to Writing Unbeatable Resumes, Warren Simons and Rose Curtis. New York: McGraw-Hill, 2004.

The Resume Handbook: How to Write Outstanding Resumes & Cover Letters for Every Situation, 4th ed., Arthur D. Rosenberg and David V. Hizer. Avon, MA: Adams Media, 2003.

Resume Magic: Trade Secrets of a Professional Resume Writer, 2nd ed., Susan Britton Whitcomb. Indianapolis, IN: JIST Publishing, 2003.

Resumes for Dummies, 4th ed., Joyce Lain Kennedy. Indianapolis, IN: Wiley, 2003.

Resumes That Knock 'Em Dead, 6th ed., Martin Yate. Avon, MA: Adams Media, 2004.

301 Smart Answers to Tough Interview Questions, Vicky Oliver. Naperville, IL: Sourcebooks, 2005.

201 Best Questions to Ask on Your Interview, John Kador. New York: McGraw-Hill, 2002.

Winning the Interview Game: Everything You Need to Know to Land the Job, Alan H. Nierenberg. New York: AMACOM, 2005.

Recommended

Resume Magic: Trade Secrets of a Professional Resume Writer, 2nd ed., Susan Britton Whitcomb. Indianapolis, IN: JIST Publishing, 2003. Before and after resume samples provide a how-to on crafting the perfect resume. Includes tips on e-resumes and tricks for scannable-text submissions.

301 Smart Answers to Tough Interview Questions, Vicky Oliver. Naperville, IL: Sourcebooks, 2005. Advice on how to handle the questions designed to unsettle, from explaining gaps in work history to acing arcane trivia volleys.

Mid-Career Options

Change Your Job, Change Your Life: Careering and Re-Careering in the New Boom/Bust Economy, 9th ed., Ron Krannich. Manassas Park, VA: Impact, 2004.

Fearless Career Change, Marky Stein. New York: McGraw-Hill, 2005.

Fire Your Boss, Stephen M. Pollan and Mark Levine. New York: HarperCollins, 2004.

I Don't Know What I Want, But I Know It's Not This: A Step-by-Step Guide to Finding Gratifying Work, Julie Jansen. New York: Penguin Books, 2003.

Over-40 Job Search Guide: 10 Strategies for Making Your Age an Advantage in Your Career, Gail Geary. Indianapolis, IN: JIST Publishing, 2004.

Radical Careering: 100 Truths to Jumpstart Your Job, Your Career, and Your Life, Sally Hogshead. New York: Gotham, 2005.

Second Acts: Creating the Life You Really Want, Building the Career You Truly Desire, Stephen M. Pollan and Mark Levine. New York: HarperCollins, 2003.

Working Identity: Unconventional Strategies for Reinventing Your Career, Hermania Ibarra. Boston: Harvard Business School Press, 2003.

Equality of Opportunity

Dancing on the Glass Ceiling, Nancy Frederick and Candy Deemer. New York: McGraw-Hill, 2004.

Job-Hunting for the So-Called Handicapped or People Who Have Disabilities, 2nd ed., Richard Nelson Bolles and Dale Susan Brown. Berkeley, CA: Ten Speed Press, 2001.

Job Search Handbook for People with Disabilities, 2nd ed., Daniel J. Ryan. Indianapolis, IN: JIST Publishing, 2004.

Lavender Road to Success: The Career Guide for the Gay Community, Kirk Snyder. Berkeley, CA: Ten Speed Press, 2003.

Resources for People with Disabilities, 2nd ed., Shawn Woodyard. Chicago: Ferguson, 2001.

Lists and Indexes of Career and Vocational Information

Encyclopedia of Careers and Vocational Guidance, 13th ed., 5 vols. Chicago: Ferguson, 2006.

*O*Net Dictionary of Occupational Titles*, 3rd ed. Indianapolis, IN: JIST Publishing, 2004.

Recommended

I Don't Know What I Want, But I Know It's Not This: A Step-by-Step Guide to Finding Gratifying Work, Julie Jansen. New York: Penguin Books, 2003. Experienced career coach identifies the top six reasons people are dissatisfied with their jobs and provides a step-by-step process for finding a career that suits every personality.

Working Identity: Unconventional Strategies for Reinventing Your Career, Hermania Ibarra. Boston: Harvard Business School Press, 2003. Help for those considering a mid-life career change.

Recommended

Dancing on the Glass Ceiling, Nancy Frederick and Candy Deemer. New York: McGraw-Hill, 2004. A former advertising executive teams with a professional executive coach to provide practical as well as inspirational advice for women in the workplace.

Job-Hunting for the So-Called Handicapped or People Who Have Disabilities, 2nd ed., Richard Nelson Bolles and Dale Susan Brown. Berkeley, CA: Ten Speed Press, 2001. From the author of *What Color Is Your Parachute?* Advice for the physically or mentally challenged on finding a career niche.

Internet Sites

Sites with Extensive Links

About.com
http://careerplanning.about.com

Beyond.com
http://www.beyond.com

Jobweb.com
http://www.jobweb.com

JIST Publishing
http://www.jist.com

Job Hunt: Online Job Search Guide and Resource Directory
http://www.job-hunt.org

Vault.com
http://www.vault.com

Vocational Information Center
http://www.khake.com

Career Development Resources

Career Magazine
http://www.careermag.com

Career Resource Homepage
http://www.careerresource.net

Job Hunters Bible
http://www.jobhuntersbible.com

Princeton Review
http://www.princetonreview.com

Quintessential Careers
http://www.quintcareers.com

Online Information and References

AT&T Toll-Free Internet Directory
http://www.tollfree.att.net

The Best Jobs in the USA Today
http://www.bestjobsusa.com

Careers.org
http://www.careers.org

Federal Jobs Digest
http://www.fedworld.gov/jobs/jobsearch.html

Job Finders Online
http://www.planningcommunications.com/jf

Job Safari
http://www.jobsafari.com

Monster Career Center
http://content.monster.com

Occupational Outlook Handbook
http://www.bls.gov/oco

SpherionExchange
http://employee.spherionexchange.com/start.cfm

U.S. Bureau of Labor Statistics Homepage
http://www.bls.gov/home.htm

US News and World Report Career Center
http://www.usnews.com/usnews/biztech/career/career_home.htm

Wall Street Journal Career Journal
http://www.careerjournal.com

Yahoo! Business and Economy
http://dir.yahoo.com/Business_and_Economy

Job Databases and Resume Posting

After College
http://www.aftercollege.com

America's Job Bank
http://www.ajb.org

Career Builder
http://www.careerbuilder.com

Career Mart
http://www.careermart.com

Employment Guide
http://www.employmentguide.com

Yahoo! Hot Jobs
http://hotjobs.yahoo.com

Idealist Nonprofit Career Center
http://www.idealist.org

Job.com
http://www.job.com

JobBank USA
http://www.jobbankusa.com

Job Web
http://www.jobweb.org

Monster Jobs
http://www.monster.com

Monstertrak
http://www.monstertrak.monster.com

NationJob.com
http://www.nationjob.com

Now Hiring
http://www.nowhiring.com

Audiovisual Materials

The following titles include, where possible, the developer's name and location or else the name and location of a distributor. Audiovisual titles may be available through several distributors.

Exploring the Working World

Career Advantage: Strategies for Success series. Video, guide. Princeton, NJ: Films Media Group.

Career Clusters series. Video. Charleston, WV: Cambridge Educational.

Career Exploration series. Video. South Charleston, WV: Meridian Education Corp.

Career Guidance Videos series. Video. South Charleston, WV: Meridian Education Corp.

Career S.E.L.F. Assessment: Finding a Career That Works for You. Video. Charleston, WV: Cambridge Educational.

Careers, Careers, Careers! Video, guide. Princeton, NJ: Films Media Group.

Careers for the 21st Century series. Video, guide. South Charleston, WV: Meridian Education Corp.

Careers without College. Video. Charleston, WV: Cambridge Educational.

The Changing Workplace: Technology and Globalization. Video. Princeton, NJ: Films Media Group.

Choices Today for Career Satisfaction Tomorrow. Video, guide. Charleston, WV: Cambridge Educational.

Complete Job Search System. Video. Charleston, WV: Cambridge Educational.

Connect on the Net: Finding a Job on the Internet. Video. Charleston, WV: Cambridge Educational.

Educational Planning for Your Career. Video. South Charleston, WV: Meridian Education Corp.

The 50 Best Jobs for the 21st Century series. Video. Indianapolis, IN: JIST Publishing.

The JIST Video Guide for Occupational Exploration series. Video. Indianapolis, IN: JIST Publishing.

Internet Careers: College Not Required. Video. Charleston, WV: Cambridge Educational.

Introduction to Career and Educational Exploration. Video. Princeton, NJ: Films Media Group.

JIST TV Series: The Job Search Channel. Video. Indianapolis, IN: JIST Publishing.

Jobs for the 21st Century. Video. Mt. Kisco, NY: Guidance Associates.

Learning for Earning. Video, guide. South Charleston, WV: Meridian Education Corp.

Log On for Success: Using Internet Job Sites. Video, guide. Charleston, WV: Cambridge Educational.

Researching Career Options: New Technologies and Current Techniques. Video. Princeton, NJ: Films Media Group.

School-to-Work Transition. Video. South Charleston, WV: Meridian Education Corp.

Ten Fastest Growing Careers: Jobs for the Future. Video. Mt. Kisco, NY: Guidance Associates.

What Would I Be Good At? Video. Mt. Kisco, NY: Guidance Associates.

What's Out There: How the World of Work is Organized. Video. Princeton, NJ: Films Media Group.

Your Career Search: Taking the First Step. Video. Mt. Kisco, NY: Guidance Associates.

Your Future: Planning Through Career Exploration. Video. South Charleston, WV: Meridian Education Corp.

Getting the Job and Getting Ahead

Career Evaluation. Video. Charleston, WV: Cambridge Educational.

Common Mistakes People Make in Interviews. Video, guide. Charleston, WV: Cambridge Educational.

Exceptional Employee: A Guide to Success on the Job. Video. Charleston, WV: Cambridge Educational.

Exceptional Interviewing Tips: A View from the Inside. Video, workbook. Charleston, WV: Cambridge Educational.

Extraordinary Answers to Common Interview Questions. Video. Charleston, WV: Cambridge Educational.

Finding a Job. Video. Charleston, WV: Cambridge Educational.

First Impressions: Etiquette and Work Habits for New Employees. Video, guide. Charleston, WV: Cambridge Educational.

From Pinkslip to Paycheck: The Road to Reemployment series. Video. Indianapolis, IN: JIST Publishing.

Getting Good Answers to Tough Interview Questions. Video. Indianapolis, IN: JIST Publishing.

Getting the Job You Really Want series. Video, workbook, guide. Indianapolis, IN: JIST Publishing.

How to Find a Job on the Internet. Video. Indianapolis, IN: JIST Publishing.

How to Be a Success at Work series. Video. Indianapolis, IN: JIST Publishing.

The Ideal Resume. Video. Charleston, WV: Cambridge Educational.

If at First: How to Get a Job and Keep It. Video. Mt. Kisco, NY: Guidance Associates.

Interview to Win Your First Job. Video. Indianapolis, IN: JIST Publishing.

Interviewing for a Job. Video. Charleston, WV: Cambridge Educational.

Job Survival Kit. Video. Charleston, WV: Cambridge Educational.

On-the-Job Success series. Video. Indianapolis, IN: JIST Publishing.

Planning Your Career. Video. Charleston, WV: Cambridge Educational.

The Portfolio Resume series. Video. Charleston, WV: Cambridge Educational.

"Quick" Job Search series. Video. Indianapolis, IN: JIST Publishing.

Succeeding on the Job. Video. Charleston, WV: Cambridge Educational.

Success in the Job World series. Video. Indianapolis, IN: JIST Publishing.

Staying on Track in Your Work Search. Video. Princeton, NJ: Films Media Group.

Power Interviewing Skills: Strategies for the Interviewee. Video. Charleston, WV: Cambridge Educational.

Take This Job and Love It: Keys to Surviving Your New Job. Video. Charleston, WV: Cambridge Educational.

Ten Commandments of Resumes. Video. Charleston, WV: Cambridge Educational.

Tough Times Job Strategies. Video, guide. Charleston, WV: Cambridge Educational.

Understanding and Using the O*NET. Video, guide. Charleston, WV: Cambridge Educational.

The Very Quick Job Search Video. Video. Indianapolis, IN: JIST Publishing.

The Video Guide to JIST's Self-Directed Job Search series. Video. Indianapolis, IN: JIST Publishing.

Web Resumes. Video. Charleston, WV: Cambridge Educational.

Computer Software

The following titles include, where possible, the developer's name and location or else the name and location of a distributor. Software titles may be available through several distributors.

Ace the Interview: The Multimedia Job Interview Guide. CD-ROM. Charleston, WV: Cambridge Educational.

Adams Media JobBank FastResume Suite. CD-ROM for Windows. Avon, MA: Adams Media.

Barron's Profiles of American Colleges on CD-ROM. Windows or Macintosh. Hauppauge, NY: Barron's Educational Series.

Cambridge Career Center. CD-ROM. Charleston, WV: Cambridge Educational.

Career Discovery Encyclopedia. CD-ROM. Chicago, IL: Ferguson.

Career Explorer. CD-ROM for Windows. Indianapolis, IN: JIST Publishing.

Career Finder Plus. CD-ROM. Indianapolis, IN: JIST Publishing.

CareerOINKs on the Web. Network. Indianapolis, IN: JIST Publishing.

Careers without College. CD-ROM. Indianapolis, IN: JIST Publishing.

Complete Resume Designer. CD-ROM. Charleston, WV: Cambridge Educational.

Custom Resume Creator. CD-ROM for Windows. Indianapolis, IN: JIST Publishing.

Decisions. CD-ROM. Indianapolis, IN: JIST Publishing.

Electronic Career Planner. CD-ROM for Windows. Indianapolis, IN: JIST Publishing.

Exploring the World of Work. CD-ROM. New York: McGraw-Hill.

JIST Presents Interview Mastery. CD-ROM. Indianapolis, IN: JIST Publishing.

Job Search series. CD-ROM. Indianapolis, IN: JIST Publishing.

Job Survival series. CD-ROM. Indianapolis, IN: JIST Publishing.

The Keys to Interviewing Success: Unlocking Your Professional Future. CD-ROM. Charleston, WV: Cambridge Educational.

Moving on Up: An Interactive Guide to Finding a Great Job. CD-ROM for Windows. Charleston, WV: Cambridge Educational.

Multimedia Career Center. CD-ROM. Charleston, WV: Cambridge Educational.

The Multimedia Career Path. CD-ROM. Charleston, WV: Cambridge Educational.

The Multimedia Guide to Occupational Exploration. CD-ROM. Charleston, WV: Cambridge Educational.

Multimedia Job Search. CD-ROM for Windows. Charleston, WV: Cambridge Educational.

Multimedia Take This Job and Love It. CD-ROM. Charleston, WV: Cambridge Educational.

OOH Career Center. CD-ROM. Charleston, WV: Cambridge Educational.

School-to-Work Career Center. CD-ROM. Charleston, WV: Cambridge Educational.

Success in the World of Work: Succeeding on the Job. CD-ROM. South Charleston, WV: Meridian Education Corp.

Targeting Success. CD-ROM. Indianapolis, IN: JIST Publishing.

General

Books

AHA Guide to the Health Care Field. Washington, DC: American Hospital Association, annual.

Careers in Health Care, 5th ed., Barbara Swanson. New York: McGraw-Hill, 2005.

Career Opportunities in Health Care, 2nd ed., Shelly Field. New York: Facts on File, 2002.

Careers in Alternative Medicine Career Resource Library, Alan Steinfeld. New York: Rosen Publishing Group, 2003.

Diversified Health Occupations, 6th ed., Louise Simmers. Albany, NY: Thomas Delmar Learning, 2003.

Exploring Health Care Careers, 2nd ed., Carole Bolster, ed. New York: Ferguson Publishing Company, 2001.

Health Care Career Starter, 2nd ed., Cheryl Jean Hancock and Brigit Dermott. Sewickley, PA: Learning Express, 2002.

Health Careers Today, 3rd ed., Judith Gerdin. St. Louis, MO: C.V. Mosby, 2003.

Health Professions Career and Education Directory, American Medical Association. Chicago: AMA, annual.

Introduction to Health Occupation: Today's Health Care Worker, 6th ed., Shirley Badasch and Doreen S. Chesbro. Upper Saddle River, NJ: Prentice Hall, 2003.

Introduction to the Health Professions, 3rd ed., Peggy Stanfield and Y. H. Hui. Sudbury, MA: Jones & Bartlett Publishers, 2002.

Job Opportunities in Health Care, Princeton, NJ: Peterson's annual.

Opportunities in Allied Health Careers, Alex Kacen. New York: McGraw-Hill, 2005.

Opportunities in Gerontology and Aging Services Careers, 2nd ed. New York: McGraw-Hill, 2002.

Petersons Job Opportunities for Health and Science Majors. Princeton, NJ: Petersons, annual.

Top 100 Health Care Careers: Your Complete Guidebook to Training and Jobs in Allied Health, Nursing, Medicine, and More, Saul Wischnitzer and Edith Wischnitzer. Indianapolis, IN: Jist Publishing, 2005.

The Yale Guide to Careers in Medicine and the Health Professions: Pathways to Medicine in the 21st Century, Robert Donaldson, Kathleen Lundgren, and Howard Spiro, eds. New Haven, CT: Yale University Press, 2003.

Internet Sites

Allied Health Careers
http://www.AlliedHealthCareers.com/

American College of Nurse-Midwives
http://www.midwife.org/

American Dental Hygienists Association: Education and Careers
http://www.adha.org/careerinfo/index.html

Career Builder
http://www.careerbuilder.com/

Career Planner
http://www.careerplanner.com/

Center for Health Careers
http://chc.hcwp.org/

EDphysician.com
http://www.edphysician.com/

Health Career Network
http://www.healthcareernet.com/

HealthCareerWeb.com
http://www.healthcareerweb.com/

MedZilla
http://www.medzilla.com/

Monster Healthcare
http://healthcare.monster.com/

National Institutes of Health, Office of Science Education Life Works
http://science.education.nih.gov/LifeWorks.nsf/

Nurse Options USA
http://www.nurseoptions.com/

Pharmaceutical Online
http://www.pharmaceuticalonline.com

Pharmacy Week
http://www.pweek.com

Physicians Employment
http://www.physemp.com/

PracticeLink
http://www.practicelink.com

Psych Web
http://www.psywww.com

RadWorking.com
http://www.radworking.com

RehabWorld
http://www.rehabworld.com

Audiovisual Materials

Career Cluster 1 Series: Health Services. DVD. Cambridge Research Group, 2002.

Careers: Scientific Occupations. Video. New York: Delphi Productions.

Dentists, Dental Assistants, and Dental Technicians

Books

Dental Assistant (Career Exploration), Rosemary Wallner. Mankato, MN: Capstone Press, 2000.

Opportunities in Dental Care Careers, Bonnie Kendall. New York: McGraw-Hill, 2000.

Pre-Dental Guide: A Guide for Successfully Getting into Dental School, Joseph S. Kim. Lincoln, NE: Writers Club Press, 2001.

Medical Assistants, Technicians, and Technologists

Books

Critical Careers: A Guide to Opportunities in Medical Equipment Service, Roger A. Bowles. Glen Rose, TX: Upstream Press, 2001.

Getting into the Physician Assistant School of Your Choice, Andrew Rodican. New York: McGraw-Hill Medical Publishing, 2003.

Medical Technicians (Careers in Focus), 3rd ed., Ferguson Publishing Staff, eds., New York: Ferguson Publishing Company, 2001.

Opportunities in Clinical Laboratory Science Careers, 2nd ed., Karen Karni. New York: McGraw-Hill, 2002.

Opportunities in Medical Imaging Careers, revised ed., Clifford J. Sherry. New York: McGraw-Hill, 2000.

Opportunities in Paramedical Careers, Alex Kacen and Terence J. Sacks. New York: McGraw-Hill, 1999.

Opportunities in Physician Assistant Careers, 2nd ed., Terrance J. Sacks and Ann L. Elderkin. New York: McGraw-Hill, 2002.

Nursing

Books

Advancing Your Career: Concepts of Professional Nursing, 3rd ed., Rose Kearney Nunnery. Philadelphia, PA: F.A. Davis Co., 2004.

Careers in Nursing, 2nd ed., Terence J. Sacks. New York: McGraw-Hill, 2003.

LPN to RN Transitions, 2nd ed., Nicki Harrington, Cynthia Lee Terry, and Felix S. Chew. Philadelphia: Lippincott Williams & Wilkins Publishers, 2002.

Mosby's Tour Guide to Nursing School: A Student's Road Survival Kit, 4th ed., Melodie Chenevert. St. Louis, MO: Mosby, 2002.

The Nursing Experience: Trends, Challenges, and Transitions, 4th ed., Lucie Young Kelly and Lucille A. Joel. New York: McGraw-Hill Medical, 2001.

101 Careers in Nursing, Jeanne M. Novotny, Doris T. Lippman, Nicole K. Sanders, and Joyce J. Fitzpatrik, eds. New York: Springer Publishing Company, 2003.

Opportunities in Nursing Careers, 2nd ed., Keville Frederickson. New York: McGraw-Hill, 2003.

Resumes for Nursing Careers, 2nd ed., editors of VGM. New York: McGraw-Hill, 2001.

Your Career in Nursing: Manage Your Future in the Changing World of Healthcare, Annette Valano. Chicago, IL: Kaplan, 2002.

Audiovisual Materials

Careers: Nursing—Get the Facts. Video. CEV Multimedia, 2003.

Pharmacy

Books

Careers with the Pharmaceutical Industry, 2nd ed., Peter D. Stonier, ed. New York: John Wiley & Sons, 2003.

Opportunities in Pharmacy Careers, Fred Gable. New York: McGraw-Hill, 2003.

Pharmacy Technician Career Starter, Felice Devine. New York: Learning Express, 2002.

Physicians and Specialized Practitioners

Books

Barron's Guide to Medical and Dental Schools, 9th ed., Saul Wischnitzer and Edith Wischnitzer. Hauppauge, NY: Barron's Educational Series, 2000.

Careers in Psychology: Opportunities in a Changing World, Tara L. Kuther and Robert D. Morgan. Florence, KY: Wadsworth Publishing, 2003.

Exploring Psychology, 5th ed., David G. Myers. New York: Worth Publishers, 2001.

Great Jobs for Psychology Majors, 2nd ed., Julie Degalan and Stephen Lambert. New York: McGraw-Hill, 2000.

Opportunities in Eye Care Careers, Kathleen M. Belikoff. New York: McGraw-Hill, 2003.

Opportunities in Physician Careers, Jan Sugar-Webb. Lincolnwood, IL: NTC Publishing Group, 1999.

Opportunities in Psychology Careers, Donald E. Super and Charles M. Super. New York: McGraw-Hill, 2001.

The Ultimate Guide to Choosing a Medical Specialty, Brian Freeman. New York: McGraw-Hill Medical, 2003.

Rehabilitation Therapists

Books

Careers in Physical Therapy, Trisha Hawkins. New York: Rosen Publishing Group, 2001.

Opportunities in Nutrition Careers, Marguerite Duffy and Carol Coles Caldwell. New York: McGraw-Hill, 1999.

Opportunities in Occupational Therapy Careers, Marguerite Abbott, Marie-Louise Franciscus, and Zona Roberta Weeks. New York: McGraw-Hill, 2000.

Opportunities in Sports and Fitness Careers, William Ray Heitzmann. New York: McGraw-Hill, 2003.

Occupations for Occupational Therapists, Matthew Molineux, ed. Malden, MA: Blackwell Publishers, 2004.

Opportunities in Physical Therapy Careers, Bernice R. Krumhansl. New York: McGraw-Hill, 1999.

Careers in Physical Therapy, Trisha Hawkins. New York: Rosen Publishing Group, 2001.

Audiovisual Materials

Career as a Respiratory Therapist. DVD. Educational Video Network, Inc., 2004.

Directory

The information in this directory was generated from the IPEDS (Integrated Postsecondary Education Data System) database of the U.S. Department of Education. It includes only regionally or nationally accredited institutions offering postsecondary occupational training in health care. Because college catalogs and directories of colleges and universities are readily available elsewhere, this directory does not include institutions that offer only bachelor's and advanced degrees.

Dental Assistant Technology

ALABAMA

Community College of the Air Force
130 West Maxwell Blvd.
Montgomery 36112-6613

ARIZONA

Apollo College
3870 North Oracle Rd.
Tucson 85705

Apollo College, Phoenix, Inc.
8503 North 27th Ave.
Phoenix 85051

Apollo College, Tri City, Inc.
630 West Southern Ave.
Mesa 85210

The Bryman School
4343 North 16th St.
Phoenix 85016

CALIFORNIA

Allan Hancock College
800 South College Dr.
Santa Maria 93454

Citrus College
1000 West Foothill Blvd.
Glendora 91741-1899

Concorde Career Institute
12412 Victory Blvd.
North Hollywood 91602

Concorde Career Institute
123 Camino De La Reina, Ste.
E125**San Diego 92108**

Concorde Career Institute
570 West Fourth St., Ste. 107
San Bernardino 92401

Diablo Valley College
321 Golf Club Rd.
Pleasant Hill 94523

Donald Vocational School
1833 West Eighth St., Ste. 200
Los Angeles 90057

Galen College of Medical and Dental
Assistants
1325 North Wishon Ave.
Fresno 93728

Galen College of Medical and Dental
Assistants
1604 Ford Ave.
Modesto 95350

Galen College of Medical and Dental
Assistants
3908 West Coldwell, Ste. A
Visalia 93277

Huntington College of Dental
Technology
250 Hospital Circle
Westminster 92683

Nova Institute of Health Technology
3000 South Robertson Blvd.
Los Angeles 90034

Nova Institute of Health Technology
520 North Euclid Ave.
Ontario 91762

Nova Institute of Health Technology
12449 Putnam St.
Whittier 90602-1023

Orange Coast College
2701 Fairview Rd.
Costa Mesa 92626

San Joaquin Valley College
201 New Stine Rd.
Bakersfield 93309

San Joaquin Valley College
295 East Sierra Ave.
Fresno 93710-3616

San Joaquin Valley College
8400 West Mineral King Ave.
Visalia 93291

Santa Rosa Junior College
1501 Mendocino Ave.
Santa Rosa 95401-4395

Western Career College
170 Bay Fair Mall
San Leandro 94578

COLORADO

Concorde Career Institute
770 Grant St.
Denver 80203

Front Range Community College
3645 West 112th Ave.
Westminster 80030

Heritage College of Health Careers
12 Lakeside Ln.
Denver 80212

CONNECTICUT

Huntington Institute, Inc.
193 Broadway
Norwich 06360

FLORIDA

Concorde Career Institute
7960 Arlington Expwy.
Jacksonville 32211

Concorde Career Institute
4202 West Spruce St.
Tampa 33607

Florida Community College at
Jacksonville
501 West State St.
Jacksonville 32202

Palm Beach Community College
4200 Congress Ave.
Lake Worth 33461

Southern College
5600 Lake Underhill Rd.
Orlando 32807

GEORGIA

Albany Technical Institute
1021 Lowe Rd.
Albany 31708

Medix Schools
2108 Cobb Pkwy.
Smyrna 30080

IDAHO

American Institute of Health
Technology, Inc.
6600 Emerald
Boise 83704

LLINOIS

Kaskaskia College
27210 College Rd.
Centralia 62801

Parkland College
2400 West Bradley Ave.
Champaign 61821

VIP Schools, Inc.
600N McClurg Ct., Ste. 304A
Chicago 60611-3044

INDIANA

Indiana University, Purdue University
at Indianapolis
355 North Lansing
Indianapolis 46202

Professional Careers Institute
2611 Waterfront Pkwy., East Dr.
Indianapolis 46214-2028

LOUISIANA

Domestic Health Care Institute
4826 Jamestown Ave.
Baton Rouge 70808

Eastern College of Health Vocations
3321 Hessmer Ave., Ste. 200
Metairie 70002

MARYLAND

Medix Schools
1017 York Rd.
Towson 21204-9840

MASSACHUSETTS

Bryman Institute, a Corinthian School
323 Boylston St.
Brookline 02146

Northeastern University
360 Huntington Ave.
Boston 02115

MICHIGAN

Delta College
University Ctr.
University Center 48710

Ferris State University
901 South State St.
Big Rapids 49307

Grand Rapids Community College
143 Bostwick Ave. NE
Grand Rapids 49503-3295

Grand Rapids Educational Center
1750 Woodworth NE
Grand Rapids 49525

Grand Rapids Educational Center
5349 West Main
Kalamazoo 49009

Ross Medical Education Center
1036 Gilbert St.
Flint 48532

Ross Medical Education Center
1188 North West Ave.
Jackson 49202

Ross Medical Education Center
913 West Holmes, Ste. 260
Lansing 48910

Ross Medical Education Center
4054 Bay Rd.
Saginaw 48603

Ross Medical Education Center
26417 Hoover Rd.
Warren 48089

MINNESOTA

Century Community and Technical
College
3300 Century Ave. N
White Bear Lake 55110

Hibbing Community College, a
Technical and Community College
1515 East 25th St.
Hibbing 55746

Lakeland Medical and Dental Academy,
Inc.
1402 West Lake St.
Minneapolis 55408

MISSISSIPPI

Hinds Community College, Raymond
Campus
Raymond 39154

MISSOURI

Al-Med Academy
10963 Saint Charles Rock Rd.
Saint Louis 63074

Concorde Career Institute
3239 Broadway
Kansas City 64111

Missouri College
10121 Manchester Rd.
Saint Louis 63122

Saint Louis Community College, Forest Park
5600 Oakland Ave.
Saint Louis 63110

NEVADA

Heritage College
3305 Spring Mountain Rd., Ste. 7
Las Vegas 89120

NEW HAMPSHIRE

New Hampshire Technical Institute
11 Institute Dr.
Concord 03301

NEW JERSEY

Berdan Institute
265 Rte. 46
Totowa 07512

Camden County College
P.O. Box 200
Blackwood 08012

Empire Technical School of New Jersey
576 Central Ave.
East Orange 07018

NEW YORK

Continental Dental Assistant School
633 Jefferson Rd.
Rochester 14623

Mandl School
254 West 54th St.
New York 10019

New York School for Medical and
Dental Assistants
116-16 Queens Blvd.
Forest Hills 11375

NORTH CAROLINA

Alamance Community College
P.O. Box 8000
Graham 27253

Guilford Technical Community College
Box 309
Jamestown 27282

OHIO

Akron Medical-Dental Institute, Inc.,
DBA Akron Institute
1625 Portage Tr.
Cuyahoga Falls 44223

Cleveland Institute of Dental-Medical
Assistants
1836 Euclid Ave.
Cleveland 44115

Cleveland Institute of Dental-Medical
Assistants
5564 Mayfield Rd.
Lyndhurst 44124

Cleveland Institute of Dental-Medical
Assistants
5733 Hopkins Rd.
Mentor 44060

Eastland Career Center
4465 South Hamilton Rd.
Groveport 43125

Institute of Medical-Dental Technology
375 Glensprings Dr., Ste. 201
Cincinnati 45246

OKLAHOMA

Kiamichi Area Vocational Technical
School SD 7, Talihina Campus
Rte. 2, Hwy. 63A
Talihina 74571

Metro Area Vocational Technical School
District 22
1900 Springlake Dr.
Oklahoma City 73111

OREGON

Apollo College, Portland, Inc.
2600 Southeast 98th Ave.
Portland 97266

Lane Community College
4000 East 30th Ave.
Eugene 97405

Portland Community College
P.O. Box 19000
Portland 97280-0990

PENNSYLVANIA

Academy of Medical Arts and Business
2301 Academy Dr.
Harrisburg 17112

Career Training Academy
703 Fifth Ave.
New Kensington 15068

Community College of Philadelphia
1700 Spring Garden St.
Philadelphia 19130

Delaware Valley Academy of Medical
and Dental Assistants
3330 Grant Ave.
Philadelphia 19114

Median School of Allied Health Careers
125 Seventh St.
Pittsburgh 15222-3400

RHODE ISLAND

Community College of Rhode Island
400 East Ave.
Warwick 02886-1807

TENNESSEE

Chattanooga State Technical
Community College
4501 Amnicola Hwy.
Chattanooga 37406

Tennessee Technology Center at
Memphis
550 Alabama Ave.
Memphis 38105-3604

Tennessee Technology Center at
Shelbyville
1405 Madison St.
Shelbyville 37160

TEXAS

Allied Health Careers
5424 Hwy. 290 W, Ste. 105
Austin 78735

Career Centers of Texas El Paso
8375 Burnham Dr.
El Paso 79907

San Antonio College of Medical and
Dental Assistants, Central
4205 San Pedro Ave.
San Antonio 78212-1899

San Antonio College of Medical and
Dental Assistants, South
3900 North 23rd
McAllen 78501

Texas State Technical College, Waco
3801 Campus Dr.
Waco 76705

UTAH

American Institute of Medical-Dental
Technology
1675 North 200 West, Bldg. 4
Provo 84604

Provo College
1450 West 820 North
Provo 84601

Utah Career College
1144 West 3300 South
Salt Lake City 84119-3330

VIRGINIA

Medical Careers Institute
605 Thimble Shoals
Newport News 23606

National Business College
1813 East Main St.
Salem 24153

Riverside Regional Medical Center,
School of Professional Nursing
500 J Clyde Morris Blvd.
Newport News 23601

WASHINGTON

Bates Technical College
1101 South Yakima Ave.
Tacoma 98405

Bellingham Technical College
3028 Lindbergh Ave.
Bellingham 98225

Eton Technical Institute
209 East Casino Rd.
Everett 98208

Eton Technical Institute
31919 Sixth Ave. S
Federal Way 98003

Eton Technical Institute
3649 Frontage Rd., St. A
Port Orchard 98366

Lake Washington Technical College
11605 132nd Ave. NE
Kirkland 98034

Seattle Vocational Institute
315 22nd Ave. S
Seattle 98144

Spokane Community College
North 1810 Greene Ave.
Spokane 99207

WISCONSIN

Fox Valley Technical College at
Appleton
1825 North Bluemound Dr.
Appleton 54913-2277

Western Wisconsin Technical College
304 North Sixth St., P.O. Box 908
La Crosse 54602-0908

Dental Hygiene Technology

ARIZONA

Phoenix College
1202 West Thomas Rd.
Phoenix 85013

CALIFORNIA

Cabrillo College
6500 Soquel Dr.
Aptos 95003

Foothill College
12345 El Monte Rd.
Los Altos Hills 94022

Pasadena City College
1570 East Colorado Blvd.
Pasadena 91106

Riverside Community College
4800 Magnolia Ave.
Riverside 92506-1299

West Los Angeles College
4800 Freshman Dr.
Culver 90230

CONNECTICUT

Tunxis Community Technical College
Rtes. 6 and 177
Farmington 06032

University of Bridgeport
380 University Ave.
Bridgeport 06601

DELAWARE

Delaware Technical and Community
College, Stanton-Wilmington
400 Stanton-Christiana Rd.
Newark 19702

FLORIDA

Miami-Dade Community College
300 Northeast Second Ave.
Miami 33132

Palm Beach Community College
4200 Congress Ave.
Lake Worth 33461

Pensacola Junior College
1000 College Blvd.
Pensacola 32504

Saint Petersburg Junior College
8580 66th St. N
Pinellas Park 34665

Santa Fe Community College
3000 Northwest 83rd St.
Gainesville 32606

GEORGIA

Darton College
2400 Gillionville Rd.
Albany 31707

Dekalb College
3251 Panthersville Rd.
Decatur 30034

Medical College of Georgia
1120 15th St.
Augusta 30912

ILLINOIS

Illinois Central College
One College Dr.
East Peoria 61635-0001

Parkland College
2400 West Bradley Ave.
Champaign 61821

Prairie State College
202 Halsted St.
Chicago Heights 60411

Southern Illinois University,
Carbondale
Faner Hall 2179
Carbondale 62901-4512

William Rainey Harper College
1200 West Algonquin Rd.
Palatine 60067-7398

INDIANA

Indiana University, Northwest
3400 Broadway
Gary 46408

Indiana University, Purdue University,
Indianapolis
355 North Lansing
Indianapolis 46202

KANSAS

Johnson County Community College
12345 College Blvd.
Overland Park 66210-1299

Wichita State University
1845 Fairmount
Wichita 67260

KENTUCKY

Lexington Community College
Cooper Dr.
Lexington 40506

LOUISIANA

Louisiana State University Medical
Center
433 Bolivar St.
New Orleans 70112

MARYLAND

Allegany College of Maryland
12401 Willowbrook Rd. SE
Cumberland 21502

Baltimore City Community College
2901 Liberty Heights Ave.
Baltimore 21215

MASSACHUSETTS

Bristol Community College
777 Elsbree St.
Fall River 02720

Forsyth School for Dental Hygienists
140 The Fenway
Boston 02115

Middlesex Community College
Springs Rd.
Bedford 01730

MICHIGAN

Ferris State University
901 South State St.
Big Rapids 49307

Grand Rapids Community College
143 Bostwick Ave. NE
Grand Rapids 49503-3295

Mott Community College
1401 East Court St.
Flint 48503

Oakland Community College
2480 Opdyke Rd.
Bloomfield Hills 48304-2266

University of Detroit, Mercy
P.O. Box 19900
Detroit 48219-0900

MINNESOTA

Normandale Community College
9700 France Ave. S
Bloomington 55431

MISSOURI

Saint Louis Community College, Forest
Park
5600 Oakland Ave.
Saint Louis 63110

NEW HAMPSHIRE

New Hampshire Technical Institute
11 Institute Dr.
Concord 03301

NEW JERSEY

Bergen Community College
400 Paramus Rd.
Paramus 07652

Camden County College
P.O. Box 200
Blackwood 08012

Middlesex County College
155 Mill Rd.
Edison 08818-3050

Union County College
1033 Springfield Ave.
Cranford 07016

NEW MEXICO

University of New Mexico, Main
Campus
Albuquerque 87131

NEW YORK

Broome Community College
P.O. Box 1017
Binghamton 13902

CUNY New York City Technical College
300 Jay St.
Brooklyn 11201

Erie Community College, North
Campus
Main St. and Youngs Rd.
Williamsville 14221

Hudson Valley Community College
80 Vandenburgh Ave.
Troy 12180

Monroe Community College
1000 East Henrietta Rd.
Rochester 14623

Onondaga Community College
4941 Onondaga Rd.
Syracuse 13215

SUNY College of Technology at
Farmingdale
Melville Rd.
Farmingdale 11735-1021

NORTH CAROLINA

Central Piedmont Community College
P.O. Box 35009
Charlotte 28235-5009

Guilford Technical Community College
Box 309
Jamestown 27282

NORTH DAKOTA

North Dakota State College of Science
800 North Sixth St.
Wahpeton 58076

OHIO

Cuyahoga Community College District
700 Carnegie Ave.
Cleveland 44115-2878

Shawnee State University
940 Second St.
Portsmouth 45662

University of Cincinnati, Raymond
Walters College
9555 Plainfield Rd.
Blue Ash 45236

Youngstown State University
One University Plaza
Youngstown 44555

OREGON

Lane Community College
4000 East 30th Ave.
Eugene 97405

PENNSYLVANIA

Community College of Philadelphia
1700 Spring Garden St.
Philadelphia 19130

Harcum College
750 Montgomery Ave.
Bryn Mawr 19010

ICS-International Correspondence
Schools
Oak St. and Pawnee Ave.
Scranton 18515

Luzerne County Community College
1333 South Prospect St.
Nanticoke 18634

Northampton County Area Community
College
3835 Green Pond Rd.
Bethlehem 18020-7599

Pennsylvania College of Technology
One College Ave.
Williamsport 17701

RHODE ISLAND

Community College of Rhode Island
400 East Ave.
Warwick 02886-1807

SOUTH CAROLINA

Greenville Technical College
P.O. Box 5616, Station B
Greenville 29606-5616

Midlands Technical College
P.O. Box 2408
Columbia 29202

Trident Technical College
P.O. Box 118067
Charleston 29423-8067

SOUTH DAKOTA

University of South Dakota
414 East Clark St.
Vermillion 57069-2390

TENNESSEE

East Tennessee State University
P.O. Box 70734
Johnson City 37614-0734

Tennessee State University
3500 John Merritt Blvd.
Nashville 37209-1561

TEXAS

Tyler Junior College
1327 South Baxter Ave.
Tyler 75711

The University of Texas Health Science
Center
P.O. Box 20036
Houston 77225

The University of Texas Health Science
Center, San Antonio
7703 Floyd Curl Dr.
San Antonio 78284

UTAH

American Institute of Medical-Dental
Technology
1675 North 200 West, Bldg. 4
Provo 84604

Weber State University
3750 Harrison Blvd.
Ogden 84408

VIRGINIA

Wytheville Community College
1000 East Main St.
Wytheville 24382

WASHINGTON

Clark College
1800 East McLoughlin Blvd.
Vancouver 98663-3598

Shoreline Community College
16101 Greenwood Ave. N
Seattle 98133

WEST VIRGINIA

West Liberty State College
West Liberty 26074

WISCONSIN

Madison Area Technical College
3550 Anderson St.
Madison 53704

Northcentral Technical College
1000 Campus Dr.
Wausau 54401-1899

Northeast Wisconsin Technical College
2740 West Mason St., P.O. Box 19042
Green Bay 54307-9042

Dental Laboratory Technology

CALIFORNIA

California Vocational College
3951 Balboa Ave.
San Francisco 94121

Huntington College of Dental
Technology
250 Hospital Circle
Westminster 92683

Nova Institute of Health Technology
12449 Putnam St.
Whittier 90602-1023

Simi Valley Adult School
3192 Los Angeles Ave.
Simi Valley 93065

ILLINOIS

Midwest Institute of Technology, Inc.
3712 West Montrose Ave.
Chicago 60618

NEW YORK

Penaranda Institute of Dental
Technology
40-17 82nd St.
Jackson Heights 11373

TENNESSEE

Tennessee Technology Center at
Memphis
550 Alabama Ave.
Memphis 38105-3604

EEG and EKG Technology

CALIFORNIA

Institute of Computer Technology
3200 Wilshire Blvd.
Los Angeles 90010

Orange Coast College
2701 Fairview Rd.
Costa Mesa 92626

FLORIDA

Pasco-Hernando Community College
36727 Blanton Rd.
Dade City 33525-7599

Technical Career Institute
4299 Northwest 36th St., Ste. 300
Miami Springs 33166

ILLINOIS

Medical Careers Institute
116 South Michigan Ave.
Chicago 60603

MICHIGAN

Carnegie Institute
550 Stephenson Hwy.
Troy 48083

MISSOURI

Saint Louis College of Health Careers
4484 West Pine
Saint Louis 63108

NEW JERSEY

Hudson County Area Vocational
Technical School, North Hudson
Center
8511 Tonnelle Ave.
North Bergen 07047

NEW YORK

Niagara County Community College
3111 Saunders Settlement Rd.
Sanborn 14132

PENNSYLVANIA

American Center Technical Arts
1930 Chestnut St.
Philadelphia 19103

TEXAS

Career Centers of Texas El Paso
8375 Burnham Dr.
El Paso 79907

Laboratory Animal Care Technology

COLORADO

Institute for Nuclear Medical Education
5660 Airport Blvd., Ste. 101
Boulder 80301

CONNECTICUT

Huntington Institute, Inc.
193 Broadway
Norwich 06360

FLORIDA

Beacon Career Institute, Inc.
2900 Northwest 183rd St.
Miami 33056

Lee County High Vocational Technical
Center, Central
3800 Michigan Ave.
Fort Myers 33916

Miriam Vocational School, Inc.
135 Southwest 57th Ave.
Miami 33144

Sarasota County Technical Institute
4748 Beneva Rd.
Sarasota 34233-1798

MINNESOTA

Saint Cloud Technical College
1540 Northway Dr.
Saint Cloud 56303

OHIO

Professional Skills Institute
20 Arco Dr.
Toledo 43607

PENNSYLVANIA

Allied Medical and Technical Careers
2901 Pittston Ave.
Scranton 18505

Allied Medical and Technical Careers
104 Woodward Hill Rd.
Edwardsville 18704

RHODE ISLAND

Community College of Rhode Island
400 East Ave.
Warwick 02886-1807

TENNESSEE

Nashville State Technical Institute
120 White Bridge Rd.
Nashville 37209

WISCONSIN

Saint Joseph's Hospital Histologic
Technician Program
611 Saint Joseph's Ave.
Marshfield 54449

Licensed Practical Nursing

ALABAMA

Bessemer State Technical College
1100 Ninth Ave.
Bessemer 35021

Bevill State Community College
100 State St.
Sumiton 35148

Central Alabama Community College
1675 Cherokee Rd.
Alexander City 35010

Douglas MacArthur State Technical
College
1708 North Main St.
Opp 36467

Gadsden State Community College
1001 George Wallace Dr.
Gadsden 35902-0227

George C Wallace State Community
College, Dothan
Rte. 6, Box 62
Dothan 36303-9234

George C Wallace State Community
College, Hanceville
801 Main St. NW
Hanceville 35077-2000

George C Wallace State Community
College, Selma
3000 Earl Goodwin Pkwy.
Selma 36702

Harry M Ayers State Technical College
1801 Coleman Rd.
Anniston 36202

J F Drake State Technical College
3421 Meridian St. N
Huntsville 35811

Jefferson Davis Community College
220 Alco Dr.
Brewton 36426

John C Calhoun State Community
College
Hwy. 31 N
Decatur 35602

Northwest Shoals Community College
800 George Wallace Blvd.
Muscle Shoals 35662

Reid State Technical College
I65 and Hwy. 83
Evergreen 36401

Shelton State Community College
9500 Old Greensboro Rd.
Tuscaloosa 35405

Southern Union State Junior College
P.O. Box 1000
Wadley 36276

Trenholm State Technical College
1225 Air Base Blvd.
Montgomery 36108

ARIZONA

Central Arizona College
8470 North Overfield Rd.
Coolidge 85228-9778

Gateway Community College
108 North 40th St.
Phoenix 85034

Mesa Community College
1833 West Southern Ave.
Mesa 85202

Mohave Community College
1971 Jagerson Ave.
Kingman 86401

Pima Community College
2202 West Anklam Rd.
Tucson 85709-0001

ARKANSAS

Arkansas Valley Technical Institute
P.O. Box 506, Hwy. 23 N
Ozark 72949

Baptist Schools of Nursing and Allied
Health
11900 College Glenn Rd., Ste. 1000
Little Rock 72210-2820

Black River Technical College
Box 468, Hwy. 304
Pocahontas 72455

Cossatot Technical College
183 Hwy. 399
De Queen 71832

Cotton Boll Technical Institute
155 and Hwy. 148
Burdette 72321

Crowley's Ridge Technical School
140 Crowley's Ridge Rd.
Forrest City 72336-0925

Foothills Technical Institute
1800 East Moore St.
Searcy 72143

Northwest Technical Institute
709 South Old Missouri Rd.
Springdale 72764

Pulaski Technical College
3000 West Scenic Dr.
North Little Rock 72118

Quapaw Technical Institute
201 Mid-America Blvd.
Hot Springs 71913

Southeast Arkansas Technical College
1900 Hazel
Pine Bluff 71603

Westark College
P.O. Box 3649
Fort Smith 72913

CALIFORNIA

Butte College
3536 Butte Campus Dr.
Oroville 95965

Casa Loma College
14445 Olive View Dr.
Sylmar 91342

Casa Loma College, Los Angeles
3761 Stocker
Los Angeles 90008

Cerro Coso Community College
3000 College Heights Blvd.
Ridgecrest 93555-7777

Citrus College
1000 West Foothill Blvd.
Glendora 91741-1899

Concorde Career Institute
12412 Victory Blvd.
North Hollywood 91606

Concorde Career Institute
570 West Fourth St., Ste. 107
San Bernardino 92401

Crafton Hills College
11711 Sand Canyon Rd.
Yucaipa 92399-1799

El Camino College
16007 Crenshaw Blvd.
Torrance 90506

Glendale Community College
1500 North Verdugo Rd.
Glendale 91208-2894

Hacienda La Puente Unified School
District, Adult Education
P.O. Box 60002
City of Industry 91716-0002

Lassen College
Hwy. 139
Susanville 96130

Los Angeles Trade Technical College
400 West Washington Blvd.
Los Angeles 90015-4181

Maric College of Medical Careers
3666 Kearny Villa Rd., Ste. 100
San Diego 92123

Maric College of Medical Careers
2030 University Dr.
Vista 92083

Merced College
3600 M St.
Merced 95348-2898

Mission College
3000 Mission College Blvd.
Santa Clara 95054-1897

Mount San Jacinto College
1499 North State St.
San Jacinto 92383

Napa Valley College
2277 Napa Vallejo Hwy.
Napa 94558

Porterville College
100 East College Ave.
Porterville 93257

Sacramento City College
3835 Freeport Blvd.
Sacramento 95822

San Diego City College
1313 12th Ave.
San Diego 92101

Santa Barbara City College
721 Cliff Dr.
Santa Barbara 93109-2394

Sierra College
5000 Rocklin Rd.
Rocklin 95677

Yuba College
2088 North Beale Rd.
Marysville 95901

COLORADO

Community College of Denver
P.O. Box 173363
Denver 80217

Front Range Community College
3645 West 112th Ave.
Westminster 80030

Northeastern Junior College
100 College Dr.
Sterling 80751

Otero Junior College
1802 Colorado Ave.
La Junta 81050

Pikes Peak Community College
5675 South Academy Blvd.
Colorado Springs 80906-5498

Pueblo Community College
900 West Orman Ave.
Pueblo 81004

Red Rocks Community College
13300 West Sixth Ave.
Lakewood 80228

San Juan Basin Area Vocational School
Box 970
Cortez 81321

T H Pickens Technical Center
500 Airport Blvd.
Aurora 80011

Trinidad State Junior College
600 Prospect St.
Trinidad 81082

Trinidad State Junior College, San Luis
Valley Education Center
1011 Main St.
Alamosa 81101

DELAWARE

Delaware Technical and Community
College, Owens
Box 610
Georgetown 19947

Delaware Technical and Community
College, Terry Campus
1832 North Dupont Pkwy.
Dover 19901

DISTRICT OF COLUMBIA

Harrison Center for Career Education
624 Ninth St. NW, 4th Fl.
Washington 20001

FLORIDA

Atlantic Vocational Technical Center
4700 Coconut Creek Pkwy.
Coconut Creek 33063

Brevard Community College, Cocoa
Campus
1519 Clearlake Rd.
Cocoa 32922

Central Florida Community College
3001 Southwest College Rd.
Ocala 34474

Charlotte Vocational Technical Center
18300 Toledo Blade Blvd.
Port Charlotte 33948-3399

Daytona Beach Community College
1200 Volusia Ave.
Daytona Beach 32114

Florida Community College at
Jacksonville
501 West State St.
Jacksonville 32202

Indian River Community College
3209 Virginia Ave.
Fort Pierce 34981

Lake City Community College
Rte. 19, Box 1030
Lake City 32025

Lake County Area Vocational-Technical
Center
2001 Kurt St.
Eustis 32726

Lee County High Technical Center,
Central
3800 Michigan Ave.
Fort Myers 33916

Lindsey Hopkins Technical Education
Center
750 Northwest 20th St.
Miami 33127

Lively Technical Center
500 North Appleyard Dr.
Tallahassee 32304

Lorenzo Walker Institute of Technology
3702 Estey Ave.
Naples 34104

Manatee Vocational Technical Center
5603 34th St. W
Bradenton 34210

Miami Lakes Technical Education
Center
5780 Northwest 158th St.
Miami Lakes 33169

North Florida Community College
Turner Davis Dr.
Madison 32340

North Technical Education Center
7071 Garden Rd.
Riviera Beach 33404

Pasco-Hernando Community College
36727 Blanton Rd.
Dade City 33525-7599

Pensacola Junior College
1000 College Blvd.
Pensacola 32504

Pinellas Technical Education Center,
Clearwater
6100 154th Ave. N
Clearwater 34620

Pinellas Technical Education Center
901 34th St. S
Saint Petersburg 33711

Robert Morgan Vocational Technical
Center
18180 Southwest 122nd Ave.
Miami 33177

Saint Augustine Technical Center
2980 Collins Ave.
Saint Augustine 32095-1919

Santa Fe Community College
3000 Northwest 83rd St.
Gainesville 32606

Sarasota County Technical Institute
4748 Beneva Rd.
Sarasota 34233-1798

Seminole Community College
100 Weldon Blvd.
Sanford 32773-6199

Sheridan Vocational Center
5400 Sheridan St.
Hollywood 33021

South Florida Community College
600 West College Dr.
Avon Park 33825

South Technical Education Center
1300 Southwest 30th Ave.
Boynton Beach 33426-9099

Washington-Holmes Area Vocational-
Technical Center
757 Hoyt St.
Chipley 32428

William T McFatter Vocational
Technical Center
6500 Nova Dr.
Davie 33317

Withlacoochee Technical Institute
1201 West Main St.
Inverness 32650

GEORGIA

Albany Technical Institute
504 College Dr.
Albany 31705

Athens Area Technical Institute
U.S. Hwy. 29 N
Athens 30610-0399

Atlanta Area Technical School
1560 Stewart Ave. SW
Atlanta 30310

Augusta Technical Institute
3116 Deans Bridge Rd.
Augusta 30906

Bainbridge College
2500 East Shotwell St.
Bainbridge 31717

Carroll Technical Institute
997 South Hwy. 16
Carrollton 30117

Chattahoochee Technical Institute
980 South Cobb Dr.
Marietta 30060-3398

Columbus Technical Institute
928 45th St.
Columbus 31904-6572

Coosa Valley Technical Institute
785 Cedar Ave.
Rome 30161

Dekalb Technical Institute
495 North Indian Creek Dr.
Clarkston 30021

East Central Technical Institute
667 Perry House Rd.
Fitzgerald 31750

Flint River Technical Institute
1533 Hwy. 19 S
Thomaston 30286

Griffin Technical Institute
501 Varsity Rd.
Griffin 30223

Heart of Georgia Technical Institute
560 Pinehill Rd.
Dublin 31021

Macon Technical Institute
3300 Macon Tech Dr.
Macon 31206

Middle Georgia Technical Institute
1311 Corder Rd.
Warner Robins 31088

Moultrie Area Technical Institute
361 Industrial Dr.
Moultrie 31768

North Georgia Technical Institute
Georgia Hwy. 197, P.O. Box 65
Clarkesville 30523

Pickens Technical Institute
100 Pickens Tech Dr.
Jasper 30143

Savannah Technical Institute
5717 White Bluff Rd.
Savannah 31405-5594

South College
709 Mall Blvd.
Savannah 31406

South Georgia Technical Institute
728 Souther Field Rd.
Americus 31709

Swainsboro Technical Institute
346 Kite Rd.
Swainsboro 30401

Thomas Technical Institute
15689 US Hwy. 19N
Thomasville 31792

Valdosta Technical Institute
4089 Valtech Rd.
Valdosta 31602-9796

HAWAII

Kapiolani Community College
4303 Diamond Head Rd.
Honolulu 96816

IDAHO

Boise State University
1910 University Dr.
Boise 83725

College of Southern Idaho
P.O. Box 1238
Twin Falls 83301

Idaho State University
741 South Seventh Ave.
Pocatello 83209

ILLINOIS

Black Hawk College, Quad-Cities
6600 34th Ave.
Moline 61265

Capital Area School of Practical
Nursing
2201 Toronto Rd.
Springfield 62707-8645

Carl Sandburg College
2232 South Lake Storey Rd.
Galesburg 61401

City Colleges of Chicago, Central Office
226 West Jackson
Chicago 60606

Danville Area Community College
2000 East Main St.
Danville 61832

Decatur School of Practical Nursing
300 East Eldorado St.
Decatur 62523

Elgin Community College
1700 Spartan Dr.
Elgin 60123

F W Olin Vocational School of Practical
Nursing
4200 Humbert Rd.
Alton 62002

Highland Community College
2998 West Pearl City Rd.
Freeport 61032-9341

Illinois Eastern Community Colleges,
Olney Central College
305 North West St.
Olney 62450

Illinois Valley Community College
815 North Orlando Smith Ave.
Oglesby 61348-9692

Jacksonville School of Practical
Nursing
32 North Central Park Plaza
Jacksonville 62650

John A Logan College
700 Logan College Rd.
Carterville 62918

John Wood Community College
150 South 48th St.
Quincy 62301-9147

Joliet Township High School Practical
Nursing
201 East Jefferson St.
Joliet 60432

Kankakee Community College
P.O. Box 888
Kankakee 60901

Kaskaskia College
27210 College Rd.
Centralia 62801

Lake Land College
5001 Lake Land Blvd.
Mattoon 61938

Rend Lake College
468 North Ken Graz Pkwy.
Ina 62846

Shawnee Community College
8364 Shawnee College Rd.
Ullin 62992

Southeastern Illinois College
3575 College Rd.
Harrisburg 62946

South Suburban College
15800 South State St.
South Holland 60473

Spoon River College
23235 North CO 22
Canton 61520

Triton College
2000 Fifth Ave.
River Grove 60171

William Rainey Harper College
1200 West Algonquin Rd.
Palatine 60067-7398

INDIANA

Ebbert Education Center
325 West 38th St.
Anderson 46013

Ivy Tech State College, Central Indiana
One West 26th St.
Indianapolis 46206-1763

Ivy Tech State College, Columbus
4475 Central Ave.
Columbus 47203

Ivy Tech State College, East Central
4301 South Cowan Rd., Box 3100
Muncie 47302

Ivy Tech State College, Lafayette
3101 South Creasy Ln., P.O. Box 6299
Lafayette 47903

Ivy Tech State College, North Central
1534 West Sample St.
South Bend 46619

Ivy Tech State College, Northeast
3800 North Anthony Blvd.
Fort Wayne 46805

Ivy Tech State College, Northwest
1440 East 35th Ave.
Gary 46409

Ivy Tech State College, South Central
8204 Hwy. 311
Sellersburg 47172

Ivy Tech State College, Southeast
590 Ivy Tech Dr.
Madison 47250

Ivy Tech State College, Southwest
3501 First Ave.
Evansville 47710

Ivy Tech State College, Wabash Valley
7999 U.S. Hwy. 41
Terre Haute 47802-4898

Ivy Tech State College, Whitewater
P.O. Box 1145
Richmond 47374

J Everett Light Career Center
1901 East 86th St.
Indianapolis 46240

Vincennes University
1002 North First St.
Vincennes 47591

IOWA

Des Moines Community College
2006 Ankeny Blvd.
Ankeny 50021

Eastern Iowa Community College
District
306 West River Dr.
Davenport 52801-1221

Hawkeye Institute of Technology
1501 East Orange Rd.
Waterloo 50704

Indian Hills Community College
525 Grandview
Ottumwa 52501

Iowa Central Community College
330 Ave. M
Fort Dodge 50501

Iowa Lakes Community College
19 South Seventh St.
Estherville 51334

Iowa Valley Community College
District
Box 536
Marshalltown 50158

Iowa Western Community College
2700 College Rd., Box 4C
Council Bluffs 51502

North Iowa Area Community College
500 College Dr.
Mason City 50401

Northeast Iowa Community College,
Calmar
Box 400, Hwy. 150 S
Calmar 52132-0400

Saint Luke's College of Nursing and
Health Sciences
2720 Stone Park Blvd.
Sioux City 51104-0263

Southeastern Community College
Drawer F, 1015 South Gear Ave.
West Burlington 52655-0605

Southwestern Community College
1501 Townline
Creston 50801

Western Iowa Technical Community
College
4647 Stone Ave., P.O. Box 5199
Sioux City 51102-5199

KANSAS

Barton County Community College
245 Northeast 30th Rd.
Great Bend 67530

Colby Community College
1255 South Range
Colby 67701

Dodge City Community College
2501 North 14th Ave.
Dodge City 67801

Flint Hills Technical School
3301 West 18th St.
Emporia 66801

Kansas City Area Vocational Technical
School
2220 North 59th St.
Kansas City 66104

KAW Area Technical School
5724 Huntoon
Topeka 66604

Manhattan Area Technical Center
3136 Dickens Ave.
Manhattan 66503

Neosho County Community College
800 West 14th St.
Chanute 66720

North Central Kansas Technical College
Box 507, Hwy. 24
Beloit 67420

Northeast Kansas Area Vocational
Technical School
1501 West Riley St., P.O. Box 277
Atchison 66002

Seward County Community College
Box 1137
Liberal 67905-1137

KENTUCKY

Galen Health Institutes
612 South Fourth St., Ste. 400
Louisville 40202

Kentucky Tech, Ashland Regional
Technology Center
4818 Roberts Dr.
Ashland 41102

Kentucky Tech, Central Kentucky AVTS
308 Vo Tech Rd.
Lexington 40511-2626

Kentucky Tech, Letcher County
Technology Center
610 Circle Dr.
Whitesburg 41858

Kentucky Technical, Hazard Regional
Technology Center
101 Vo-Tech Dr.
Hazard 41701

Kentucky Technical, Jefferson
Vocational Technical School
727 West Chestnut St.
Louisville 40203-2036

Kentucky Technical, Somerset Regional
Technology Center
230 Airport Rd.
Somerset 42501

Mayo Regional Technology Center
Third St.
Paintsville 41240

Spencerian College
4627 Dixie Hwy.
Louisville 40216

West Kentucky Tech
5200 Blandville Rd.
Paducah 42002

LOUISIANA

Cameron College
2740 Canal St.
New Orleans 70119

Delta-Ouachita Regional Technical
Institute
609 Vocational Pkwy.
West Monroe 71291

Huey P Long Technical Institute
303 South Jones St.
Winnfield 71483

Louisiana Technical College,
Alexandria Campus
4311 South MacArthur Dr.
Alexandria 71302-3137

Louisiana Technical College, Bastrop
Campus
Kammell St.
Bastrop 71221-1120

Louisiana Technical College, Florida
Parishes
P.O. Box 130
Greensburg 70441

Louisiana Technical College, Gulf Area
Campus
1115 Clover St.
Abbeville 70510

Louisiana Technical College, Jefferson
Campus
5200 Blair Dr.
Metairie 70001

Louisiana Technical College, Jefferson
Davis Campus
P.O. Box 1327
Jennings 70546

Louisiana Technical College, Lafayette
Campus
1101 Bertrand Dr.
Lafayette 70502-4909

Louisiana Technical College, Lamar
Salter Campus
15014 Lake Charles Hwy.
Leesville 71446

Louisiana Technical College, Northwest
Louisiana
P.O. Box 835
Minden 71058-0835

Louisiana Technical College, Ruston
Campus
1010 James St.
Ruston 71273-1070

Louisiana Technical College,
Shreveport-Bossier
2010 North Market St.
Shreveport 71137

Louisiana Technical College, Sidney N
Collier
3727 Louisa St.
New Orleans 70126

Louisiana Technical College, Slidell
Campus
1000 Canulette Rd.
Slidell 70459

Louisiana Technical College, Sowela
Campus
3820 J Bennet Johnston Ave.
Lake Charles 70615

Louisiana Technical College, Sullivan
Campus
1710 Sullivan Dr.
Bogalusa 70427

Louisiana Technical College, T H Harris
Campus
337 East South St.
Opelousas 70570

Louisiana Technical College, West
Jefferson Campus
475 Manhattan Blvd.
Harvey 70058

Louisiana Tech College System, Young
Memorial
900 Youngs Rd.
Morgan City 70380

Our Lady of the Lake College of Medical
Technology
5345 Brittany Dr.
Baton Rouge 70808

MAINE

Central Maine Medical Center School of
Nursing
300 Main St.
Lewiston 04240

Eastern Maine Technical College
354 Hogan Rd.
Bangor 04401

Northern Maine Technical College
33 Edgemont Dr.
Presque Isle 04769

Southern Maine Technical College
Fort Rd.
South Portland 04106

MARYLAND

Harford Community College
401 Thomas Run Rd.
Bel Air 21015

Johnston School of Practical Nursing
201 East University Pkwy.
Baltimore 21218-2895

Wor-Wic Community College
32000 Campus Dr.
Salisbury 21801-7131

MASSACHUSETTS

Assabet Valley Regional Vocational
Technical School
215 Fitchburg St.
Marlborough 01752

Becker College, Worcester
61 Sever St.
Worcester 01615-0071

Berkshire Community College
1350 West St.
Pittsfield 01201-5786

Blue Hills Regional Technical School
800 Randolph St.
Canton 02021

Bristol Community College
777 Elsbree St.
Fall River 02720

Diman Regional Technical Institute
Stonehaven Rd.
Fall River 02723

Essex Agricultural Technical Institute
562 Maple St.
Hathorne 01937

Fisher College
118 Beacon St.
Boston 02116

Lemuel Shattuck Hospital School of
Practical Nursing
180 Morton St.
Jamaica Plain 02130

Massachusetts Bay Community College
50 Oakland St.
Wellesley Hills 02181

Massachusetts Soldiers Home School of
Practical Nursing
91 Crest Ave.
Chelsea 02150

Northern Essex Community College
Elliott Way
Haverhill 01830-2399

Quincy College
34 Coddington St.
Quincy 02169

Southeastern Technical Institute
250 Foundry St.
South Easton 02375

Tewksbury Hospital School of Practical
Nursing
365 East St.
Tewksbury 01876

Upper Cape Cod Regional Vocational
Technical School
220 Sandwich Rd.
Bourne 02532

Worcester Technical Institute
251 Belmont St.
Worcester 01605

Youville Hospital School of Practical
Nursing
15 Walnut Park at Aquinas College
Newton 02158

MICHIGAN

Alpena Community College
666 Johnson St.
Alpena 49707

Bay De Noc Community College
2001 North Lincoln Rd.
Escanaba 49289

Delta College
University Ctr.
University Center 48710

Gogebic Community College
East 4946 Jackson Rd.
Ironwood 49938

Grand Rapids Community College
143 Bostwick Ave. NE
Grand Rapids 49503-3295

Jackson Community College
2111 Emmons Rd.
Jackson 49201-8399

Kalamazoo Valley Community College
6767 West O Ave.
Kalamazoo 49009

Kirtland Community College
10775 North Saint Helen Rd.
Roscommon 48653

Mid Michigan Community College
1375 South Clare Ave.
Harrison 48625

Montcalm Community College
2800 College Dr.
Sidney 48885

Mott Community College
1401 East Court St.
Flint 48503

Muskegon Community College
221 South Quarterline Rd.
Muskegon 49442

Northern Michigan University
1401 Presque Isle
Marquette 49855

Oakland Community College
2480 Opdyke Rd.
Bloomfield Hills 48304-2266

Saint Clair County Community College
P.O. Box 5015, 323 Erie
Port Huron 48061-5015

Schoolcraft College
18600 Haggerty Rd.
Livonia 48152

West Shore Community College
3000 North Stiles Rd.
Scottville 49454

MINNESOTA

Alexandria Technical College
1601 Jefferson St.
Alexandria 56308

Central Lakes College, Brainerd
501 West College Dr.
Brainerd 56401

Dakota County Technical College
1300 East 145th St.
Rosemount 55068

Fergus Falls Community College
1414 College Way
Fergus Falls 56537

Hennepin Technical College
9000 Brooklyn Blvd.
Plymouth 55445

Lake Superior College
2101 Trinity Rd.
Duluth 55811

Minneapolis Community and Technical
College
1501 Hennepin Ave.
Minneapolis 55403-1779

Minnesota West Community and
Technical College
1450 College Way
Worthington 56187

Northwest Community and Technical
College
Hwy. 1 E
Thief River Falls 56701

Northwest Technical College, Detroit
Lakes
900 Hwy. 34 E
Detroit Lakes 56501

Northwest Technical College, East
Grand Forks
Hwy. 220 N
East Grand Forks 56721

Rainy River Community College
1501 Hwy. 71
International Falls 56649

Red Wing-Winona Technical College,
Red Wing Campus
308 Pioneer Rd.
Red Wing 55066

Red Wing-Winona Technical College,
Winona Campus
1250 Homer Rd., P.O. Box 409
Winona 55987

Ridgewater College, A Community and
Technical College, Willmar
P.O. Box 1097
Willmar 56201

Riverland Community College
1900 Eighth Ave. NW
Austin 55912

Saint Cloud Technical College
1540 Northway Dr.
Saint Cloud 56303

Saint Paul Technical College
235 Marshall Ave.
Saint Paul 55102

South Central Technical College,
Faribault
1225 Southwest Third St.
Faribault 55021

South Central Technical College,
Mankato
1920 Lee Blvd.
North Mankato 56003

MISSISSIPPI

East Mississippi Community College
P.O. Box 158
Scooba 39358

Hinds Community College, Raymond
Campus
Raymond 39154

Holmes Community College
Hill St.
Goodman 39079

Jones County Junior College
900 South Court St.
Ellisville 39437

Meridian Community College
910 Hwy. 19 N
Meridian 39307

Mississippi Delta Community College
P.O. Box 668
Moorhead 38761

Mississippi Gulf Coast Community
College
Central Office, P.O. Box 67
Perkinston 39573

Northeast Mississippi Community
College
Cunningham Blvd.
Booneville 38829

Northwest Mississippi Community
College
510 North Panola, Hwy. 51 N
Senatobia 38668

Pearl River Community College
Station A
Poplarville 39470

Southwest Mississippi Community
College
College Dr.
Summit 39666

MISSOURI

Columbia Area Vocational Technical
School
4203 South Providence Rd.
Columbia 65203

Cox Health Systems School of
Radiologic Technology
3801 South National Ave.
Springfield 65807

Gibson Technical Center
P.O. Box 169
Reeds Spring 65737

Hannibal Area Vocational Technical
School
4550 McMasters Ave.
Hannibal 63401

Jefferson College
1000 Viking Dr.
Hillsboro 63050

Lutheran Medical Center School of
Nursing
3547 South Jefferson Ave.
Saint Louis 63118

Mexico Public School Practical Nursing
620 East Monroe
Mexico 65265

Mineral Area College
P.O. Box 1000
Flat River 63601-1000

Nichols Career Center
609 Union
Jefferson City 65101

North Central Missouri College
1301 Main St.
Trenton 64683

Northwest Missouri Area Vocational
Technical School
1515 South Munn
Maryville 64468

Poplar Bluff School District Practical
Nurse Program
P.O. Box 47
Poplar Bluff 63901

Rolla Technical Institute
1304 East Tenth St.
Rolla 65401

Saint Charles County Community
College
4601 Mid Rivers Mall Dr.
Saint Peters 63376

Saint Louis Board of Education,
Practical Nursing Program
3815 McCausland Ave.
Saint Louis 63109

Saint Louis College of Health Careers
4484 West Pine
Saint Louis 63108

Sanford-Brown College
12006 Manchester Rd.
Des Peres 63131

Sikeston Area Vocational Technical
School
1002 Virginia St.
Sikeston 63801

State Fair Community College
3201 West 16th
Sedalia 65301-2199

Waynesville Technical Academy
810 Roosevelt
Waynesville 65583

MONTANA

Helena College of Technology of
University of Montana
1115 North Roberts St.
Helena 59601

Montana State University, College of
Technology, Billings
3803 Central Ave.
Billings 59102

Montana State University, College of
Technology, Great Falls
2100 16th Ave. S
Great Falls 59405

NEBRASKA

Central Community College Area
P.O. Box 4903
Grand Island 68802

Metropolitan Community College Area
5300 North 30th St.
Omaha 68111

Mid Plains Community College
416 North Jeffers
North Platte 69101

Northeast Community College
801 East Benjamin, P.O. Box 469
Norfolk 68702-0469

Southeast Community College Area
1111 O St., Ste. 111
Lincoln 68520

Western Nebraska Community College
1601 East 27th St. NE
Scottsbluff 69361-1899

NEVADA

Community College of Southern
Nevada
3200 East Cheyenne Ave.
Las Vegas 89030

NEW HAMPSHIRE

Saint Joseph's Hospital School of
Practical Nursing
Five Woodward Ave.
Nashua 03060

NEW JERSEY

Bergen Pines County Hospital School of
Practical Nursing
230 East Ridgewood Ave.
Paramus 07652

Charles E Gregory School of Nursing
Old Bridge Medical Arts. Bldg. 1
Hospital
Old Bridge 08857

Mountainside Hospital School of
Nursing
One Bay Ave.
Montclair 07042

Salem Community College
460 Hollywood Ave.
Carneys Point 08069

Union County College
1033 Springfield Ave.
Cranford 07016

NEW MEXICO

Clovis Community College
417 Schepps Blvd.
Clovis 88101

Northern New Mexico Community
College
1002 North Onate St.
Espanola 87532

NEW YORK

Iona College
715 North Ave.
New Rochelle 10801

Isabella G Hart School of Practical
Nursing
1425 Portland Ave.
Rochester 14621

Marion S Whelan School of Nursing of
Geneva General Hospital
196-198 North St.
Geneva 14456

Niagara County Community College
3111 Saunders Settlement Rd.
Sanborn 14132

North Country Community College
20 Winona Ave., P.O. Box 89
Saranac Lake 12983

Oswego County Boces
179 Colorado Rte. 64
Mexico 13114

Saint Francis School of Practical
Nursing
2221 West State St.
Olean 14760-1984

SUNY Westchester Commmunity
College
75 Grasslands Rd.
Valhalla 10595

NORTH CAROLINA

Asheville Buncombe Technical
Community College
340 Victoria Rd.
Asheville 28801

Caldwell Community College and
Technical Institute
Box 600
Lenoir 28645

Carteret Community College
3505 Arendell St.
Morehead City 28557

Central Carolina Community College
1105 Kelly Dr.
Sanford 27330

Durham Technical Community College
1637 Lawson St.
Durham 27703

Forsyth Technical Community College
2100 Silas Creek Pkwy.
Winston-Salem 27103

Montgomery Community College
P.O. Box 787
Troy 27371

Richmond Community College
P.O. Box 1189
Hamlet 28345

Rockingham Community College
P.O. Box 38, Hwy 65 W, County Home
Rd.
Wentworth 27375-0038

Rowan-Cabarrus Community College
Box 1595
Salisbury 28145-1595

Surry Community College
P.O. Box 304
Dobson 27017-0304

NORTH DAKOTA

Dickinson State University
Third St. and Eighth Ave. W
Dickinson 58601

North Dakota State College of Science
800 North Sixth St.
Wahpeton 58076

OHIO

Akron Adult Vocational Services
147 Park St.
Akron 44308

Akron School of Practical Nursing
619 Sumner St.
Akron 44311

Apollo Career Center
3325 Shawnee Rd.
Lima 45806-1454

Ashtabula County Joint Vocational
School
1565 State Rte. 167
Jefferson 44047

Belmont Technical College
120 Fox Shannon Place
Saint Clairsville 43950

Butler County JVS District, D Russel
Lee Career Center
3603 Hamilton Middletown Rd.
Hamilton 45011

Canton City School Practical Nurse
Program
1253 Third St. SE
Canton 44707-4798

Central School of Practical Nursing
4600 Carnegie Ave.
Cleveland 44103

Choffin Career Center
200 East Wood St.
Youngstown 44503

Clark State Community College
570 East Leffel Ln.
Springfield 45505

Ehove School of Practical Nursing,
Ehove Career Center
316 West Mason Rd.
Milan 44846

Gallia Jackson Vinton JUSD
Box 157
Rio Grande 45674

Hannah E Mullins School of Practical
Nursing
1200 East Sixth St.
Salem 44460-1757

Health Occupations Program,
Columbus Public School
100 Arcadia Ave.
Columbus 43202

Hocking Technical College
3301 Hocking Pkwy.
Nelsonville 45764

Jefferson Community College
4000 Sunset Blvd.
Steubenville 43952-3598

Lorain County Community College
1005 Abbe Rd. N
Elyria 44035

Marymount School of Practical Nursing
12300 McCracken Rd.
Garfield Heights 44125

North Central Technical College
2441 Kenwood Circle, P.O. Box 698
Mansfield 44901

Northwest State Community College
22-600 South Rte. 34
Archbold 43502-9542

Ohio Hi Point Joint Vocational School
District
2280 SR 540
Bellefontaine 43311-9594

Parma School of Practical Nursing
6726 Ridge Rd.
Parma 44129

Pickaway Ross Joint Vocational School
District
895 Crouse Chapel Rd.
Chillicothe 45601-9010

Portage Lakes Career Center
4401 Shriver Rd.
Greensburg 44232-0248

Scioto County Joint Vocational School
District
P.O. Box 766
Lucasville 45648

Toledo School of Practical Nursing
1602 Washington St., Whitney Building
Toledo 43624

Upper Valley Joint Vocational School
8811 Career Dr.
Piqua 45356

W Howard Nicol School of Practical
Nursing
4401 Shriver Rd.
Green 44232-0248

Walsh University
2020 Easton St. NW
North Canton 44720-3396

Washington State Community College
710 Colegate Dr.
Marietta 45750

Wayne Adult School of Practical
Nursing
518 West Prospect St.
Smithville 44677-0378

OKLAHOMA

Caddo-Kiowa Area Vocational Technical
School
P.O. Box 190
Fort Cobb 73038

Francis Tuttle Area Vocational
Technical Center
12777 North Rockwell Ave.
Oklahoma City 73142-2789

Gordon Cooper Area Vocational
Technical School
One John C Bruton Blvd.
Shawnee 74801

Great Plains Area Vocational Technical
School
4500 West Lee Blvd.
Lawton 73505

Kiamichi AVTS SD #7, Hugo
107 South 15th
Hugo 74743

Kiamichi AVTS SD #7, McCurtain
Campus
Box 177, Rte. 3, Hwy. 70 N
Idabel 74745

Kiamichi AVTS SD #7, Poteau
1509 South McKenna
Poteau 74953

Metro Area Vocational Technical School
District 22
1900 Springlake Dr.
Oklahoma City 73111

Pioneer Area Vocational Technical
School
2101 North Ash
Ponca City 74601

Pontotoc Area Vocational Technical
School
601 West 33rd
Ada 74820

Red River Area Vocational Technical
School
3300 West Bois Darc
Duncan 73533

Southwest Area Vocational Technical
Center
711 West Tamarack
Altus 73521

OREGON

Blue Mountain Community College
P.O. Box 100
Pendleton 97801

Central Oregon Community College
2600 Northwest College Way
Bend 97701

Chemeketa Community College
4000 Lancaster Dr. NE
Salem 97305

Clackamas Community College
19600 Molalla Ave.
Oregon City 97045

Lane Community College
4000 East 30th Ave.
Eugene 97405

PENNSYLVANIA

Altoona Area Vocational Technical
School
1500 Fourth Ave.
Altoona 16602

Fayette County Area Vocational
Technical School of Practical
Nursing
RD 2, Box 122A
Uniontown 15401

Frankford Hospital School of Nursing
4918 Penn St.
Philadelphia 19124

Franklin County Career and
Technology Center
2463 Loop Rd.
Chambersburg 17201

Gannon University
109 West Sixth St.
Erie 16541

Harrisburg Area Community College,
Harrisburg
One Hacc Dr.
Harrisburg 17110

Lawrence County Vocational Technical
School Practical Nursing
750 Phelps Way
New Castle 16101-5099

Lehigh Carbon Community College
4525 Education Park Dr.
Schnecksville 18078-2598

Mercer County Area Vocational
Technical School
776 Greenville Rd.
Mercer 16137-0152

Northampton County Area Community
College
3835 Green Pond Rd.
Bethlehem 18017-7599

Pennsylvania College of Technology
One College Ave.
Williamsport 17701

Roxborough Memorial Hospital School
of Nursing
5800 Ridge Ave.
Philadelphia 19128

Saint Francis Medical Center School of
Nursing
400 45th St.
Pittsburgh 15201

Saint Luke's Hospital School of Nursing
801 Ostrum
Bethlehem 18015

Schuykill County Area Vocational
Technical School
101 Technology Dr.
Frackville 17931

Western Area Career and Technology
Center
688 Western Ave.
Canonsburg 15317

Wilkes-Barre Area Vocational-Technical
School of Practical Nursing
P.O. Box 1699, North End Station
Jumper Rd.
Wilkes-Barre 18705-0699

RHODE ISLAND

Community College of Rhode Island
400 East Ave.
Warwick 02886-1807

SOUTH CAROLINA

Greenville Technical College
P.O. Box 5616, Station B
Greenville 29606-5616

Midlands Technical College
P.O. Box 2408
Columbia 29202

Orangeburg Calhoun Technical College
3250 Saint Matthew's Rd.
Orangeburg 29118

Piedmont Technical College
P.O. Drawer 1467
Greenwood 29648

Spartanburg Technical College
Business I-85
Spartanburg 29305

Trident Technical College
P.O. Box 118067
Charleston 29423-8067

SOUTH DAKOTA

Lake Area Technical Institute
230 11th St. NE
Watertown 57201

Western Dakota Vocational Technical
Institute
800 Mickelson Dr.
Rapid City 57701

TENNESSEE

Chattanooga State Technical
Community College
4501 Amnicola Hwy.
Chattanooga 37406

Tennessee Technology Center at Athens
P.O. Box 848, 1635 Vo Tech Dr.
Athens 37371-0848

Tennessee Technology Center at
Covington
P.O. Box 249
Covington 38019

Tennessee Technology Center at
Crossville
P.O. Box 2959
Crossville 38557

Tennessee Technology Center at
Dickson
740 Hwy. 46
Dickson 37055

Tennessee Technology Center at
Elizabethton
1500 Arney St.
Elizabethton 37643

Tennessee Technology Center at
Harriman
P.O. Box 1109
Harriman 37748

Tennessee Technology Center at
Jacksboro
Rte. 1
Jacksboro 37757

Tennessee Technology Center at
Jackson
2468 Westover Rd.
Jackson 38301

Tennessee Technology Center at
Knoxville
1100 Liberty St.
Knoxville 37919

Tennessee Technology Center at
Livingston
740 High Tech Dr.
Livingston 38570

Tennessee Technology Center at
McMinnville
241 Vo Tech Dr.
McMinnville 37110

Tennessee Technology Center at
Memphis
550 Alabama Ave.
Memphis 38105-3604

Tennessee Technology Center at
Morristown
821 West Louise Ave.
Morristown 37813

Tennessee Technology Center at
Nashville
100 White Bridge Rd.
Nashville 37209

Tennessee Technology Center at Paris
312 South Wilson St.
Paris 38242

Tennessee Technology Center at
Shelbyville
1405 Madison St.
Shelbyville 37160

Tennessee Technology Center at
Whiteville
P.O. Box 489
Whiteville 38075

TEXAS

Amarillo College
P.O. Box 447
Amarillo 79178

Austin Community College
5930 Middle Fiskville Rd.
Austin 78752

Baptist Hospital System, Institute of
Health Education
111 Dallas St.
San Antonio 78205

Bee County College
3800 Charco Rd.
Beeville 78102

Blinn College
902 College Ave.
Brenham 77833

Central Texas College
P.O. Box 1800
Killeen 76540-1800

Cisco Junior College
Rte. 3, Box 3
Cisco 76437

Clarendon College
P.O. Box 968
Clarendon 79226

Del Mar College
101 Baldwin
Corpus Christi 78404-3897

Delta Career Institute
1310 Pennsylvania Ave.
Beaumont 77701

El Centro College
Main and Lamar
Dallas 75202

Galveston College
4015 Ave. Q
Galveston 77550

Hill College
P.O. Box 619
Hillsboro 76645

Houston Community College System
22 Waugh Dr.
Houston 77270-7849

Howard County Junior College District
1001 Birdwell Ln.
Big Spring 79720

Huntsville Memorial Hospital School
Vocational Nursing
3000 IH-45
Huntsville 77340

Kilgore College
1100 Broadway
Kilgore 75662-3299

Lamar University, Orange
410 Front St.
Orange 77630-5899

Lamar University, Port Arthur
1500 Proctor St.
Port Arthur 77640

Laredo Community College
West End Washington St.
Laredo 78040

Lee College
200 Lee Dr.
Baytown 77520-4703

McLennan Community College
1400 College Dr.
Waco 76708

Memorial Hospital, Memoral City
School of Vocational Nursing
920 Frostwood
Houston 77024-2434

Navarro College
3200 West Seventh
Corsicana 75110

North Harris Montgomery Community
College District
250 North Sam Houston Pkwy. E, Ste.
300
Houston 77060

Northeast Texas Community College
FM 1735
Mount Pleasant 75456

Odessa College
201 West University
Odessa 79764

Panola College
1109 West Panola St.
Carthage 75633

Paris Junior College
2400 Clarksville St.
Paris 75460

PCI Health Training Center
8101 John Carpenter Fwy.
Dallas 75247

Ranger College
College Circle
Ranger 76470

Saint Philip's College
1801 Martin Luther King Dr.
San Antonio 78203

San Jacinto College, North Campus
5800 Uvalde
Houston 77049

San Jacinto College, South Campus
13735 Beamer Rd.
Houston 77089-6009

Schreiner College
2100 Memorial Blvd.
Kerrville 78028

South Plains College
1401 College Ave.
Levelland 79336

Tarleton State University
Tarleton Station
Stephenville 76402

Temple College
2600 South First St.
Temple 76504-7435

Texarkana College
2500 North Robison Rd.
Texarkana 75599

Texas Southmost College
80 Fort Brown
Brownsville 78520

Texas State Technical College,
Sweetwater
300 College Dr.
Sweetwater 79556

Trinity Valley Community College
500 South Prairieville
Athens 75751

Vernon Regional Junior College
4400 College Dr.
Vernon 76384-4092

Victoria College
2200 East Red River
Victoria 77901

Weatherford College
308 East Park Ave.
Weatherford 76086

Western Texas College
6200 College Ave.
Snyder 79549-9502

Wharton County Junior College
911 Boling Hwy.
Wharton 77488

UTAH

College of Eastern Utah
400 East 400 North
Price 84501

Davis Applied Technology Center
550 East 300 South
Kaysville 84037

Salt Lake Community College
P.O. Box 30808
Salt Lake City 84130

Uintah Basin Applied Technology
Center
1100 East Lagoon St. (124-5)
Roosevelt 84066

Utah Valley State College
800 West 1200 South
Orem 84058

Weber State University
3750 Harrison Blvd.
Ogden 84408

VIRGINIA

Computer Dynamics Institute, Inc.
5361 Virginia Beach Blvd.
Virginia Beach 23462

Medical Careers Institute
605 Thimble Shoals
Newport News 23606

Petersburg Public Schools Practical
Nursing Program
Blandford School, 816 East Bank St.
Petersburg 23803

Richmond Memorial Hospital School of
Practical Nursing
1300 Westwood Ave.
Richmond 23227

Tidewater Technical
616 Denbigh Blvd.
Newport News 23608

WASHINGTON

Bates Technical College
1101 South Yakima Ave.
Tacoma 98405

Bellingham Technical College
3028 Lindbergh Ave.
Bellingham 98225

Centralia College
600 West Locust St.
Centralia 98531

Clark College
1800 East McLoughlin Blvd.
Vancouver 98663-3598

Columbia Basin College
2600 North 20th Ave.
Pasco 99301

Everett Community College
801 Wetmore Ave.
Everett 98201

Grays Harbor College
1620 Edward P Smith Dr.
Aberdeen 98520

Green River Community College
12401 Southeast 320th St.
Auburn 98092

Lower Columbia College
P.O. Box 3010
Longview 98632

Olympic College
1600 Chester Ave.
Bremerton 98310-1699

Seattle Community College, North
Campus
9600 College Way N
Seattle 98103

Skagit Valley College
2405 College Way
Mount Vernon 98273

South Puget Sound Community College
2011 Mottman Rd. SW
Olympia 98512

Spokane Community College
North 1810 Greene Ave.
Spokane 99207

Walla Walla Community College
500 Tausick Way
Walla Walla 99362

Wenatchee Valley College
1300 Fifth St.
Wenatchee 98801

Yakima Valley Community College
P.O. Box 1647
Yakima 98907

WEST VIRGINIA

B M Spurr School of Practical Nursing
800 Wheeling Ave.
Glen Dale 26038

Fred W Eberle School of Practical
Nursing
Rte. 5, Box 2
Buckhannon 26201

James Rumsey Technical Institute
Rte. 6, Box 268
Martinsburg 25401

Logan-Mingo School of Practical
Nursing
Box 1747, Three Mile Curve
Logan 25601

Mercer County Technical Education
Center
1397 Stafford Dr.
Princeton 24740

Roane-Jackson Technical Center
4800 Spencer Rd.
Leroy 25252-9700

Wood County Vocational School of
Practical Nursing
1515 Blizzard Dr.
Parkersburg 26101-6424

WISCONSIN

Chippewa Valley Technical College
620 West Clairemont Ave.
Eau Claire 54701

Fox Valley Technical College at
Appleton
1825 North Bluemound Dr.
Appleton 54913-2277

Madison Area Technical College
3550 Anderson St.
Madison 53704

Milwaukee Area Technical College
700 West State St.
Milwaukee 53233-1443

Moraine Park Technical College
235 North National Ave.
Fond Du Lac 54936-1940

WYOMING

Central Wyoming College
2660 Peck Ave.
Riverton 82501

Sheridan College
3059 Coffeen Ave.
Sheridan 82801

Western Wyoming Community College
2500 College Dr.
Rock Springs 82902

Medical Assistant Technology

ALABAMA

Capps College
3100 Cottage Hill Rd., Bldg. 5
Mobile 36606

Community College of the Air Force
130 West Maxwell Blvd.
Montgomery 36112-6613

Gadsden Business College
750 Forrest Ave.
Gadsden 35901

Gadsden Business College, Anniston
P.O. Box 1559
Anniston 36202-1575

George C Wallace State Community
College, Dothan
Rte. 6, Box 62
Dothan 36303-9234

ARIZONA

Apollo College
3870 North Oracle Rd.
Tucson 85705

Apollo College, Phoenix, Inc.
8503 North 27th Ave.
Phoenix 85051

Apollo College, Tri City, Inc.
630 West Southern Ave.
Mesa 85210

The Bryman School
4343 North 16th St.
Phoenix 85016

Gateway Community College
108 North 40th St.
Phoenix 85034

Long Medical Institute
4126 North Black Canyon Hwy.
Phoenix 85017

Occupational Training Center
4136 North 75th Ave., Ste. 200
Phoenix 85033

Pima Medical Institute
3350 East Grant Rd.
Tucson 85716

Tucson College
7302-10 East 22nd St.
Tucson 85710

ARKANSAS

Eastern College of Health Vocations
6423 Forbing Rd.
Little Rock 72209

CALIFORNIA

American School of X-Ray
13723-1/2 Harvard Place
Gardena 90249

Andon College
1700 McHenry Village Way
Modesto 95354

Andon College
1201 North El Dorado St.
Stockton 95202

Assert, Inc.
16745 Saticoy St.
Van Nuys 91406

California Paramedical and Technical
College
4550 La Sierra Ave.
Riverside 92505

Chabot College
25555 Hesperian Blvd.
Hayward 94545

Citrus College
1000 West Foothill Blvd.
Glendora 91741-1899

City College of San Francisco
50 Phelan Ave.
San Francisco 94112

Concorde Career Institute
12412 Victory Blvd.
North Hollywood 91606

Concorde Career Institute
570 West Fourth St., Ste. 107
San Bernardino 92401

Concorde Career Institute
123 Camino De La Reina, Ste. E125
San Diego 92108

Donald Vocational School
1833 West Eighth St., Ste. 200
Los Angeles 90057

Educorp Career Institute
230 East Third St.
Long Beach 90802

Foothill College
12345 El Monte Rd.
Los Altos Hills 94022

Galen College of Medical and Dental
Assistants
1325 North Wishon Ave.
Fresno 93728

Galen College of Medical and Dental
Assistants
1604 Ford Ave.
Modesto 95350

Galen College of Medical and Dental
Assistants
3908 West Coldwell, Ste. A
Visalia 93277

Hacienda La Puente Unified School
District, Adult Education
P.O. Box 60002
City of Industry 91716-0002

Institute for Business and Technology
2550 Scott Blvd.
Santa Clara 95050

Institute of Computer Technology
3200 Wilshire Blvd.
Los Angeles 90010

Maric College of Medical Careers
3666 Kearny Villa Rd., Ste. 100
San Diego 92120

Maric College of Medical Careers, Vista
Campus
2030 University Dr.
Vista 92083

McKinnon Institute of Professional
Massage and Bodywork
3798 Grand Ave.
Oakland 94610-1594

Modern Technology School
1232 East Katella Ave.
Anaheim 92805

Modern Technology School of X-Ray
6180 Laurel Canyon Blvd.
North Hollywood 91606

MTI Business College, Inc.
6006 North El Dorado St.
Stockton 95207-4349

National Career Education
6060 Sunrise Vista Dr.
Citrus Heights 95610

Newbridge College
1840 East 17th St., Ste. 140
Santa Ana 92705

Nova Institute of Health Technology
3000 South Robertson Blvd.
Los Angeles 90034

Nova Institute of Health Technology
520 North Euclid Ave.
Ontario 91762

Nova Institute of Health Technology
12449 Putnam St.
Whittier 90602-1023

Platt College, San Diego
6250 El Cajon Blvd.
San Diego 92115

San Joaquin Valley College
201 New Stine Rd.
Bakersfield 93309

San Joaquin Valley College
295 East Sierra Ave.
Fresno 93710-3616

San Joaquin Valley College
8400 West Mineral King Ave.
Visalia 93291

Santa Barbara Business College
211 South Real Rd.
Bakersfield 93309

Santa Barbara Business College
4333 Hansen Ave.
Fremont 94536

Santa Barbara Business College, Santa
Maria Branch
303 East Plaza Dr., Ste. 1
Santa Maria 93454

Sawyer College, A Corinthian School
8475 Jackson Rd.
Sacramento 95826

Shasta College
P.O. Box 496006
Redding 96049

Simi Valley Adult School
3192 Los Angeles Ave.
Simi Valley 93065

Skadron College
295 East Caroline St., Ste. D
San Bernardino 92408

Travel and Trade Career Institute
3635 Atlantic Ave.
Long Beach 90807

United Education Institute
3727 West Sixth St., Ste. 317
Los Angeles 90020

Watterson College
150 South Los Robles Blvd., Ste. 100
Pasadena 91101

Western Career College
8909 Folsom Blvd.
Sacramento 95826

Western Career College
170 Bay Fair Mall
San Leandro 94578

COLORADO

Blair College
828 Wooten Rd.
Colorado Springs 80915

Concorde Career Institute
770 Grant St.
Denver 80203

Denver Technical College at Colorado
Springs
225 South Union Blvd.
Colorado Springs 80910

Heritage College of Health Careers
12 Lakeside Ln.
Denver 80212

PPI Health Careers School
2345 North Academy Blvd.
Colorado Springs 80909

CONNECTICUT

Branford Hall Career Institute
One Summit Pl.
Branford 06405

Huntington Institute, Inc.
193 Broadway
Norwich 06360

Stone Academy
1315 Dixwell Ave.
Hamden 06514

DELAWARE

Star Technical Institute
Graystone Plaza, 631 West Newport Pike
Wilmington 19804

DISTRICT OF COLUMBIA

Harrison Center for Career Education
624 Ninth St. NW, 4th Fl.
Washington 20001

FLORIDA

Career Training Institute
3326 Edgewater Dr.
Orlando 32804

Concorde Career Institute
7960 Arlington Expwy.
Jacksonville 32211

Concorde Career Institute
4000 North State Rd. 7
Lauderdale Lakes 33319

Concorde Career Institute
285 Northwest 199th St.
Miami 33169

Concorde Career Institute
4202 West Spruce St.
Tampa 33607

Keiser College
1500 Northwest 49th St.
Fort Lauderdale 33309

Miami Lakes Technical Education
Center
5780 Northwest 158th St.
Miami Lakes 33169

Miami Technical College
14701 Northwest Seventh Ave.
North Miami 33168

Miriam Vocational School, Inc.
135 Southwest 57th Ave.
Miami 33144

National School of Technology, Inc.
4410 West 16th Ave., Ste. 52
Hialeah 33012

National School of Technology, Inc.
16150 Northeast 17th Ave.
North Miami Beach 33162

Orlando College
5421 Diplomat Circle
Orlando 32810

Politechnical Institute of Florida
500 West 29th St.
Hialeah 33012

Ross Technical Institute
1490 South Military Trail
West Palm Beach 33415-9141

Santa Fe Community College
3000 Northwest 83rd St.
Gainesville 32606

Tampa College
3924 Coconut Palm Dr.
Tampa 33619

Technical Career Institute
4299 Northwest 36th St., Ste. 300
Miami Springs 33166

Webster College, Inc.
2127 Grand Blvd.
Holiday 34691

William T McFatter Vocational
Technical Center
6500 Nova Dr.
Davie 33317

GEORGIA

Atlanta Area Technical School
1560 Stewart Ave. SW
Atlanta 30310

Augusta Technical Institute
3116 Deans Bridge Rd.
Augusta 30906

Georgia Medical Institute
40 Marietta St. NW, Ste. 1333
Atlanta 30303

Gwinnett Technical Institute
5150 Sugarloaf Pkwy.
Lawrenceville 30043

Medix Schools
2108 Cobb Pkwy.
Smyrna 30008

Valdosta Technical Institute
4089 Valtech Rd.
Valdosta 31602-9796

HAWAII

Medical Assistant School of Hawaii, Inc.
33 South King, Ste. 223
Honolulu 96813

IDAHO

American Institute of Health
Technology, Inc.
6600 Emerald
Boise 83704

College of Southern Idaho
P.O. Box 1238
Twin Falls 83301

Ricks College
Rexburg 83460-4107

INDIANA

Davenport College, Merrillville
8200 Georgia St.
Merrillville 46410

International Business College
3811 Illinois Rd.
Fort Wayne 46804

Ivy Tech State College, North Central
1534 West Sample St.
South Bend 46619

Ivy Tech State College, Northeast
3800 North Anthony Blvd.
Fort Wayne 46805

Ivy Tech State College, South Central
8204 Hwy. 311
Sellersburg 47172

Ivy Tech State College, Southwest
3501 First Ave.
Evansville 47710

Michiana College
1030 East Jefferson Blvd.
South Bend 46617

Professional Careers Institute
2611 Waterfront Pkwy., East Dr.
Indianapolis 46214-2028

IOWA

Des Moines Community College
2006 Ankeny Blvd.
Ankeny 50021

Kirkwood Community College
P.O. Box 2068
Cedar Rapids 52406

Palmer College of Chiropractic
1000 Brady St.
Davenport 52803

KANSAS

Johnson County Community College
12345 College Blvd.
Overland Park 66210-1299

Southwest Kansas Technical School
2215 North Kansas
Liberal 67905-1599

Topeka Technical College
1620 Northwest Gage
Topeka 66618

KENTUCKY

Kentucky College of Business
628 East Main St.
Lexington 40508

Owensboro Junior College of Business
1515 East 18th St., Box 1350
Owensboro 42302

RETS Medical and Business Institute
1102 South Virginia St.
Hopkinsville 42240

Spencerian College
4627 Dixie Hwy.
Louisville 40216

LOUISIANA

Ayers Institute, Inc.
2924 Knight St., Ste. 318
Shreveport 71105

Cameron College
2740 Canal St.
New Orleans 70119

Coastal College, Hammond
4304 Yokum Rd.
Hammond 70403

Domestic Health Care Institute
4826 Jamestown Ave.
Baton Rouge 70808

Eastern College of Health Vocations
3321 Hessemer Ave., Ste. 200
Metairie 70002

Remington College
303 Rue Louis XIV
Lafayette 70508

MAINE

Andover College
901 Washington Ave.
Portland 04103

Beal College
629 Main St.
Bangor 04401

Mid-State College
88 East Hardscrabble Rd.
Auburn 04210

MARYLAND

Essex Community College
7201 Rossville Blvd.
Baltimore 21237

Medix Schools
1017 York Rd.
Towson 21204-9840

MASSACHUSETTS

Aquinas College at Newton
15 Walnut Park
Newton 02158

Bunker Hill Community College
250 New Rutherford Ave.
Boston 02129

Fisher College
118 Beacon St.
Boston 02116

The Salter School
1243 Main St.
Springfield 01103

The Salter School
155 Ararat St.
Worcester 01606

MICHIGAN

Carnegie Institute
550 Stephenson Hwy.
Troy 48083

Delta College
University Ctr.
University Center 48710

Detroit Business Institute
1249 Washington Blvd., Ste. 1200
Detroit 48226

Detroit Business Institute, Downriver
19100 Fort St.
Riverview 48192

Grand Rapids Educational Center
1750 Woodworth NE
Grand Rapids 49525

Grand Rapids Educational Center
5349 West Main
Kalamazoo 49009

Lansing Community College
419 North Capitol Ave.
Lansing 48901-7210

Macomb Community College
14500 Twelve Mile Rd.
Warren 48093-3896

Payne-Pulliam School of Trade and
Commerce, Inc.
2345 Cass Ave.
Detroit 48201-3305

Ross Business Institute
37065 South Gratiot
Clinton Township 48036

Ross Business Institute
22293 Eureka
Taylor 48180

Ross Medical Education Center
1036 Gilbert St.
Flint 48532

Ross Medical Education Center
2035 28th St. SE
Grand Rapids 49508

Ross Medical Education Center
1188 North West Ave.
Jackson 49202

Ross Medical Education Center
913 West Holmes, Ste. 260
Lansing 48910

Ross Medical Education Center
Park Row Mall, 950 Norton Ave.
Roosevelt Park 49441

Ross Medical Education Center
4054 Bay Rd.
Saginaw 48603

Ross Medical Education Center
26417 Hoover Rd.
Warren 48089

Ross Medical Education Center
2495 Elizabeth Lake Rd.
Waterford 48328

Ross Technical Institute
4703 Washtenaw
Ann Arbor 48108-1411

Ross Technical Institute
5757 Whitmore Lake Rd., Ste. 800
Brighton 48116

Ross Technical Institute
20820 Greenfield Rd., Ste. 101
Oak Park 48237

Schoolcraft College
18600 Haggerty Rd.
Livonia 48152

MINNESOTA

Duluth Business University, Inc.
412 West Superior St.
Duluth 55802

Globe College of Business
175 Fifth St. E, Ste. 201, Box 60
Saint Paul 55101-2901

Lakeland Medical and Dental Academy,
Inc.
1402 West Lake St.
Minneapolis 55408

Medical Institute of Minnesota
5503 Green Valley Dr.
Bloomington 55437

Northwest Technical College, East
Grand Forks
Hwy. 220 N
East Grand Forks 56721

Rochester Community and Technical
College
851 30th Ave. SE
Rochester 55904-4999

MISSISSIPPI

Northeast Mississippi Community
College
Cunningham Blvd.
Booneville 38829

MISSOURI

Al-Med Academy
10963 Saint Charles Rock Rd.
Saint Louis 63074

Concorde Career Institute
3239 Broadway
Kansas City 64111

Metro Business College
1407 Southwest Blvd.
Jefferson City 65109

Metro Business College
1202 East Hwy. 72
Rolla 65401

Metro Business College of Cape
Girardeau
1732 North Kings Hwy.
Cape Girardeau 63701

Midwest Institute for Medical Assistants
112 West Jefferson
Kirkwood 63122

Missouri College
10121 Manchester Rd.
Saint Louis 63122

Saint Louis College of Health Careers
4484 West Pine
Saint Louis 63108

Springfield College
1010 West Sunshine
Springfield 65807

Tad Technical Institute
7910 Troost Ave.
Kansas City 64131

NEBRASKA

Institute of Computer Science
808 South 74th Place, 7400 Court
Building
Omaha 68114

Omaha College of Health Careers
10845 Harney St.
Omaha 68154

Southeast Community College Area
1111 O St., Ste. 111
Lincoln 68520

NEVADA

Canterbury Career Schools
2215C Renaissance Dr.
Las Vegas 89119

NEW JERSEY

American Business Academy
66 Moore St.
Hackensack 07601

Berdan Institute
265 Rte. 46
Totowa 07512

Business Training Institute
Four Forest Ave.
Paramus 07652

Dover Business College
15 East Blackwell St.
Dover 07801

Dover Business College
East 81 & Rte. 4 W
Paramus 07652

Drake College of Business
125 Broad St.
Elizabeth 07201

Ho-Ho-Kus School
50 South Franklin Tpke.
Ramsey 07446

Omega Institute
7050 Rte. 38 E
Pennsauken 08109

Star Technical Institute
4313 RR 130 S
Edgewater Park 08010

Star Technical Institute
1255 Rte. 70
Lakewood 08701

Star Technical Institute
1386 South Delsea Dr.
Vineland 08360

Star Technical Institute, Deptford
1450 Clements Bridge Rd.
Deptford 08096

NEW MEXICO

Franklin College
2400 Louisiana Blvd. NE, Ste. 200
Albuquerque 87110

Pima Medical Institute
2201 San Pedro NE, Bldg. 3, Ste. 100
Albuquerque 87110

NEW YORK

Bayley Seton Hospital School Physician
Assistants
75 Vanderbilt Ave.
Staten Island 10304-3850

Bryant and Stratton Business Institute,
Buffalo
1028 Main St.
Buffalo 14202

Hudson Valley Community College
80 Vandenburgh Ave.
Troy 12180

Mandl School
254 West 54th St.
New York 10019

New York School for Medical and
Dental Assistants
116-16 Queens Blvd.
Forest Hills 11375

Suburban Technical School
175 Fulton Ave.
Hempstead 11550

NORTH CAROLINA

Central Piedmont Community College
P.O. Box 35009
Charlotte 28235-5009

Miller-Motte Business College
606 South College Rd.
Wilmington 28403

NORTH DAKOTA

Interstate Business College
520 East Main Ave.
Bismarck 58501

Interstate Business College
2720 32nd Ave. SW
Fargo 58103

OHIO

Akron Medical-Dental Institute, Inc.
DBA Akron Institute
1625 Portage Tr.
Cuyahoga Falls 44223

American School of Technology
2100 Morse Rd., Bldg. 4599
Columbus 43229

Aristotle Institute of Medical-Dental
Technology
5900 Westerville Rd.
Westerville 43081

Belmont Technical College
120 Fox Shannon Place
Saint Clairsville 43950

Boheckers Business College, Ravenna
326 East Main St.
Ravenna 44266

Cleveland Institute of Dental-Medical
Assistants
1836 Euclid Ave.
Cleveland 44115

Cleveland Institute of Dental-Medical
Assistants
5564 Mayfield Rd.
Lyndhurst 44124

Cleveland Institute of Dental-Medical
Assistants
5733 Hopkins Rd.
Mentor 44060

Columbus Paraprofessional Institute
1900 East Grandville Rd., Bldg. A, Ste.
210
Columbus 43229

Cuyahoga Community College District
700 Carnegie Ave.
Cleveland 44115-2878

Institute of Medical-Dental Technology
4452 Eastgate Blvd., Ste. 209
Cincinnati 45245

Institute of Medical-Dental Technology
375 Glensprings Dr., Ste. 201
Cincinnati 45246

Knox County Career Center
306 Martinsburg Rd.
Mount Vernon 43050

Mahoning County Joint Vocational
School District
7300 North Palmyra Rd.
Canfield 44406

Professional Skills Institute
20 Arco Dr.
Toledo 43607

RETS Technical Center
116 Westpark Rd.
Centerville 45459

Sawyer College of Business
3150 Mayfield Rd.
Cleveland Heights 44118

Southwestern College of Business
225 West First St.
Dayton 45402

Stautzenberger College
5355 Southwyck Blvd.
Toledo 43614

Technology Education College
288 South Hamilton Rd.
Columbus 43213

Tri-County Vocational School
15675 St. Rte. 691
Nelsonville 45764

Trumbull County Joint Vocational
School District
528 Educational Hwy.
Warren 44483

University of Toledo
2801 West Bancroft
Toledo 43606

Warren County Career Center
3525 North St. Rte. 48
Lebanon 45036-1099

OKLAHOMA

Central Oklahoma Area Vocational
Technical School
1720 South Main
Sapulpa 74066

De Marge College North
3608 Northwest 58th
Oklahoma City 73112

Francis Tuttle Area Vocational
Technical Center
12777 North Rockwell Ave.
Oklahoma City 73142-2789

Platt College
309 South Ann Arbor
Oklahoma City 73128

Southern Oklahoma Technology Center
2610 Sam Noble Pkwy.
Ardmore 73401

Wright Business School
2219 Southwest 74th St., Ste. 124
Oklahoma City 73159

OREGON

Apollo College, Portland, Inc.
2600 Southeast 98th Ave.
Portland 97266

Pioneer Pacific College
25195 Southwest Parkway Ave.
Wilsonville 97070

Western Business College
425 Southwest Washington
Portland 97204

PENNSYLVANIA

Academy of Medical Arts and Business
2301 Academy Dr.
Harrisburg 17112

Allied Medical and Technical Careers
2901 Pittston Ave.
Scranton 18505

Allied Medical and Technical Careers
104 Woodward Hill Rd.
Edwardsville 18704

Altoona Area Vocational Technical
School
1500 Fourth Ave.
Altoona 16602

Antonelli Medical and Professional
Institute
1700 Industrial Hwy.
Pottstown 19464

Berks Technical Institute
2205 Ridgewood Rd.
Wyomissing 19610-1168

Career Training Academy
105 Mall Blvd., Ste. 300 W
Monroeville 15146

Career Training Academy
703 Fifth Ave.
New Kensington 15068

Delaware Valley Academy of Medical
and Dental Assistants
3300 Grant Ave.
Philadelphia 19114

Duffs Business Institute
110 Ninth St.
Pittsburgh 15222

ICM School of Business and Medical
Careers
10-14 Wood St.
Pittsburgh 15222

J H Thompson Academies
2910 State St.
Erie 16508

Median School of Allied Health Careers
125 Seventh St.
Pittsburgh 15222-3400

North Hills School of Health
Occupations
1500 Northway Mall
Pittsburgh 15237

Sawyer School
717 Liberty Ave.
Pittsburgh 15222

Thompson Institute
5650 Derry St.
Harrisburg 17111

Thompson Institute
3440 Market St.
Philadelphia 19104

SOUTH CAROLINA

Central Carolina Technical College
506 North Guignard Dr.
Sumter 29150

Trident Technical College
P.O. Box 118067
Charleston 29423-8067

TENNESSEE

Draughons Junior College
1860 Wilma Rudolph Blvd.
Clarksville 37040

Fugazzi College
5042 Linbar Dr., Ste. 200
Nashville 37211

TEXAS

The Academy of Health Care
Professions
1919 Northloop W, Ste. 170
Houston 77008

Bradford School of Business
4669 Southwest Fwy., Ste. 300
Houston 77027

Career Centers of Texas El Paso
8375 Burnham Dr.
El Paso 79907

PCI Health Training Center
8101 John Carpenter Fwy.
Dallas 75247

San Antonio College of Medical and
Dental Assistants, Central
4205 San Pedro Ave.
San Antonio 78212-1899

San Antonio College of Medical and
Dental Assistants, South
3900 North 23rd
McAllen 78501

Southern Careers Institute, Inc.
2301 South Congress, Ste. 27
Austin 78704

Southern Careers Institute, South Texas
1414 North Jackson Rd.
Pharr 78577

Southwest School of Business and
Technical Careers
602 West South Cross
San Antonio 78221

Western Technical Institute
4710 Alabama St.
El Paso 79930

UTAH

American Institute of Medical-Dental
Technology
1675 North 200 West, Bldg. 4
Provo 84604

Stevens-Henager College of Business,
Ogden
2168 Washington Blvd.
Ogden 84401

Stevens-Henager College of Business,
Provo
25 East 1700 South
Provo 84606-6157

Utah Career College
1144 West 3300 South
Salt Lake City 84119-3330

VIRGINIA

Commonwealth College, Virginia Beach
301 Centre Pointe Dr.
Virginia Beach 23462

Dominion Business School
4142-1 Melrose Ave.
Roanoke 24017

Medical Careers Institute
605 Thimble Shoals
Newport News 23606

Tidewater Technical
1760 East Little Creek Rd.
Norfolk 23518

Tidewater Technical
2697 Dean Dr., Ste. 100
Virginia Beach 23452

WASHINGTON

Eton Technical Institute
209 East Casino Rd.
Everett 98208

Eton Technical Institute
31919 Sixth Ave. S
Federal Way 98003

Eton Technical Institute
3649 Frontage Rd., Ste. A
Port Orchard 98366

Pima Medical Institute
1627 Eastlake Ave. E
Seattle 98102

Seattle Vocational Institute
315 22nd Ave. S
Seattle 98144

Spokane Community College
North 1810 Greene Ave.
Spokane 99207

WEST VIRGINIA

Boone County Career & Technical
Center
HC 81, Box 50B
Danville 25053

Huntington Junior College
900 Fifth Ave.
Huntington 25701

Opportunities Industrialization Center,
North Central West Virginia
120 Jackson St.
Fairmont 26554

West Virginia Career College
148 Willey St.
Morgantown 26505

WISCONSIN

Blackhawk Technical College
P.O. Box 5009
Janesville 53547

Madison Area Technical College
3550 Anderson St.
Madison 53704

Mid-State Technical College, Main
Campus
500 32nd St. N
Wisconsin Rapids 54494

Milwaukee Area Technical College
700 West State St.
Milwaukee 53233-1443

Northeast Wisconsin Technical College
2740 West Mason St., P.O. Box 19042
Green Bay 54307-9042

Waukesha County Technical College
800 Main St.
Pewaukee 53072

Western Wisconsin Technical College
304 North Sixth St., P.O. Box 908
La Crosse 54602-0908

Wisconsin Indianhead Technical
College
505 Pine Ridge Dr.
Shell Lake 54871

Medical and Biological Laboratory Technology

ALABAMA

Capps College
3100 Cottage Hill Rd., Bldg. 5
Mobile 36606

Community College of the Air Force
130 West Maxwell Blvd.
Montgomery 36112-6613

Jefferson State Community College
2601 Carson Rd.
Birmingham 35215-3098

University of Alabama at Birmingham
Administration Bldg., Ste. 1070-2010
Birmingham 35294-0110

ARIZONA

Apollo College
3870 North Oracle Rd.
Tucson 85705

Apollo College, Phoenix, Inc.
8503 North 27th Ave.
Phoenix 85051

Long Medical Institute
4126 North Black Canyon Hwy.
Phoenix 85017

Occupational Training Center
4136 North 75th Ave., Ste. 200
Phoenix 85033

Phoenix College
1202 West Thomas Rd.
Phoenix 85013

Tucson College
7302-10 East 22nd St.
Tucson 85710

ARKANSAS

Arkansas Valley Technical Institute
P.O. Box 506, Hwy. 23 N
Ozark 72949

Carti School of Radiation Therapy
Technology
P.O. Box 55050
Little Rock 72215

CALIFORNIA

American School of X-Ray
13723-1/2 Harvard Place
Gardena 90249

Associated Technical College
1670 Wilshire Blvd.
Los Angeles 90017

Butte College
3536 Butte Campus Dr.
Oroville 95965

El Camino College
16007 Crenshaw Blvd.
Torrance 90506

Glendale Career College
1015 Grandview Ave.
Glendale 91201

Grossmont College
8800 Grossmont College Dr.
El Cajon 92020

Hacienda La Puente Unified School
District, Adult Education
P.O. Box 60002
City of Industry 91716-0002

Ila Polytechnic Institute
202 West Lincoln Ave., Ste. H
Orange 92665-1058

Institute for Business and Technology
2550 Scott Blvd.
Santa Clara 95050

Loma Linda University
Loma Linda 92350

McKinnon Institute of Professional
Massage and Bodywork
3798 Grand Ave.
Oakland 94610-1594

Modern Technology School
1232 East Katella Ave.
Anaheim 92805

Modern Technology School of X-Ray
6180 Laurel Canyon Blvd., Ste. 101
North Hollywood 91606

National Career Education
6060 Sunrise Vista Dr.
Citrus Heights 95610

Newbridge College
1840 East 17th St., Ste. 140
Santa Ana 92705

Nova Institute of Health Technology
3000 South Robertson Blvd.
Los Angeles 90034

Nova Institute of Health Technology
12449 Putnam St.
Whittier 90602-1023

Orange Coast College
2701 Fairview Rd.
Costa Mesa 92626

Simi Valley Adult School
3192 Los Angeles Ave.
Simi Valley 93065

COLORADO

PPI Health Careers School
2345 North Academy Blvd.
Colorado Springs 80909

Regis University
3333 Regis Blvd.
Denver 80221-1099

CONNECTICUT

Department of Education Hartford
Hospital School of Allied Health
312 Conklin Blvd., 80 Seymour St.
Hartford 06115

Gateway Community Technical College
60 Sargent Dr.
New Haven 06511

Housatonic Community Technical
College
900 Lafayette Blvd.
Bridgeport 06604

Huntington Institute, Inc.
193 Broadway
Norwich 06360

DELAWARE

Delaware Technical and Community
College, Owens
Box 610
Georgetown 19947

Delaware Technical and Community
College, Stanton, Wilmington
400 Stanton-Christiana Rd.
Newark 19702

DISTRICT OF COLUMBIA

Harrison Center for Career Education
624 Ninth St. NW, 4th Fl.
Washington 20001

FLORIDA

Beacon Career Institute, Inc.
2900 Northwest 183rd St.
Miami 33056

Brevard Community College, Cocoa
Campus
1519 Clearlake Rd.
Cocoa 32922

Brewster Technical Center
2222 North Tampa St.
Tampa 33602-2196

Florida Community College at
Jacksonville
501 West State St.
Jacksonville 32202

Keiser College
1500 Northwest 49th St.
Fort Lauderdale 33309

Lake City Community College
Rte. 19, Box 1030
Lake City 32025

Lee County Technical Center, Central
3800 Michigan Ave.
Fort Myers 33916

Miami-Dade Community College
300 Northeast Second Ave.
Miami 33132

Miriam Vocational School, Inc.
135 Southwest 57th Ave.
Miami 33144

National School of Technology, Inc.
4410 West 16th Ave., Ste. 52
Hialeah 33012

National School of Technology, Inc.
16150 Northeast 17th Ave.
North Miami Beach 33162

Pasco-Hernando Community College
36727 Blanton Rd.
Dade City 33525-7599

Santa Fe Community College
3000 Northwest 83rd St.
Gainesville 32606

Sarasota County Technical Institute
4748 Beneva Rd.
Sarasota 34233-1798

Sheridan Vocational Center
5400 Sheridan St.
Hollywood 33021

Ultrasound Diagnostic School
10199 Southside Blvd., Ste. 106
Jacksonville 32256

Ultrasound Diagnostic School
9950 Princess Palm Ave., Reg 11, Ste. 120
Tampa 33619

William T McFatter Vocational
Technical Center
6500 Nova Dr.
Davie 33317

GEORGIA

Columbus State University
4225 University Ave.
Columbus 31907-5645

Dekalb Technical Institute
495 North Indian Creek Dr.
Clarkston 30021

Grady Health System Professional
Schools
80 Butler St.
Atlanta 30335-3801

ILLINOIS

Medical Careers Institute
116 South Michigan Ave.
Chicago 60603

Methodist Medical Center of Illinois,
School of Nursing
221 Northeast Glen Oak Ave.
Peoria 61636

Oakton Community College
1600 East Golf Rd.
Des Plaines 60016

Swedish American Hospital School of
Medical Technology
1400 Charles St.
Rockford 61104-2298

Triton College
2000 Fifth Ave.
River Grove 60171

INDIANA

Vincennes University
1002 North First St.
Vincennes 47591

IOWA

Des Moines Community College
2006 Ankeny Blvd.
Ankeny 50021

Iowa Methodist Medical Center, School
of Radiologic Technology
1200 Pleasant St.
Des Moines 50309-1453

Palmer College of Chiropractic
1000 Brady St.
Davenport 52803

Saint Luke's College of Nursing and
Health Sciences
2720 Stone Park Blvd.
Sioux City 51104-0263

KANSAS

Seward County Community College
Box 1137
Liberal 67905-1137

Wichita Area Technical College
201 North Water
Wichita 67202-1292

KENTUCKY

Spencerian College
4627 Dixie Hwy.
Louisville 40216

University of Louisville
2301 South Third St.
Louisville 40292-0001

LOUISIANA

Delgado Community College
501 City Park Ave.
New Orleans 70119

Eastern College of Health Vocations
3321 Hessmer Ave., Ste. 200
Metairie 70002

MARYLAND

Hagerstown Business College
18618 Crestwood Dr.
Hagerstown 21742

Ultrasound Diagnostic School
1320 Fenwick Ln., Ste. 206
Silver Spring 20910

MASSACHUSETTS

Middlesex Community College
Springs Rd.
Bedford 01730

Northeastern University
360 Huntington Ave.
Boston 02115

Springfield Technical Community
College
One Armory Square
Springfield 01105

Ultrasound Diagnostic School
33 Boston Post Rd. W, Ste. 140
Marlborough 01752

MICHIGAN

Carnegie Institute
550 Stephenson Hwy.
Troy 48083

Krainz Woods Academy of Medical
Laboratory Technology
4327 East Seven Mile Rd.
Detroit 48234

Marygrove College
8425 West McNichols Rd.
Detroit 48221

Northern Michigan University
1401 Presque Isle
Marquette 49855

Oakland Community College
2480 Opdyke Rd.
Bloomfield Hills 48304-2266

Schoolcraft College
18600 Haggerty Rd.
Livonia 48152

MINNESOTA

Fergus Falls Community College
1414 College Way
Fergus Falls 56537

Hibbing Community College, a
Technical and Community College
1515 East 25th St.
Hibbing 55746

Lake Superior College
2101 Trinity Rd.
Duluth 55811

Lakeland Medical and Dental Academy,
Inc.
1402 West Lake St.
Minneapolis 55408

Mayo School of Health-Related Sciences
200 First St. SW
Rochester 55905

Medical Institute of Minnesota
5503 Green Valley Dr.
Bloomington 55437

North Hennepin Community College
7411 85th Ave. N
Brooklyn Park 55445

Northwest Technical College, East
Grand Forks
Hwy. 220 N
East Grand Forks 56721

Saint Cloud Technical College
1540 Northway Dr.
Saint Cloud 56303

Saint Paul Technical College
235 Marshall Ave.
Saint Paul 55102

MISSISSIPPI

Mississippi Gulf Coast Community
College
Central Office, P.O. Box 67
Perkinston 39573

MISSOURI

Al-Med Academy
10963 Saint Charles Rock Rd.
Saint Louis 63074

Saint John's Regional Health Center
School of Radiologic Technology
1235 East Cherokee
Springfield 65804

Saint Louis Community College, Forest
Park
5600 Oakland Ave.
Saint Louis 63110

NEW JERSEY

Bergen Community College
400 Paramus Rd.
Paramus 07652

Drake College of Business
125 Broad St.
Elizabeth 07201

Omega Institute
7050 Rte. 38 E
Pennsauken 08109

Star Technical Institute
1255 Rte. 70
Lakewood 08701

Ultrasound Diagnostic School
675 Rte. 1, Second Fl.
Iselin 08830

University of Medicine and Dentistry of
New Jersey
30 Bergen St.
Newark 07107

NEW MEXICO

Albuquerque Technical Vocational
Institute
525 Buena Vista SE
Albuquerque 87106

New Mexico Junior College
5317 Lovington Hwy.
Hobbs 88240

Pima Medical Institute
2201 San Pedro NE, Bldg. 3, Ste. 100
Albuquerque 87110

NEW YORK

Dutchess Community College
53 Pendell Rd.
Poughkeepsie 12601

Hudson Valley Community College
80 Vandenburgh Ave.
Troy 12180

Institute of Allied Medical Professions
405 Park Ave., Ste. 501
New York 10022

Mandl School
254 West 54th St.
New York 10019

Monroe Community College
1000 East Henrietta Rd.
Rochester 14623

New York School for Medical and
Dental Assistants
116-16 Queens Blvd.
Forest Hills 11375

NYU Medical Center Allied Health
Education
483 First Ave.
New York 10016

SUNY College of Technology at
Farmingdale
Melville Rd.
Farmingdale 11735-1021

SUNY Westchester Commmunity
College
75 Grasslands Rd.
Valhalla 10595

Syrit College
1760 53rd St.
Brooklyn 11204

Ultrasound Diagnostic School
One Old Country Rd.
Carle Place 11514

Ultrasound Diagnostic School
2269 Saw Mill River Rd.
Elmsford 10523

Ultrasound Diagnostic School
120 East 16th St., Second Fl.
New York 10003

NORTH CAROLINA

Alamance Community College
P.O. Box 8000
Graham 27253

Caldwell Community College and
Technical Institute
Box 600
Lenoir 28645

Halifax Community College
P.O. Drawer 809
Weldon 27890

Northern Hospital of Surry County
School of Medical Laboratory
Technology
830 Rockford St., P.O. Box 1101
Mount Airy 27030

Pitt Community College
Hwy. 11 S, P.O. Drawer 7007
Greenville 27835-7007

Southwestern Community College
447 College Dr.
Sylva 28779

Wake Technical Community College
9101 Fayetteville Rd.
Raleigh 27603-5696

NORTH DAKOTA

Trinity School of Clinical Laboratory
Science
Three Burdick Expwy.
Minot 58701

OHIO

Akron Medical-Dental Institute, Inc.,
DBA Akron Institute
1625 Portage Tr.
Cuyahoga Falls 44223

Cincinnati State Technical and
Community College
3520 Central Pkwy.
Cincinnati 45223

Cleveland Institute of Dental-Medical
Assistants
1836 Euclid Ave.
Cleveland 44115

Cleveland Institute of Dental-Medical
Assistants
5564 Mayfield Rd.
Lyndhurst 44124

Cleveland Institute of Dental-Medical
Assistants
5733 Hopkins Rd.
Mentor 44060

Columbus State Community College
550 East Spring St.
Columbus 43216

Cuyahoga Community College District
700 Carnegie Ave.
Cleveland 44115-2878

Kettering College Medical Arts
3737 Southern Blvd.
Kettering 45429-1299

Marion Technical College
1467 Mount Vernon Ave.
Marion 43302-5694

Owens Community College
30335 Oregon Rd.
Toledo 43699-1947

Professional Skills Institute
20 Arco Dr.
Toledo 43607

Riverside School of Medical Technology
1600 North Superior St.
Toledo 43604

Tri-Rivers Career Center
2222 Marion Mount Gilead Rd.
Marion 43302

Trumbull County Joint Vocational
School District
528 Educational Hwy.
Warren 44483

OKLAHOMA

Tulsa Community College
6111 East Skelly Dr.
Tulsa 74135

OREGON

Concorde Career Institute
1827 Northeast 44th Ave.
Portland 97213

PENNSYLVANIA

Abington Memorial Hospital Medical
Technology Program
1200 Old York Rd.
Abington 19001

Allied Medical and Technical Careers
104 Woodward Hill Rd.
Edwardsville 18704

Allied Medical and Technical Careers
2901 Pittston Ave.
Scranton 18505

Chambersburg Hospital Medical
Laboratory Technical School
112 North Seventh St.
Chambersburg 17201

Community College of Allegheny
County, Pittsburgh
800 Allegheny Ave.
Pittsburgh 15233-1895

Community College of Philadelphia
1700 Spring Garden St.
Philadelphia 19130

Conemaugh Valley Memorial Hospital
1086 Franklin St.
Johnstown 15905-4398

Divine Providence Hospital School of
Medical Technology
1100 Grampian Blvd.
Williamsport 17754

Edinboro University of Pennsylvania
Edinboro 16444

Gwynedd-Mercy College
Sumneytown Pike
Gwynedd Valley 19437

Johnson Technical Institute
3427 North Main Ave.
Scranton 18508-1495

Mount Aloysius College
7373 Admiral Peary Hwy.
Cresson 16630-1999

North Hills School of Health
Occupations
1500 Northway Mall
Pittsburgh 15237

Pennsylvania State University, New
Kensington
3550 Seventh Street Rd.
New Kensington 15068

Ultrasound Diagnostic School
5830 Ellsworth Ave., Ste. 102
Pittsburgh 15232

Western School of Health & Business
Careers
411 Seventh Ave.
Pittsburgh 15219

RHODE ISLAND

Community College of Rhode Island
400 East Ave.
Warwick 02886-1807

SOUTH CAROLINA

Central Carolina Technical College
506 North Guignard Dr.
Sumter 29150

Midlands Technical College
P.O. Box 2408
Columbia 29202

Orangeburg Calhoun Technical College
3250 Saint Matthew's Rd.
Orangeburg 29118

Trident Technical College
P.O. Box 118067
Charleston 29423-8067

SOUTH DAKOTA

Presentation College
1500 North Main
Aberdeen 57401

Southeast Technical Institute
2301 Career Place
Sioux Falls 57107

TENNESSEE

Nashville State Technical Institute
120 White Bridge Rd.
Nashville 37209

Roane State Community College
276 Patton Ln.
Harriman 37748

Shelby State Community College
P.O. Box 40568
Memphis 38174-0568

TEXAS

The Academy of Health Care
Professions
1919 Northloop W, Ste. 170
Houston 77008

Austin Community College
5930 Middle Fiskville Rd.
Austin 78752

Del Mar College
101 Baldwin
Corpus Christi 78404-3897

El Centro College
Main and Lamar
Dallas 75202

El Paso Community College
P.O. Box 20500
El Paso 79998

Houston Community College System
22 Waugh Dr.
Houston 77270-7849

Microcomputer Technology Institute
7277 Regency Square Blvd.
Houston 77036

Saint Philip's College
1801 Martin Luther King Dr.
San Antonio 78203

San Antonio College of Medical and
Dental Assistants, Central
4205 San Pedro Ave.
San Antonio 78212-1899

Texas State Technical College, Waco
3801 Campus Dr.
Waco 76705

Ultrasound Diagnostic School
1333 Corporate Dr., Ste. 200
Irving 75038

Wadley Regional Medical Center School
of Medical Technology
1000 Pine St.
Texarkana 75501

WASHINGTON

Pima Medical Institute
1627 Eastlake Ave. E
Seattle 98102

Shoreline Community College
16101 Greenwood Ave. N
Seattle 98133

Spokane Community College
North 1810 Greene Ave.
Spokane 99207

WEST VIRGINIA

Boone County Career & Technical
Center
HC 81, Box 50B
Danville 25053

West Virginia University Hospital
School of Radiation Technology
Medical Center Dr., P.O. Box 8062
Morgantown 26506-8062

WISCONSIN

Chippewa Valley Technical College
620 West Clairemont Ave.
Eau Claire 54701

Madison Area Technical College
3550 Anderson St.
Madison 53704

Milwaukee Area Technical College
700 West State St.
Milwaukee 53233-1443

Saint Joseph's Hospital Histologic
Technician Program
611 Saint Joseph's Ave.
Marshfield 54449

Saint Luke's Medical Center, School of
Diagnostic Medical Sonography
2900 West Oklahoma Ave.
Milwaukee 53215

Western Wisconsin Technical College
304 North Sixth St., P.O. Box 908
La Crosse 54602-0908

Medical Emergency Technology

ALABAMA

Bessemer State Technical College
1100 Ninth Ave.
Bessemer 35021

George C Wallace State Community
College, Hanceville
801 Main St. NW
Hanceville 35077-2000

University of Alabama at Birmingham
Administration Bldg., Ste. 1070-2010
Birmingham 35294-2010

University of Alabama in Huntsville
301 Sparkman Dr.
Huntsville 35899

University of South Alabama
307 North University Blvd.
Mobile 36688-0002

ARIZONA

Phoenix College
1202 West Thomas Rd.
Phoenix 85013

Pima Community College
2202 West Anklam Rd.
Tucson 85709-0001

CALIFORNIA

Crafton Hills College
11711 Sand Canyon Rd.
Yucaipa 92399-1799

Daniel Freeman Hospital Paramedic
School
333 North Prairie Ave.
Inglewood 90301-4514

Imperial Valley College
P.O. Box 158
Imperial 92251-0158

Pacoima Skills Center, Los Angeles
Unified School District
13545 Van Nuys Blvd.
Pacoima 91331

Simi Valley Adult School
3192 Los Angeles Ave.
Simi Valley 93065

Skyline College
3300 College Dr.
San Bruno 94066

COLORADO

Aims Community College
Box 69
Greeley 80632

Colorado Mountain College
P.O. Box 10001
Glenwood Springs 81602

Morgan Community College
17800 County Rd. 20
Fort Morgan 80701

San Juan Basin Area Vocational School
Box 970
Cortez 81321

FLORIDA

Brevard Community College, Cocoa
Campus
1519 Clearlake Rd.
Cocoa 32922

Broward Community College
225 East Las Olas Blvd.
Fort Lauderdale 33301

Central Florida Community College
3001 Southwest College Rd.
Ocala 34474

Daytona Beach Community College
1200 Volusia Ave.
Daytona Beach 32114

Hillsborough Community College
P.O. Box 31127
Tampa 33631-3127

Indian River Community College
3209 Virginia Ave.
Fort Pierce 34981

Lake City Community College
Rte. 19, Box 1030
Lake City 32025

Lake County Area Vocational Technical
Center
2001 Kurt St.
Eustis 32726

Manatee Vocational Technical Center
5603 34th St. W
Bradenton 34210

Palm Beach Community College
4200 Congress Ave.
Lake Worth 33461

Pasco-Hernando Community College
36727 Blanton Rd.
Dade City 33525-7599

Pensacola Junior College
1000 College Blvd.
Pensacola 32504

Saint Petersburg Junior College
8580 66th St. N
Pinellas Park 34665

Santa Fe Community College
3000 Northwest 83rd St.
Gainesville 32606

Seminole Community College
100 Weldon Blvd.
Sanford 32773-6199

South Florida Community College
600 West College Dr.
Avon Park 33825

Tallahassee Community College
444 Appleyard Dr.
Tallahassee 32304-2895

Valencia Community College
P.O. Box 3028
Orlando 32802

GEORGIA

Dekalb Technical Institute
495 North Indian Creek Dr.
Clarkston 30021

Gwinnett Technical Institute
5150 Sugarloaf Pkwy.
Lawrenceville 30043

ILLINOIS

City Colleges of Chicago, Central Office
226 West Jackson
Chicago 60606

Southeastern Illinois College
3575 College Rd.
Harrisburg 62946

INDIANA

Sawyer College, Hammond
6040 Hohman Ave.
Hammond 46320

IOWA

North Iowa Area Community College
500 College Dr.
Mason City 50401

KANSAS

Allen County Community College
1801 North Cottonwood
Iola 66749

Cloud County Community College
2221 Campus Dr., Box 1002
Concordia 66901-1002

Colby Community College
1255 South Range
Colby 67701

Johnson County Community College
12345 College Blvd.
Overland Park 66210-1299

Salina Area Vocational Technical
School
2562 Scanlan Ave.
Salina 67401

LOUISIANA

Huey P Long Technical Institute
303 South Jones St.
Winnfield 71483

Louisiana Technical College, Hammond
Area Campus
111 Pride Ave.
Hammond 70404

MARYLAND

Baltimore City Community College
2901 Liberty Heights Ave.
Baltimore 21215

MICHIGAN

Davenport College Career Center
3030 Easter SE
Grand Rapids 49508

Lansing Community College
419 North Capitol Ave.
Lansing 48901-7210

MINNESOTA

Century Community and Technical
College
3300 Century Ave. N
White Bear Lake 55110

MISSISSIPPI

University of Mississippi Medical
Center
2500 North State St.
Jackson 39216

MISSOURI

Cape Girardeau Area Vocational
Technical School
301 North Clark Ave.
Cape Girardeau 63701

Rolla Area Vocational-Technical School
1304 East Tenth St.
Rolla 65401

MONTANA

Montana State University, College of
Technology, Great Falls
2100 16th Ave. S
Great Falls 59405

NEW HAMPSHIRE

New Hampshire Technical Institute
11 Institute Dr.
Concord 03301

NEW YORK

Hudson Valley Community College
80 Vandenburgh Ave.
Troy 12180

NORTH DAKOTA

Med Center One EMS Education
Box 5525
Bismarck 58505

OHIO

Akron Adult Vocational Services
147 Park St.
Akron 44308

Butler County JVS District, D Russel
Lee Career Center
3603 Hamilton Middletown Rd.
Hamilton 45011

Columbus State Community College
550 East Spring St.
Columbus 43216

Lima Technical College
4240 Campus Dr.
Lima 45804

Tri-Rivers Career Center
2222 Marion Mount Gilead Rd.
Marion 43302

OKLAHOMA

Oklahoma City Community College
7777 South May Ave.
Oklahoma City 73159

TENNESSEE

Shelby State Community College
P.O. Box 40568
Memphis 38174-0568

Walters State Community College
500 South Davy Crockett Pkwy.
Morristown 37813-6899

TEXAS

Texas State Technical College,
Sweetwater
300 College Dr.
Sweetwater 79556

UTAH

Bridgerland Applied Technology Center
1301 North 600 West
Logan 84321

WISCONSIN

Blackhawk Technical College
P.O. Box 5009
Janesville 53547

Fox Valley Technical College at
Appleton
1825 North Bluemound Dr.
Appleton 54913-2277

Gateway Technical College
3520 30th Ave.
Kenosha 53144-1690

Lakeshore Technical College
1290 North Ave.
Cleveland 53015

Madison Area Technical College
3550 Anderson St.
Madison 53704

Mid-State Technical College
500 32nd St. N
Wisconsin Rapids 54494

Moraine Park Technical College
235 North National Ave.
Fond Du Lac 54936-1940

Northcentral Technical College
1000 Campus Dr.
Wausau 54401-1899

Northeast Wisconsin Technical College
2740 West Mason St., P.O. Box 19042
Green Bay 54307-9042

Waukesha County Technical College
800 Main St.
Pewaukee 53072

Medical Illustrating

ARIZONA

Pima Medical Institute
957 South Dobson
Mesa 85202

CALIFORNIA

West Hills Community College
300 Cherry Ln.
Coalinga 93210

MICHIGAN

Muskegon Community College
221 South Quarterline Rd.
Muskegon 49442

OHIO

Ohio State University, Main Campus
1800 Cannon Dr., Rm. 1210
Columbus 43210

Medical Record Technology

ALABAMA

Capps College
3100 Cottage Hill Rd., Bldg. 5
Mobile 36606

Community College of the Air Force
130 West Maxwell Blvd.
Montgomery 36112-6613

University of Alabama at Birmingham,
   Walker College
1411 Indiana Ave.
Jasper 35501

ARIZONA

Arizona Institute of Business and
   Technology
925 South Gilbert Rd., Ste. 201
Mesa 85204

Arizona Institute of Business and
   Technology
6049 North 43rd Ave.
Phoenix 85019

The Bryman School
4343 North 16th St.
Phoenix 85016

Gateway Community College
108 North 40th St.
Phoenix 85034

Tucson College
7302-10 East 22nd St.
Tucson 85710

ARKANSAS

Foothills Technical Institute
1800 East Moore St.
Searcy 72143

CALIFORNIA

Allan Hancock College
800 South College Dr.
Santa Maria 93454

California College for Health Science
222 West 24th St.
National City 91950

California Paramedical and Technical
   College
4550 La Sierra Ave.
Riverside 92505

Career Development Center
255 East Bonita Ave.
Pomona 91767

Concorde Career Institute
570 West Fourth St., Ste. 107
San Bernardino 92401

Concorde Career Institute
123 Camino De La Reina, Ste. E25
San Diego 92108

Empire College School of Business
3033 Cleveland Ave.
Santa Rosa 95403

Hacienda La Puente Unified School
   District, Adult Education
P.O. Box 60002
City of Industry 91716-0002

Institute for Business and Technology
2550 Scott Blvd.
Santa Clara 95050

Larson Training Centers, Inc.
2041 West Orangewood Ave.
Orange 92668

Maric College of Medical Careers
3666 Kearny Villa Rd., Ste. 100
San Diego 92123

Maric College of Medical Careers
2030 University Dr.
Vista 92083

Mount Saint Mary's College
12001 Chalon Rd.
Los Angeles 90049

MTI Business College, Inc.
6006 North El Dorado St.
Stockton 95207-4349

National Career Education
6060 Sunrise Vista Dr.
Citrus Heights 95610

Sawyer College A Corinthian School
8475 Jackson Rd.
Sacramento 95826

Newbridge College
1840 East 17th St., Ste. 140
Santa Ana 92705

Nova Institute of Health Technology
12449 Putnam St.
Whittier 90602-1023

San Joaquin Valley College
8400 West Mineral King Ave.
Visalia 93291

Santa Barbara Business College
211 South Real Rd.
Bakerfield 93309

Summit Career College
1330 East Cooley Dr.
Colton 92324

COLORADO

Arapahoe Community College
2500 West College Dr.
Littleton 80160-9002

Concorde Career Institute
770 Grant St.
Denver 80203

Denver Academy of Court Reporting,
   Main Campus
7920 Samuel Dr., Ste. 200
Denver 80221-2792

Heritage College of Health Careers
12 Lakeside Ln.
Denver 80212

DELAWARE

Star Technical Institute
Graystone Plaza, 631 West Newport Pike
Wilmington 19804

FLORIDA

Atlantic Vocational Technical Center
4700 Coconut Creek Pkwy.
Coconut Creek 33063

Beacon Career Institute, Inc.
2900 Northwest 183rd St.
Miami 33056

Brewster Technical Center
2222 North Tampa St.
Tampa 33602-2196

Concorde Career Institute
7960 Arlington Expwy.
Jacksonville 32211

Concorde Career Institute
4202 West Spruce St.
Tampa 33607

Daytona Beach Community College
1200 Volusia Ave.
Daytona Beach 32114

Miami-Dade Community College
300 Northeast Second Ave.
Miami 33132

Pasco-Hernando Community College
36727 Blanton Rd.
Dade City 33525-7599

Pensacola Junior College
1000 College Blvd.
Pensacola 32504

Sarasota County Technical Institute
4748 Beneva Rd.
Sarasota 34233-1798

Sheridan Vocational Center
5400 Sheridan St.
Hollywood 33021

Withlacoochee Technical Institute
1201 West Main St.
Inverness 32650

GEORGIA

Medix Schools
2108 Cobb Pkwy.
Smyrna 30080

HAWAII

Heald College School of Business and
   Technology
1500 Kapiolani Blvd.
Honolulu 96816

Medical Assistant School of Hawaii, Inc.
33 South King, Ste. 223
Honolulu 96813

IDAHO

American Institute of Health
   Technology, Inc.
6600 Emerald
Boise 83704

ILLINOIS

American Health Information
   Management Association
919 North Michigan Ave., Ste. 1400
Chicago 60611

Belleville Area College
2500 Carlyle Rd.
Belleville 62221

Lewis and Clark Community College
5800 Godfrey Rd.
Godfrey 62035

Medical Careers Institute
116 South Michigan Ave.
Chicago 60603

INDIANA

Indiana University, Northwest
3400 Broadway
Gary 46408

Professional Careers Institute
2611 Waterfront Pkwy., East Dr.
Indianapolis 46214-2028

Saint Margaret Hospital Medical
   Technology Program
5454 Hohman Ave.
Hammond 46320

IOWA

Indian Hills Community College
525 Grandview
Ottumwa 52501

KANSAS

Dodge City Community College
2501 North 14th Ave.
Dodge City 67801

KENTUCKY

Eastern Kentucky University
Lancaster Ave.
Richmond 40475

Interactive Learning Systems
11 Spiral Dr., Bldg. 13, Ste. 8
Florence 41042

LOUISIANA

American School of Business
702 Professional Dr. N
Shreveport 71105

Ayers Institute, Inc.
2924 Knight St., Ste. 318
Shreveport 71105

MARYLAND

Essex Community College
7201 Rossville Blvd.
Baltimore 21237

Medix Schools
1017 York Rd.
Towson 21204-9840

MASSACHUSETTS

Bryman Institute, A Corinthian School
323 Boylston St.
Brookline 02146

MICHIGAN

Baker College of Flint
G1050 West Bristol Rd.
Flint 48507

Baker College of Muskegon
1903 Marquette Ave.
Muskegon 49442

Carnegie Institute
550 Stephenson Hwy.
Troy 48083

Davenport College, Kalamazoo
4123 West Main St.
Kalamazoo 49006-2791

Dorsey Business Schools
31542 Gratiot
Roseville 48066

Dorsey Business Schools
15755 Northline Rd.
Southgate 48195

Dorsey Business Schools
34841 Veterans Plaza
Wayne 48184

Ferris State University
901 South State St.
Big Rapids 49307

Grand Rapids Educational Center
1750 Woodworth NE
Grand Rapids 49525

Grand Rapids Educational Center
5349 West Main
Kalamazoo 49009

Henry Ford Community College
5101 Evergreen Rd.
Dearborn 48128

Lawton School
20755 Greenfield Rd., Ste. 300
Southfield 48075

SER Business and Technical Insti tute
9301 Michigan Ave.
Detroit 47210-2095

MINNESOTA

Hennepin Technical College
9000 Brooklyn Blvd.
Plymouth 55445

Northwest Technical College, East
Grand Forks
Hwy. 220 N
East Grand Forks 56721

Saint Paul Technical College
235 Marshall Ave.
Saint Paul 55102

MISSISSIPPI

Amherst Career Center
201 West Park Ave.
Greenwood 38930

MISSOURI

Concorde Career Institute
3239 Broadway
Kansas City 64111

Miss Vanderschmidt's Secretarial School
4625 Lindell Blvd.
Saint Louis 63108

Missouri College
10121 Manchester Rd.
Saint Louis 63122

Penn Valley Community College
3201 Southwest Trafficway
Kansas City 64111

Saint Louis College of Health Careers
4484 West Pine
Saint Louis 63108

Sikeston Area Vocational Technical
School
1002 Virginia St.
Sikeston 63801

NEBRASKA

College of Saint Mary
1901 South 72nd St.
Omaha 68124

NEVADA

Nevada School of Insurance, Las Vegas
3305 Spring Mountain Rd., Ste. 50
Las Vegas 89102

NEW JERSEY

Berdan Institute
265 Rte. 46
Totowa 07512

Business Training Institute
Four Forest Ave.
Paramus 07652

Star Technical Institute
1255 Rte. 70
Lakewood 08701

NEW MEXICO

Albuquerque Technical Vocational
Institute
525 Buena Vista SE
Albuquerque 87106

NEW YORK

CUNY Borough of Manhattan
Community College
199 Chambers St.
New York 10007

Monroe Community College
1000 East Henrietta Rd.
Rochester 14623

NORTH CAROLINA

Central Piedmont Community College
P.O. Box 35009
Charlotte 28235-5009

Kings College
322 Lamar Ave.
Charlotte 28204

Pitt Community College
Hwy. 11 S, P.O. Drawer 7007
Greenville 27835-7007

OHIO

Chase School of Medical Transcription
Ten West Streetsboro St., Ste. 101-303
Hudson 44236

Cincinnati State Technical and
Community College
3520 Central Pkwy.
Cincinnati 45223

Cleveland Institute of Dental-Medical
Assistants
1836 Euclid Ave.
Cleveland 44115

Cleveland Institute of Dental-Medical
Assistants
5564 Mayfield Rd.
Lyndhurst 44124

Cleveland Institute of Dental-Medical
Assistants
5733 Hopkins Rd.
Mentor 44060

Pioneer Career and Technical Center, A
Vocational School District
27 Ryan Rd.
Shelby 44875

Remington College
14445 Broadway Ave.
Cleveland 44125

OKLAHOMA

De Marge College North
3608 Northwest 58th
Oklahoma City 73112

Francis Tuttle Area Vocational-
Technical Center
12777 North Rockwell Ave.
Oklahoma City 73142-2789

Pontotoc Area Vocational Technical
School
601 West 33rd
Ada 74820

Wright Business School
2219 Southwest 74th St., Ste. 124
Oklahoma City 73159

OREGON

Chemeketa Community College
4000 Lancaster Dr. NE
Salem 97305

Concorde Career Institute
1827 Northeast 44th Ave.
Portland 97213

Portland Community College
P.O. Box 19000
Portland 97280-0990

PENNSYLVANIA

Allied Medical and Technical Careers
104 Woodward Hill Rd.
Edwardsville 18704

Allied Medical and Technical Careers
2901 Pittston Ave.
Scranton 18505

Antonelli Medical and Professional
Institute
1700 Industrial Hwy.
Pottstown 19464

Bidwell Training Center, Inc.
1815 Metropolitan St.
Pittsburgh 15233

Community College of Allegheny
County, Pittsburgh
800 Allegheny Ave.
Pittsburgh 15233-1895

Computer Learning Network
2900 Fairway Dr.
Altoona 16602

Delaware County Community College
901 South Media Line Rd.
Media 19063-1094

Median School of Allied Health Careers
125 Seventh St.
Pittsburgh 15222-3400

National Education Center, Allentown
Business School Campus
1501 Lehigh St.
Allentown 18103

Thompson Institute
3440 Market St.
Philadelphia 19104

RHODE ISLAND

New England Institute of Technology
2500 Post Rd.
Warwick 02886

SOUTH DAKOTA

National American University
321 Kansas City St.
Rapid City 57701

TENNESSEE

Fugazzi College
5042 Linbar Dr., Ste. 200
Nashville 37211

Nashville State Technical Institute
120 White Bridge Rd.
Nashville 37209

Roane State Community College
276 Patton Ln.
Harriman 37748

TEXAS

The Academy of Health Care
Professions
1919 Northloop W, Ste. 170
Houston 77008

American Commercial College
3177 Executive Dr.
San Angelo 76904

Career Centers of Texas El Paso
8375 Burnham Dr.
El Paso 79907

PCI Health Training Center
8101 John Carpenter Fwy.
Dallas 75247

Saint Philip's College
1801 Martin Luther King Dr.
San Antonio 78203

San Antonio College of Medical and
Dental Assistants, Central
4205 San Pedro Ave.
San Antonio 78212-1899

Texas School of Business, Inc.
711 Airtex Dr.
Houston 77073

Texas School of Business, Southwest,
Inc.
10250 Bissonnet
Houston 77036

Texas State Technical College,
Harlingen
2424 Boxwood
Harlingen 78550-3697

UTAH

Bridgerland Applied Technology Center
1301 North 600 West
Logan 84321

Provo College
1450 West 820 N
Provo 84601

VIRGINIA

Computer Dynamics Institute, Inc.
5361 Virginia Beach Blvd.
Virginia Beach 23462

Medical Careers Institute
605 Thimble Shoals
Newport News 23606

WASHINGTON

Clark College
1800 East McLoughlin Blvd.
Vancouver 98663-3598

Eton Technical Institute
209 East Casino Rd.
Everett 98208

Eton Technical Institute
31919 Sixth Ave. S
Federal Way 98003

Eton Technical Institute
3649 Frontage Rd., St. A
Port Orchard 98366

Lower Columbia College
P.O. Box 3010
Longview 98632

Spokane Community College
North 1810 Greene Ave.
Spokane 99207

Tacoma Community College
5900 South 12th St.
Tacoma 98465

WEST VIRGINIA

Marshall University
400 Hal Greer Blvd.
Huntington 25755

West Virginia Business College
1052 Main St.
Wheeling 26003

WISCONSIN

Chippewa Valley Technical College
620 West Clairemont Ave.
Eau Claire 54701

Gateway Technical College
3520 30th Ave.
Kenosha 53144-1690

Mid-State Technical College
500 32nd St. N
Wisconsin Rapids 54494

Milwaukee Area Technical College
700 West State St.
Milwaukee 53233-1443

Northeast Wisconsin Technical College
2740 West Mason St., P.O. Box 19042
Green Bay 54307-9042

Waukesha County Technical College
800 Main St.
Pewaukee 53072

Western Wisconsin Technical College
304 North Sixth St., P.O. Box 908
La Crosse 54602-0908

Nurse's Aide

ALABAMA

Bevill State Community College
100 State St.
Sumiton 35148

Reid State Technical College
165 and Hwy. 83
Evergreen 36401

Trenholm State Technical College
1225 Air Base Blvd.
Montgomery 36108

ARIZONA

Eastern Arizona College
Church St.
Thatcher 85552-0769

Gateway Community College
108 North 40th St.
Phoenix 85034

Pima Community College
2202 West Anklam Rd.
Tucson 85709-0001

Pima Medical Institute
3350 East Grant Rd.
Tucson 85716

Tucson College
7302-10 East 22nd St.
Tucson 85710

ARKANSAS

Arkansas Valley Technical Institute
P.O. Box 506, Hwy. 23 N
Ozark 72949

Black River Technical College
Box 468, Hwy. 304
Pocahontas 72455

Crowley's Ridge Technical Institute
140 Crowley's Ridge Rd.
Forrest City 72335-0925

Eastern College of Health Vocations
6423 Forbing Rd.
Little Rock 72209

Great Rivers Vocational Technical
School
P.O. Box 747, Hwy. One NE
McGehee 71654

University of Arkansas Community
College, Batesville
P.O. Box 3350
Batesville 72503

CALIFORNIA

Allan Hancock College
800 South College Dr.
Santa Maria 93454

American School of X-Ray
13723-1/2 Harvard Place
Gardena 90249

Butte College
3536 Butte Campus Dr.
Oroville 95965

Educorp Career College
230 East Third St.
Long Beach 90802

Hacienda La Puente Unified School
District, Adult Education
P.O. Box 60002
City of Industry 91716-0002

Mission College
3000 Mission College Blvd.
Santa Clara 95054-1897

Nova Institute of Health Technology
520 North Euclid Ave.
Ontario 91762

Santa Rosa Junior College
1501 Mendocino Ave.
Santa Rosa 95401-4395

Simi Valley Adult School
3192 Los Angeles Ave.
Simi Valley 93065

COLORADO

Colorado Mountain College
P.O. Box 10001
Glenwood Springs 81602

PPI Health Careers School
2345 North Academy Blvd.
Colorado Springs 80909

Trinidad State Junior College, San Luis
Valley Education Center
1011 Main St.
Alamosa 81101

FLORIDA

Atlantic Vocational Technical Center
4700 Coconut Creek Pkwy.
Coconut Creek 33063

Beacon Career Institute, Inc.
2900 Northwest 183rd St.
Miami 33056

Brevard Community College, Cocoa
Campus
1519 Clearlake Rd.
Cocoa 32922

Brewster Technical Center
2222 North Tampa St.
Tampa 33602-2196

Charlotte Vocational Technical Center
18300 Toledo Blade Blvd.
Port Charlotte 33948-3399

Daytona Beach Community College
1200 Volusia Ave.
Daytona Beach 32114

Florida Community College at
Jacksonville
501 West State St.
Jacksonville 32202

Lorenzo Walker Institute of Technology
3702 Estey Ave.
Naples 33942

Lee County High Technical Center,
Central
3800 Michigan Ave.
Fort Myers 33916

Lindsey Hopkins Technical Education
Center
750 Northwest 20th St.
Miami 33127

Manatee Vocational Technical Center
5603 34th St. W
Bradenton 34210

Miriam Vocational School, Inc.
135 Southwest 57th Ave.
Miami 33144

Pensacola Junior College
1000 College Blvd.
Pensacola 32504

Pinellas Technical Education Centers
901 34th St. S
Saint Petersburg 33711

Radford M Locklin Vocational Technical
Center
5330 Berryhill Rd.
Milton 32570

Robert Morgan Vocational Technical
Center
18180 Southwest 122nd Ave.
Miami 33177

Santa Fe Community College
3000 Northwest 83rd St.
Gainesville 32606

Sarasota County Technical Institute
4748 Beneva Rd.
Sarasota 34233-1798

Seminole Community College
100 Weldon Blvd.
Sanford 32773-6199

South Florida Community College
600 West College Dr.
Avon Park 33825

Suwannee-Hamilton Area Vocational
and Adult Center
415 Southwest Pinewood Dr.
Live Oak 32060

U.S. Schools
100 North Plaza
Miami 33147

Washington-Holmes Area Vocational-
Technical Center
757 Hoyt St.
Chipley 32428

Withlacoochee Technical Institute
1201 West Main St.
Inverness 32650

GEORGIA

Kerr Business College
2528 Centerwest Pkwy., Bldg. A
Augusta 30909

Meadows Junior College
1170 Brown Ave.
Columbus 31906

ILLINOIS

Belleville Area College
2500 Carlyle Rd.
Belleville 62221

Career Academy
20 North Michigan Ave., Ste. 302
Chicago 60601

City Colleges of Chicago, Central Office
226 West Jackson Blvd.
Chicago 60606

John Wood Community College
150 South 48th St.
Quincy 62301-9147

Kishwaukee College
21193 Malta Rd.
Malta 60150

Lake Land College
5001 Lake Land Blvd.
Mattoon 61938

Lewis and Clark Community College
5800 Godfrey Rd.
Godfrey 62035

McHenry County College
8900 U.S. Hwy. 14
Crystal Lake 60012

Rock Valley College
3301 North Mulford Rd.
Rockford 61114

Sauk Valley Community College
173 Illinois Rte. 2
Dixon 61021

Shawnee Community College
8364 Shawnee College Rd.
Ullin 62992

Waubonsee Community College
IL Rte. 47 at Harter Rd.
Sugar Grove 60554-0901

IOWA

North Iowa Area Community College
500 College Dr.
Mason City 50401

KANSAS

Cloud County Community College
2221 Campus Dr., Box 1002
Concordia 66901-1002

Colby Community College
1255 South Range
Colby 67701

KAW Area Technical School
5724 Huntoon
Topeka 66604

Salina Area Vocational Technical
School
2562 Scanlan Ave.
Salina 67401

Southwest Kansas Technical School
P.O. Box 1599
Liberal 67905-1599

KENTUCKY

Kentucky Tech, Ashland Regional
Technology Center
4818 Roberts Dr.
Ashland 41102

LOUISIANA

Ascension College
320 East Ascension St.
Gonzales 70737

Cameron College
2740 Canal St.
New Orleans 70119

Charles B Coreil Technical Institute
Industrial Park Ward I
Ville Platte 70586

Coastal College, Hammond
4304 Yokum Rd.
Hammond 70403

Domestic Health Care Institute
4826 Jamestown Ave.
Baton Rouge 70808

Eastern College of Health Vocations
3321 Hessmer Ave., Ste. 200
Metairie 70002

Elaine P Nunez Community College
3710 Paris Rd.
Chalmette 70043

Huey P Long Technical Institute
303 South Jones St.
Winnfield 71483

Louisiana Technical College, Ascension
Campus
P.O. Box 38
Sorrento 70778

Louisiana Technical College, Avoyelles
Campus
508 Choupique St.
Cottonport 71327

Louisiana Technical College, Baton
Rouge Campus
3250 North Acadian Twy. E
Baton Rouge 70805

Louisiana Technical College, Claiborne
Campus
3001 Minden Rd.
Homer 71040

Louisiana Technical College,
Evangeline Campus
P.O. Box 68
Saint Martinville 70582

Louisiana Technical College, Mansfield
Campus
943 Oxford Rd.
Mansfield 71052

Louisiana Technical College, Sabine
Valley Campus
1255 Fisher Rd.
Many 71449

Louisiana Technical College, T H Harris
Campus
337 East South St.
Opelousas 70570

Louisiana Technical College, Thibodaux
Lafourche Campus
1425 Tiger Dr.
Thibodaux 70302

MASSACHUSETTS

Assabet Valley Regional Vocational
Technical School
215 Fitchburg St.
Marlborough 01752

MICHIGAN

Detroit Business Institute
1249 Washington Blvd., Ste. 1200
Detroit 48226

Ross Medical Education Center
1036 Gilbert St.
Flint 48532

Ross Medical Education Center
913 West Holmes, Ste. 260
Lansing 48910

Ross Medical Education Center
Park Row Mall, 950 Norton Ave.
Roosevelt Park 49441

Ross Medical Education Center
4054 Bay Rd.
Saginaw 48603

Ross Technical Institute
20820 Greenfield Rd., Ste. 101
Oak Park 48237

MINNESOTA

Century Community and Technical
College
3300 Century Ave. N
White Bear Lake 55110

Itasca Community College
1851 Hwy. 169 E
Grand Rapids 55744

Lake Superior College
2101 Trinity Rd.
Duluth 55811

MISSISSIPPI

Northwest Mississippi Community
College
510 North Panola, Hwy. 51 N
Senatobia 38668

MISSOURI

Cape Girardeau Area Vocational
Technical School
301 North Clark Ave.
Cape Girardeau 63701

Saint Louis College of Health Careers
4484 West Pine
Saint Louis 63108

Sikeston Area Vocational Technical
School
1002 Virginia St.
Sikeston 63801

MONTANA

Dawson Community College
300 College Dr.
Glendive 59330

Montana State University, College of
Technology, Great Falls
2100 16th Ave. S
Great Falls 59405

NEBRASKA

Opportunity Industrialization Center
Omaha
2725 North 24th St.
Omaha 68110

NEW MEXICO

Albuquerque Technical Vocational
Institute
525 Buena Vista SE
Albuquerque 87106

Crownpoint Institute of Technology
P.O. Box 849
Crownpoint 87313

Franklin College
2400 Louisiana Blvd. NE, Ste. 200
Albuquerque 87110

Pima Medical Institute
2201 San Pedro NE, Bldg. 3, Ste. 100
Albuquerque 87110

NEW YORK

Municipal Training Center
44 Court St., 7th Fl.
Brooklyn 11201

Silhouette
3187 Steinway St.
Long Island City 11103

Suburban Technical School
175 Fulton Ave.
Hempstead 11550

Superior Career Institute, Inc.
254 West 29th St., 3rd Fl.
New York 10011

Travel Institute
15 Park Row
New York 10038

NORTH CAROLINA

Brunswick Community College
P.O. Box 30
Supply 28462

Coastal Carolina Community College
444 Western Blvd.
Jacksonville 28546-6877

Craven Community College
800 College Ct.
New Bern 28562

Piedmont Community College
P.O. Box 1197
Roxboro 27573

Roanoke-Chowan Community College
Rte. 2, Box 46A
Ahoskie 27910

Robeson Community College
P.O. Box 1420
Lumberton 28359

OHIO

Gallia Jackson Vinton JUSD
Box 157
Rio Grande 45674

Madison Local Schools, Madison Adult
Education
600 Esley Ln.
Mansfield 44905

Tri-Rivers Career Center
2222 Marion Mount Gilead Rd.
Marion 43302

OKLAHOMA

Southwest Area Vocational Technical
Center
711 West Tamarack
Altus 73521

Tulsa Colorado Area Vocational
Technical School District 18, Peoria
3850 North Peoria
Tulsa 74106

OREGON

Southwestern Oregon Community
College
1988 Newmark Ave.
Coos Bay 97420

PENNSYLVANIA

Advanced Career Training
McClatchy Bldg., 2nd Fl., Southwest
Corner 69th
Upper Darby 19082

Allied Medical and Technical Careers
2901 Pittston Ave.
Scranton 18505

Allied Medical and Technical Careers
104 Woodward Hill Rd.
Edwardsville 18704

American Center for Technical Arts and
Sciences
1616 Orthodoy St.
Philadelphia 19124

Antonelli Medical and Professional
Institute
1700 Industrial Hwy.
Pottstown 19464

McKeesport Hospital School of Nursing
Assistants
1500 Fifth Ave.
McKeesport 15132

Pennsylvania State University, Lehigh
Valley Berks, Lehigh
6090 Mohr Ln.
Fogelsville 18051-9733

Presbyterian Home Nurse Assistant
School
P.O. Box 551
Philipsburg 16866

SOUTH CAROLINA

Trident Technical College
P.O. Box 118067
Charleston 29423-8067

TENNESSEE

Davidson Technical College
212 Pavilion Blvd.
Nashville 37217-1002

Draughons Junior College
1860 Wilma Rudolph Blvd.
Clarksville 37040

Tennessee Technology Center at
Elizabethton
1500 Arney St.
Elizabethton 37643

Tennessee Technology Center at
Hohenwald
813 West Main
Hohenwald 38462-2201

Tennessee Technology Center at
Knoxville
1100 Liberty St.
Knoxville 37919

Tennessee Technology Center at
Memphis
550 Alabama Ave.
Memphis 38105-3604

Tennessee Technology Center at Paris
312 South Wilson St.
Paris 38242

TEXAS

Delta Career Institute
1310 Pennsylvania Ave.
Beaumont 77701

Houston Medical Career Training, Inc.
2420 Garland Dr.
Houston 77087

Southwest School of Business and
Technical Careers
602 West South Cross
San Antonio 78221

Texas State Technical College,
Harlingen
2424 Boxwood
Harlingen 78550-3697

Transworld Academy, Inc.
6220 West Park, Ste. 110
Houston 77057

UTAH

Bridgerland Applied Technology Center
1301 North 600 West
Logan 84321

Salt Lake Community College, Skills
Center
South City Campus, 1575 South State St.
Salt Lake City 84115

VIRGINIA

Blue Ridge Nursing Home School
Commerce St., P.O. Box 459
Stuart 24171

Medical Careers Institute
605 Thimble Shoals
Newport News 23606

Southside Training Skill Center
Nottoway County
P.O. Box 258
Crewe 23930

Tidewater Technical
616 Denbigh Blvd.
Newport News 23602

Tidewater Technical
1760 East Little Creek Rd.
Norfolk 23518

Tidewater Technical
2697 Dean Dr., Ste. 100
Virginia Beach 23452

WASHINGTON

Bates Technical College
1101 South Yakima Ave.
Tacoma 98405

Lower Columbia College
P.O. Box 3010
Longview 98632

Yakima Valley Community College
P.O. Box 1647
Yakima 98907

WEST VIRGINIA

Opportunities Industrialization Center,
North Central West Virginia
120 Jackson St.
Fairmont 26554

WISCONSIN

Blackhawk Technical College
P.O. Box 5009
Janesville 53547

Fox Valley Technical College at
Appleton
1825 North Bluemound Dr.
Appleton 54913-2277

Gateway Technical College
3520 30th Ave.
Kenosha 53144-1690

Lakeshore Technical College
1290 North Ave.
Cleveland 53015

Madison Area Technical College
3550 Anderson St.
Madison 53704

Mid-State Technical College, Main
Campus
500 32nd St. N
Wisconsin Rapids 54494

Milwaukee Area Technical College
700 West State St.
Milwaukee 53233-1443

Moraine Park Technical College
235 North National Ave.
Fond Du Lac 54936-1940

Nicolet Area Technical College
P.O. Box 518, County Highway G
Rhinelander 54501

Northcentral Technical College
1000 Campus Dr.
Wausau 54401-1899

Northeast Wisconsin Technical College
2740 West Mason St., P.O. Box 19042
Green Bay 54307-9042

Southwest Wisconsin Technical College
1800 Bronson Blvd.
Fennimore 53809

Waukesha County Technical College
800 Main St.
Pewaukee 53072

Western Wisconsin Technical College
304 North Sixth St., P.O. Box 908
La Crosse 54602-0908

Wisconsin Indianhead Technical
College
505 Pine Ridge Dr.
Shell Lake 54871

Occupational Therapy Technology

CALIFORNIA

Imperial Valley College
P.O. Box 158
Imperial 92251-0158

COLORADO

Aims Community College
Box 69
Greeley 80632

CONNECTICUT

Manchester Community Technical
College
60 Bidwell St.
Manchester 06040-1046

FLORIDA

Charlotte Vocational Technical Center
18300 Toledo Blade Blvd.
Port Charlotte 33948-3399

ILLINOIS

College of Du Page
425 22nd St.
Glen Ellyn 60137-6599

IOWA

Kirkwood Community College
P.O. Box 2068
Cedar Rapids 52406

KANSAS

Allen County Community College
1801 North Cottonwood
Iola 66749

Cloud County Community College
2221 Campus Dr., Box 1002
Concordia 66901-1002

Colby Community College
1255 South Range
Colby 67701

Kansas City Area Vocational Technical
School
2220 North 59th St.
Kansas City 66104

KAW Area Technical School
5724 Huntoon
Topeka 66604

Neosho County Community College
800 West 14th St.
Chanute 66720

North Central Kansas Technical College
Box 507, Hwy. 24
Beloit 67420

Salina Area Vocational Technical
School
2562 Scanlan Ave.
Salina 67401

Wichita Area Technical College
201 North Water
Wichita 67202-1292

LOUISIANA

Northeast Louisiana University
700 University Ave.
Monroe 71209

MASSACHUSETTS

Quinsigamond Community College
670 West Boylston St.
Worcester 01606

MICHIGAN

Grand Rapids Community College
143 Bostwick Ave. NE
Grand Rapids 49503-3295

Schoolcraft College
18600 Haggerty Rd.
Livonia 48152

Wayne County Community College
801 West Fort St.
Detroit 48226

MINNESOTA

Century Community and Technical
College
3300 Century Ave. N
White Bear Lake 55110

Hibbing Community College, A
Technical and Community College
1515 East 25th St.
Hibbing 55746

Lake Superior College
2101 Trinity Rd.
Duluth 55811

MISSOURI

Jefferson College
1000 Viking Dr.
Hillsboro 63050

Saint Louis Community College, Forest
Park
5600 Oakland Ave.
Saint Louis 63110

NEW YORK

CUNY La Guardia Community College
31-10 Thomson Ave.
Long Island City 11101

Erie Community College, North
Campus
Main St. and Youngs Rd.
Williamsville 14221

Herkimer County Community College
Reservoir Rd.
Herkimer 13350-1598

Rockland Community College
145 College Rd.
Suffern 10901

NORTH DAKOTA

North Dakota State College of Science
800 North Sixth St.
Wahpeton 58076

OKLAHOMA

Metro Area Vocational Technical School
District 22
1900 Springlake Dr.
Oklahoma City 73111

Oklahoma City Community College
7777 South May Ave.
Oklahoma City 73159

PENNSYLVANIA

Community College of Allegheny
County, Pittsburgh
800 Allegheny Ave.
Pittsburgh 15233-1895

Harcum College
750 Montgomery Ave.
Bryn Mawr 19010

Median School of Allied Health Careers
125 Seventh St.
Pittsburgh 15222-3400

Mount Aloysius College
7373 Admiral Peary Hwy.
Cresson 16630-1999

TENNESSEE

Shelby State Community College
P.O. Box 40568
Memphis 38174-0568

TEXAS

Houston Community College System
22 Waugh Dr.
Houston 77270-7849

WASHINGTON

Green River Community College
12401 Southeast 320th St.
Auburn 98092

Spokane Falls Community College
West 3410 Fort George Wright Dr.
Spokane 99224

WISCONSIN

Fox Valley Technical College at
Appleton
1825 North Bluemound Dr.
Appleton 54913-2277

Madison Area Technical College
3550 Anderson St.
Madison 53704

Milwaukee Area Technical College
700 West State St.
Milwaukee 53233-1443

Optical Technology

ARIZONA

The Bryman School
4343 North 16th St.
Phoenix 85016

CALIFORNIA

National Career Education
6060 Sunrise Vista Dr.
Citrus Heights 95610

FLORIDA

Miami-Dade Community College
300 Northeast Second Ave.
Miami 33132

MASSACHUSETTS

Worcester Technical Institute
251 Belmont St.
Worcester 01605

MICHIGAN

Detroit Institute of Ophthalmology
15415 East Jefferson Ave.
Grosse Pointe Park 48230

Ferris State University
901 South State St.
Big Rapids 49307

NEW YORK

Allied Health Program in Orthoptics &
Opthalmic Technology
310 East 14th St.
New York 10003

CUNY New York City Technical College
300 Jay St.
Brooklyn 11201

Erie Community College, North
Campus
Main St. and Youngs Rd.
Williamsville 14221

Interboro Institute
450 West 56th St.
New York 10019

TEXAS

San Antonio College of Medical and
Dental Assistants, Central
4205 San Pedro Ave.
San Antonio 78212-1899

UTAH

American Institute of Medical-Dental
Technology
1675 North 200 West, Bldg. 4
Provo 84604

WISCONSIN

Lakeshore Technical College
1290 North Ave.
Cleveland 53015

Pharmaceutical Technology

ALABAMA

Community College of the Air Force
130 West Maxwell Blvd.
Montgomery 36112-6613

ARIZONA

Apollo College
3870 North Oracle Rd.
Tucson 85705

Long Medical Institute
4126 North Black Canyon Hwy.
Phoenix 85017

Pima Community College
2202 West Anklam Rd.
Tucson 85709-0001

CALIFORNIA

American Career College
4021 Rosewood Ave., First Fl.
Los Angeles 90004

California Paramedical and Technical
College
3745 Long Beach Blvd.
Long Beach 90807

California Paramedical and Technical
College
4550 La Sierra Ave.
Riverside 92505

Concorde Career Institute
570 West Fourth St., Ste. 107
San Bernardino 92401

Donald Vocational School
1833 West Eighth St., Ste. 200
Los Angeles 90057

Healthstaff Training Institute, Inc.
1505 East 17th St., Ste. 122
Santa Ana 92705

Western Career College
170 Bay Fair Mall
San Leandro 94578

COLORADO

Concorde Career Institute
770 Grant St.
Denver 80203

FLORIDA

Beacon Career Institute, Inc.
2900 Northwest 183rd St.
Miami 33056

Technical Career Institute
4299 Northwest 36th St., Ste. 300
Miami Springs 33166

IDAHO

American Institute of Health
Technology, Inc.
6600 Emerald
Boise 83704

MICHIGAN

Ferris State University
901 South State St.
Big Rapids 49307

MINNESOTA

Century Community and Technical
College
3300 Century Ave. N
White Bear Lake 55110

MISSOURI

Al-Med Academy
10963 Saint Charles Rock Rd.
Saint Louis 63074

Saint Louis College of Health Careers
4484 West Pine
Saint Louis 63108

OREGON

Apollo College, Portland, Inc.
2600 Southeast 98th Ave.
Portland 97266

PENNSYLVANIA

Allied Medical and Technical Careers
2901 Pittston Ave.
Scranton 18505

Allied Medical and Technical Careers
104 Woodward Hill Rd.
Edwardsville 18704

Bidwell Training Center, Inc.
1815 Metropolitan St.
Pittsburgh 15233

North Hills School of Health
Occupations
1500 Northway Mall
Pittsburgh 15237

TEXAS

Amarillo College
P.O. Box 447
Amarillo 79178

WASHINGTON

Seattle Community College, North
Campus
9600 College Way N
Seattle 98103

WISCONSIN

Milwaukee Area Technical College
700 West State St.
Milwaukee 53233-1443

Physical Therapy Technology

ALABAMA

Community College of the Air Force
130 West Maxwell Blvd.
Montgomery 36112-6613

George C Wallace State Community
College, Hanceville
801 Main St. NW
Hanceville 35077-2000

University of Alabama at Birmingham
Administration Bldg., Ste. 1070-2010
Birmingham 35294-0110

ARIZONA

Long Medical Institute
4126 North Black Canyon Hwy.
Phoenix 85017

ARKANSAS

University of Central Arkansas
201 Donaghey Ave.
Conway 72035-0001

CALIFORNIA

Cerritos College
11110 Alondra Blvd.
Norwalk 90650

De Anza College
21250 Stevens Creek Blvd.
Cupertino 95014

Imperial Valley College
P.O. Box 158
Imperial 92251-0158

Loma Linda University
Loma Linda 92350

Watterson College Pacific
150 South Los Robles Blvd., Ste. 100
Pasadena 91101

COLORADO

Aims Community College
Box 69
Greeley 80632

CONNECTICUT

Manchester Community Technical
College
60 Bidwell St.
Manchester 06040-1046

FLORIDA

Broward Community College
225 East Las Olas Blvd.
Fort Lauderdale 33301

Charlotte Vocational Technical Center
18300 Toledo Blade Blvd.
Port Charlotte 33948-3399

Miami-Dade Community College
300 Northeast Second Ave.
Miami 33132

Saint Petersburg Junior College
8580 66th St.
Pinellas Park 34665

GEORGIA

Gwinnett Technical Institute
5150 Sugarloaf Pkwy.
Lawrenceville 30043

IDAHO

American Institute of Health
Technology, Inc.
6600 Emerald
Boise 83704

ILLINOIS

Belleville Area College
2500 Carlyle Rd.
Belleville 62221

Morton College
3801 South Central Ave.
Cicero 60804

KANSAS

Allen County Community College
1801 North Cottonwood
Iola 66749

Cloud County Community College
2221 Campus Dr., Box 1002
Concordia 66901-1002

Colby Community College
1255 South Range
Colby 67701

Kansas City Area Technical School
2220 North 59th St.
Kansas City 66104

KAW Area Technical School
5724 Huntoon
Topeka 66604

Neosho County Community College
800 West 14th St.
Chanute 66720

North Central Kansas Technical College
Box 507, Hwy. 24
Beloit 67420

Salina Area Vocational Technical
School
2562 Scanlan Ave.
Salina 67401

Wichita Area Technical College
201 North Water
Wichita 67202-1292

MARYLAND

Baltimore City Community College
2901 Liberty Heights Ave.
Baltimore 21215

MASSACHUSETTS

Becker College, Worcester
61 Sever St.
Worcester 01615-0071

Newbury College, Inc.
129 Fisher Ave.
Brookline 02146

MICHIGAN

Delta College
University Ctr.
University Center 48710

Macomb Community College
14500 Twelve Mile Rd.
Warren 48093-3896

MINNESOTA

Anoka-Ramsey Community College
11200 Mississippi Blvd.
Coon Rapids 55433-3470

College of Saint Catherine, Minneapolis
601 25th Ave. S
Minneapolis 55454

MISSOURI

Jefferson College
1000 Viking Dr.
Hillsboro 63050

NEW JERSEY

University of Medicine and Dentistry of
New Jersey
30 Bergen St.
Newark 07107

NEW YORK

CUNY Kingsborough Community
College
2001 Oriental Blvd.
Brooklyn 11235

CUNY La Guardia Community College
31-10 Thomson Ave.
Long Island City 11101

Genesee Community College
One College Rd.
Batavia 14020

Nassau Community College
One Education Dr.
Garden City 11530

Suffolk County Community College,
Ammerman Campus
533 College Rd.
Selden 11784

NORTH CAROLINA

Central Piedmont Community College
P.O. Box 35009
Charlotte 28235-5009

OHIO

Cuyahoga Community College District
700 Carnegie Ave.
Cleveland 44115-2878

Kent State University, East Liverpool
Regional Campus
400 East Fourth St.
East Liverpool 43920

Stark State College of Technology
6200 Frank Ave. NW
Canton 44720

OKLAHOMA

Metro Area Vocational Technical School
District 22
1900 Springlake Dr.
Oklahoma City 73111

OREGON

Mount Hood Community College
26000 Southeast Stark St.
Gresham 97030

PENNSYLVANIA

Community College of Allegheny
County, Pittsburgh
800 Allegheny Ave.
Pittsburgh 15233-1895

Harcum College
750 Montgomery Ave.
Bryn Mawr 19010

Lehigh Carbon Community College
4525 Education Park Dr.
Schnecksville 18078-2598

Pennsylvania State University, Hazleton
Highacres
Hazleton 18201

SOUTH CAROLINA

Trident Technical College
P.O. Box 118067
Charleston 29423-8067

TENNESSEE

Volunteer State Community College
1480 Nashville Pike
Gallatin 37066-3188

TEXAS

Amarillo College
P.O. Box 447
Amarillo 79178

Houston Community College System
22 Waugh Dr.
Houston 77270-7849

Tarrant County Junior College
1500 Houston St.
Fort Worth 76102

Transworld Academy, Inc.
6220 West Park, Ste. 110
Houston 77057

VIRGINIA

Northern Virginia Community College
4001 Wakefield Chapel Rd.
Annandale 22003

WASHINGTON

Green River Community College
12401 Southeast 320th St.
Auburn 98092

WISCONSIN

Milwaukee Area Technical College
700 West State St.
Milwaukee 53233-1443

Northeast Wisconsin Technical College
2740 West Mason St., P.O. Box 19042
Green Bay 54307-9042

Psychiatric and Mental Health Technology

ALABAMA

Chauncey Sparks State Technical
  College
Hwy. 431 S
Eufaula 36027

Gadsden State Community College
1001 George Wallace Dr.
Gadsden 35902-0227

George C Wallace State Community
  College, Hanceville
801 Main St. NW
Hanceville 35077-2000

ALASKA

University of Alaska, Anchorage
3211 Providence Dr.
Anchorage 99508

University of Alaska, Fairbanks
Signers Hall
Fairbanks 99775

ARIZONA

Apollo College
3870 North Oracle Rd.
Tucson 85705

Apollo College, Tri City, Inc.
630 West Southern Ave.
Mesa 85210

Glendale Community College
6000 West Olive Ave.
Glendale 85302

Maricopa Skill Center
1245 East Buckeye
Phoenix 85034-4101

Phoenix College
1202 West Thomas Rd.
Phoenix 85013

Pima Community College
2202 West Anklam Rd.
Tucson 85709-0001

Rio Salado Community College
2323 West 14th St.
Tempe 85281

CALIFORNIA

Allan Hancock College
800 South College Dr.
Santa Maria 93454

American River College
4700 College Oak Dr.
Sacramento 95841

American School of X-Ray
13723-1/2 Harvard Place
Gardena 90249

Butte College
3536 Butte Campus Dr.
Oroville 95965

California Paramedical and Technical
  College
4550 La Sierra Ave.
Riverside 92505

California Paramedical and Technical
  College
3745 Long Beach Blvd.
Long Beach 90807

Citrus College
1000 West Foothill Blvd.
Glendora 91741-1899

Cypress College
9200 Valley View
Cypress 90630

De Anza College
21250 Stevens Creek Blvd.
Cupertino 95014

Foothill College
12345 El Monte Rd.
Los Altos Hills 94022

Fresno City College
1101 East University Ave.
Fresno 93741

Glendale Community College
1500 North Verdugo Rd.
Glendale 91208-2894

Hacienda La Puente Unified School
  District, Adult Education
P.O. Box 60002
City of Industry 91716-0002

Hypnosis Motivation Institute
18607 Ventura Blvd., Ste. 310
Tarzana 91356

Hypnotism Training Institute of Los
  Angeles
700 South Central
Glendale 91204

Imperial Valley College
P.O. Box 158
Imperial 92251-0158

L & P School of Professional
  Hypnotherapy
12941 Gilbert, Ste. D
Garden Grove 92841

Marin Regional Occupational Program
P.O. Box 4925
San Rafael 94913

Merced College
3600 M St.
Merced 95348-2898

Mission College
3000 Mission College Blvd.
Santa Clara 95054-1897

Mount San Antonio College
1100 North Grand
Walnut 91789

Mueller College of Holistic Studies
4607 Park Blvd.
San Diego 92116

Napa Valley College
2277 Napa Vallejo Hwy.
Napa 94558

Pacific College of Oriental Medicine
7445 Mission Valley Rd., Ste. 105
San Diego 92108

Pacific Oaks College
Five Westmoreland Place
Pasadena 91103

Porterville College
100 East College Ave.
Porterville 93257

Santa Rosa Junior College
1501 Mendocino Ave.
Santa Rosa 95401-4395

Simi Valley Adult School
3192 Los Angeles Ave.
Simi Valley 93065

Ventura College
4667 Telegraph Rd.
Ventura 93003

Yuba College
2088 North Beale Rd.
Marysville 95901

COLORADO

Aims Community College
Box 69
Greeley 80632

Community College of Denver
P.O. Box 173363
Denver 80217

Modern Institute of Reflexology
7043 West Colfax Ave.
Lakewood 80215

Morgan Community College
17800 County Rd. 20
Fort Morgan 80701

Red Rocks Community College
13300 West Sixth Ave.
Lakewood 80228

CONNECTICUT

Asnuntuck Community Technical
  College
170 Elm St.
Enfield 06082

Housatonic Community Technical
  College
900 Lafayette Blvd.
Bridgeport 06604

Manchester Community Technical
  College
60 Bidwell St.
Manchester 06040-1046

Middlesex Community Technical
  College
100 Training Hill Rd.
Middletown 06457

Mitchell College
437 Pequot Ave.
New London 06320

Northwestern Connecticut Community
  Technical College
Park Place E
Winsted 06098

Norwalk Community Technical College
188 Richards Ave.
Norwalk 06854

Tunxis Community Technical College
Rtes. 6 and 177
Farmington 06032

DELAWARE

Delaware Technical and Community
  College, Owens
Box 610
Georgetown 19947

Delaware Technical and Community
  College Stanton, Wilmington
400 Stanton-Christiana Rd.
Newark 19702

Delaware Technical and Community
  College, Terry
1832 North Dupont Pkwy.
Dover 19901

DISTRICT OF COLUMBIA

Howard University
2400 Sixth St. NW
Washington 20059

FLORIDA

Charlotte Vocational Technical Center
18300 Toledo Blade Blvd.
Port Charlotte 33948-3399

Daytona Beach Community College
1200 Volusia Ave.
Daytona Beach 32114

Florida Community College at
  Jacksonville
501 West State St.
Jacksonville 32202

Lee County High Technical Center,
  Central
3800 Michigan Ave.
Fort Myers 33916

Sarasota County Technical Institute
4748 Beneva Rd.
Sarasota 34233-1798

Seminole Community College
100 Weldon Blvd.
Sanford 32773-6199

Sheridan Vocational Center
5400 Sheridan St.
Hollywood 33021

GEORGIA

Dekalb College
3251 Panthersville Rd.
Decatur 30034

ILLINOIS

City Colleges of Chicago, Harold
  Washington College
30 East Lake St.
Chicago 60601

College of Du Page
425 22nd St.
Glen Ellyn 60137-6599

Elgin Community College
1700 Spartan Dr.
Elgin 60123

Moraine Valley Community College
10900 South 88th Ave.
Palos Hills 60465-0937

Prairie State College
202 Halsted St.
Chicago Heights 60411

Swedish American Hospital School of
  Radiography
1400 Charles St.
Rockford 61104-2298

Triton College
2000 Fifth Ave.
River Grove 60171

Waubonsee Community College
IL Rte. 47 at Harter Rd.
Sugar Grove 60554-0901

William Rainey Harper College
1200 West Algonquin Rd.
Palatine 60067-7398

INDIANA

Indiana University, Purdue University,
  Fort Wayne
2101 Coliseum Blvd. E
Fort Wayne 46805

IOWA

Iowa Lakes Community College
19 South Seventh St.
Estherville 51334

KANSAS

Allen County Community College
1801 North Cottonwood
Iola 66749

Cloud County Community College
2221 Campus Dr., Box 1002
Concordia 66901-1002

Colby Community College
1255 South Range
Colby 67701

Cowley County Community College
125 South Second St.
Arkansas City 67005

Kansas City Area Technical School
2220 North 59th St.
Kansas City 66104

KAW Area Technical School
5724 Huntoon
Topeka 66604

Neosho County Community College
800 West 14th St.
Chanute 66720

North Central Kansas Technical College
Box 507, Hwy. 24
Beloit 67420

Salina Area Vocational Technical
    School
2562 Scanlan Ave.
Salina 67401

Washburn University of Topeka
1700 College Ave.
Topeka 66621

Wichita Area Technical College
201 North Water
Wichita 67260

KENTUCKY

Northern Kentucky University
University Dr.
Highland Heights 41099

LOUISIANA

Southern University, New Orleans
6400 Press Dr.
New Orleans 70126

MAINE

University of Maine at Augusta
46 University Dr.
Augusta 04330-9410

MARYLAND

Allegany College of Maryland
12401 Willowbrook Rd. SE
Cumberland 21502

Anne Arundel Community College
101 College Pkwy.
Arnold 21012

Baltimore City Community College
2901 Liberty Heights Ave.
Baltimore 21215

Dundalk Community College
7200 Sollers Point Rd.
Dundalk 21222

Essex Community College
7201 Rossville Blvd.
Baltimore 21237

MASSACHUSETTS

Bristol Community College
777 Elsbree St.
Fall River 02720

Bunker Hill Community College
250 New Rutherford Ave.
Boston 02129

Lawrence Memorial Hospital School of
    Nursing
170 Governors Ave.
Medford 02155

Middlesex Community College
Springs Rd.
Bedford 01730

Mount Wachusett Community College
444 Green St.
Gardner 01440

North Shore Community College
One Ferncroft Rd.
Danvers 01923

Northern Essex Community College
Elliott Way
Haverhill 01830-2399

Quinsigamond Community College
670 West Boylston St.
Worcester 01606

Springfield Technical Community
    College
One Armory Square
Springfield 01105

Stonehill College
Washington St.
North Easton 02357

MICHIGAN

Delta College
University Ctr.
University Center 48710

Lansing Community College
419 North Capitol Ave.
Lansing 48901-7210

Macomb Community College
14500 Twelve Mile Rd.
Warren 48093-3896

Mott Community College
1401 East Court St.
Flint 48503

Oakland Community College
2480 Opdyke Rd.
Bloomfield Hills 48304-2266

Wayne County Community College
801 West Fort St.
Detroit 48226

MINNESOTA

College of Saint Catherine, Minneapolis
601 25th Ave. S
Minneapolis 55454

Minneapolis Community and Technical
    College
1501 Hennepin Ave.
Minneapolis 55403-1779

Saint Cloud Technical College
1540 Northway Dr.
Saint Cloud 56303

University of Minnesota, Crookston
105 Selvig Hall
Crookston 56716

MISSOURI

Jefferson College
1000 Viking Dr.
Hillsboro 63050

NEBRASKA

Central Community College Area
P.O. Box 4903
Grand Island 68802

Omaha College of Health Careers
10845 Harney St.
Omaha 68154

Opportunity Industrialization Center
    Omaha
2725 North 24th St.
Omaha 68110

Southeast Community College Area
1111 O St., Ste. 111
Lincoln 68520

NEW HAMPSHIRE

Keene State College
229 Main
Keene 03431

New Hampshire Technical Institute
11 Institute Dr.
Concord 03301

NEW JERSEY

Camden County College
P.O. Box 200
Blackwood 08012

Star Technical Institute, Deptford
1450 Clements Bridge Rd.
Deptford 08096

NEW MEXICO

Hypnosis Career Institute
10701 Lomas NE, Ste. 216
Albuquerque 87112

Northern New Mexico Community
    College
1002 North Onate St.
Espanola 87532

NEW YORK

CUNY Kingsborough Community
    College
2001 Oriental Blvd.
Brooklyn 11235

Erie Community College, City Campus
121 Ellicott St.
Buffalo 14203

Mercy College, Main Campus
555 Broadway
Dobbs Ferry 10522

Rochester Institute of Technology
One Lamb Memorial Dr.
Rochester 14623-5603

Saint Joseph's College, Main Campus
245 Clinton Ave.
Brooklyn 11205-3688

Saint Joseph's College, Suffolk Campus
155 West Roe Blvd.
Patchogue 11772-2399

Sullivan County Community College
1000 Le Roy Rd.
Loch Sheldrake 12759-4002

NORTH CAROLINA

Duke University
103 Allen Building
Durham 27708

Southeastern Community College
4564 Chadburn Hwy.
Whiteville 28472

Wake Technical Community College
9101 Fayetteville Rd.
Raleigh 27603-5696

Wayne Community College
3000 Wayne Memorial Dr.
Goldsboro 27533-8002

Western Piedmont Community College
1001 Burkemont Ave.
Morganton 28655-9978

OHIO

Belmont Technical College
120 Fox Shannon Place
Saint Clairsville 43950

Columbus State Community College
550 East Spring St.
Columbus 43216

English Nanny and Governess School
30 South Franklin St.
Chagrin Falls 44022

Kettering College Medical Arts
3737 Southern Blvd.
Kettering 45429-1299

Muskingum Area Technical College
1555 Newark Rd.
Zanesville 43701

North Central Technical College
2441 Kenwood Circle, P.O. Box 698
Mansfield 44901

Sinclair Community College
444 West Third St.
Dayton 45402

University of Toledo
2801 West Bancroft
Toledo 43606

OKLAHOMA

Central Oklahoma Area Vocational
    Technical School
Three Court Circle
Drumright 74030

Kiamichi Area Vocational Technical
    School SD #7, McCurtain
Rte. 3, Box 177, Hwy. 70 N
Idabel 74745

Metro Area Vocational Technical School
    District 22
1900 Springlake Dr.
Oklahoma City 73111

OREGON

Chemeketa Community College
4000 Lancaster Dr. NE
Salem 97305

Mount Hood Community College
26000 Southeast Stark St.
Gresham 97030

PENNSYLVANIA

Bucks County Community College
Swamp Rd.
Newtown 18940

Community College of Allegheny
    County, Pittsburgh
800 Allegheny Ave.
Pittsburgh 15233-1895

Community College of Philadelphia
1700 Spring Garden St.
Philadelphia 19130

Edinboro University of Pennsylvania
Edinboro 16444

Harcum College
750 Montgomery Ave.
Bryn Mawr 19010

Manor Junior College
700 Fox Chase Rd.
Jenkintown 19046

Mercer County Area Vocational
    Technical School
776 Greenville Rd.
Mercer 16137-0152

Pennsylvania College of Technology
One College Ave.
Williamsport 17701

Pennsylvania State University, Main
    Campus
201 Old Main
University Park 16802

Reading Area Community College
P.O. Box 1706
Reading 19603-1706

Sawyer School
717 Liberty Ave.
Pittsburgh 15222

Seton Hill College
Seton Hill Dr.
Greensburg 15601

RHODE ISLAND

Community College of Rhode Island
400 East Ave.
Warwick 02886-1807

SOUTH CAROLINA

York Technical College
452 South Anderson Rd.
Rock Hill 29730

SOUTH DAKOTA

Lake Area Technical Institute
230 11th St. NE
Watertown 57201

TENNESSEE

Shelby State Community College
P.O. Box 40568
Memphis 38174-0568

TEXAS

Career Academy, Inc.
32 Oak Lawn Village
Texarkana 75501

Career Centers of Texas El Paso, Inc.
8375 Burnham Dr.
El Paso 79907

Cisco Junior College
Rte. 3, Box 3
Cisco 76437

Eastfield College
3737 Motley Dr.
Mesquite 75150

El Paso Community College
P.O. Box 20500
El Paso 79998

Houston Community College System
22 Waugh Dr.
Houston 77270-7849

Howard County Junior College District
1001 Birdwell Ln.
Big Spring 79720

McLennan Community College
1400 College Dr.
Waco 76708

PCI Health Training Center
8101 John Carpenter Fwy.
Dallas 75247

San Antonio College of Medical and
  Dental Assistants, Central
4205 San Pedro Ave.
San Antonio 78229

Tarrant County Junior College
1500 Houston St.
Fort Worth 76102

UTAH

Bridgerland Applied Technology Center
1301 North 600 West
Logan 84321

VERMONT

Community College of Vermont
Box 120
Waterbury 05676

VIRGINIA

Blue Ridge Community College
P.O. Box 80
Weyers Cave 24486

Central Virginia Community College
3506 Wards Rd.
Lynchburg 24502

Danville Community College
1008 South Main St.
Danville 24541

Eastern Shore Community College
29300 Lankford Hwy.
Melfa 23410

Germanna Community College
2130 Germanna Hwy.
Locust Grove 22508

J Sargeant Reynolds Community
  College
P.O. Box 85622
Richmond 23285-5622

John Tyler Community College
13101 Jefferson Davis Hwy.
Chester 23831-5399

Lord Fairfax Community College
173 Skirmisher Ln.
Middletown 22645

Mountain Empire Community College
Drawer 700
Big Stone Gap 24219

New River Community College
Drawer 1127
Dublin 24084-1127

Northern Virginia Community College
4001 Wakefield Chapel Rd.
Annandale 22003

Patrick Henry Community College
P.O. Box 5311
Martinsville 24115-5311

Paul D Camp Community College
P.O. Box 737, 100 North College Dr.
Franklin 23851

Rappahannock Community College
12745 College Dr.
Glenns 23149

Southside Virginia Community College
109 Campus Dr.
Alberta 23821

Southwest Virginia Community College
Box SVCC
Richlands 24641

Thomas Nelson Community College
P.O. Box 9407
Hampton 23670

Tidewater Community College
121 College Pl.
Norfolk 23510

Virginia Highlands Community College
P.O. Box 828
Abingdon 24210-0828

Virginia Western Community College
3095 Colonial Ave.
Roanoke 24015

WASHINGTON

Edmonds Community College
20000 68th Ave. W
Lynnwood 98036

Lake Washington Technical College
11605 132nd Ave. NE
Kirkland 98034

Pierce College
9401 Farwest Dr. SW
Tacoma 98498

Spokane Falls Community College
West 3410 Fort George Wright Dr.
Spokane 99224

Tacoma Community College
5900 South 12th St.
Tacoma 98465

Yakima Valley Community College
P.O. Box 1647
Yakima 98907

WEST VIRGINIA

Opportunities Industrialization Center,
  North Central West Virginia
120 Jackson St.
Fairmont 26554

WISCONSIN

C Ross Educational Center
2821 North Fourth St.
Milwaukee 53212

Chippewa Valley Technical College
620 West Clairemont Ave.
Eau Claire 54701

Lac Courte Oreilles Ojibwa Community
  College
Rte. 2, Box 2357
Hayward 54843

Waukesha County Technical College
800 Main St.
Pewaukee 53072

Western Wisconsin Technical College
304 North Sixth St., P.O. Box 908
La Crosse 54602-0908

Wisconsin Indianhead Technical
  College
505 Pine Ridge Dr.
Shell Lake 54871

Radiologic Technology

ALABAMA

Community College of the Air Force
130 West Maxwell Blvd.
Montgomery 36112-6613

Gadsden State Community College
1001 George Wallace Dr.
Gadsden 35902-0227

George C Wallace State Community
  College, Hanceville
801 Main St. NW
Hanceville 35077-2000

Jefferson State Community College
2601 Carson Rd.
Birmingham 35215-3098

University of Alabama at Birmingham
Administration Bldg., Ste. 1070-2010
Birmingham 35294-0110

University of South Alabama
307 North University Blvd.
Mobile 36688-0002

ARIZONA

The Bryman School
4343 North 16th St.
Phoenix 85016

Gateway Community College
108 North 40th St.
Phoenix 85034

ARKANSAS

Arkansas Valley Technical Institute
P.O. Box 506, Hwy. 23 N
Ozark 72949

Carti School of Radiation Therapy
  Technology
P.O. Box 55050
Little Rock 72215

Sparks Regional Medical Center School
  of Radiography
1311 South I St.
Fort Smith 72917-7006

CALIFORNIA

American School of X-Ray
13723-1/2 Harvard Place
Gardena 90249

Butte College
3536 Butte Campus Dr.
Oroville 95965

Cabrillo College
6500 Soquel Dr.
Aptos 95003

Chaffey Community College
5885 Haven Ave.
Rancho Cucamonga 91737-3002

Charles R Drew University of Medicine
  and Science
1730 East 118th St.
Los Angeles 90059

Cypress College
9200 Valley View
Cypress 90630

Educorp Career College
230 East Third St.
Long Beach 90802

Foothill College
12345 El Monte Rd.
Los Altos Hills 94022

Fresno City College
1101 East University Ave.
Fresno 93741

Loma Linda University
Loma Linda 92350

Long Beach City College
4901 East Carson St.
Long Beach 90808

Merced College
3600 M St.
Merced 95348-2898

Modern Technology School of X-Ray
6180 Laurel Canyon Blvd., Ste. 101
North Hollywood 91606

Mount San Antonio College
1100 North Grand
Walnut 91789

Nova Institute of Health Technology
3000 South Robertson Blvd.
Los Angeles 90034

Nova Institute of Health Technology
12449 Putnam St.
Whittier 90602-1023

Orange Coast College
2701 Fairview Rd.
Costa Mesa 92626

San Diego Mesa College
7250 Mesa College Dr.
San Diego 92111-4998

San Joaquin General Hospital School of
  Radiation Technology
P.O. Box 1020
Stockton 95201

Santa Barbara City College
721 Cliff Dr.
Santa Barbara 93109-2394

Santa Rosa Junior College
1501 Mendocino Ave.
Santa Rosa 95401-4395

Yuba College
2088 North Beale Rd.
Marysville 95901

COLORADO

Community College of Denver
P.O. Box 173363
Denver 80217

CONNECTICUT

Gateway Community Technical College
60 Sargent Dr.
New Haven 06511

Saint Vincent's College
2800 Main St.
Bridgeport 06606

DELAWARE

Delaware Technical and Community
  College, Stanton, Wilmington
400 Stanton-Christiana Rd.
Newark 19702

DISTRICT OF COLUMBIA

George Washington University
2121 Eye St. NW
Washington 20052

FLORIDA

Hillsborough Community College
P.O. Box 31127
Tampa 33631-3127

National School of Technology, Inc.
4410 West 16th Ave., Ste. 52
Hialeah 33012

Pensacola Junior College
1000 College Blvd.
Pensacola 32504

Saint Petersburg Junior College
8580 66th St. N
Pinellas Park 34665

Santa Fe Community College
3000 Northwest 83rd St.
Gainesville 32606

GEORGIA

De Kalb Medical Center School of
Radiologic Technology
2701 North Decatur Rd.
Decatur 30033

Grady Health System Professional
Schools
80 Butler St.
Atlanta 30335-3801

Medical Center, Inc., School of
Radiologic Technology
710 Center St., Hospital Drawer 85
Columbus 31994-2299

Medical College of Georgia
1120 15th St.
Augusta 30912

HAWAII

Kapiolani Community College
4303 Diamond Head Rd.
Honolulu 96816

ILLINOIS

Belleville Area College
2500 Carlyle Rd.
Belleville 62221

College of Du Page
425 22nd St.
Glen Ellyn 60137-6599

Cook County Hospital School of X-Ray
Technology
1825 West Harrison St.
Chicago 60612

Kaskaskia College
27210 College Rd.
Centralia 62801

Methodist Medical Center of Illinois,
School of Nursing
221 Northeast Glen Oak Ave.
Peoria 61636

Moraine Valley Community College
10900 South 88th Ave.
Palos Hills 60465-0937

Rockford Memorial Hospital School of
X-Ray Technology
2400 North Rockton Ave.
Rockford 61103

Southern Illinois University,
Carbondale
Faner Hall 2179
Carbondale 62901-4512

Swedish American Hospital School of
Medical Technology
1400 Charles St.
Rockford 61104-2298

Triton College
2000 Fifth Ave.
River Grove 60171

INDIANA

Ball State University
2000 University Ave.
Muncie 47306

Fort Wayne School of Radiography
700 Broadway
Fort Wayne 46802

Indiana University, Purdue University,
Indianapolis
355 North Lansing
Indianapolis 46202

IOWA

University of Iowa
Jessup Hall
Iowa City 52242

KANSAS

Fort Hays State University
600 Park St.
Hays 67601-4099

Labette Community College
200 South 14th
Parsons 67357

Washburn University of Topeka
1700 College Ave.
Topeka 66621

KENTUCKY

Kentucky Technical, Bowling Green
Regional Technical Center
845 Loop Dr.
Bowling Green 42101-3601

Lexington Community College
Cooper Dr.
Lexington 40506

Morehead State University
University Blvd.
Morehead 40351

LOUISIANA

Delgado Community College
501 City Park Ave.
New Orleans 70119

MAINE

Southern Maine Technical College
Fort Rd.
South Portland 04106

MARYLAND

Essex Community College
7201 Rossville Blvd.
Baltimore 21237

Prince Georges Community College
301 Largo Rd.
Largo 20774-2199

MASSACHUSETTS

Bunker Hill Community College
250 New Rutherford Ave.
Boston 02129

Holyoke Community College
303 Homestead Ave.
Holyoke 01040

Massasoit Community College
One Massasoit Blvd.
Brockton 02402

Northeastern University
360 Huntington Ave.
Boston 02115

Springfield Technical Community
College
One Armory Square
Springfield 01105

MICHIGAN

Carnegie Institute
550 Stephenson Hwy.
Troy 48083

Ferris State University
901 South State St.
Big Rapids 49307

Grand Rapids Community College
143 Bostwick Ave. NE
Grand Rapids 49503-3295

Lansing Community College
419 North Capitol Ave.
Lansing 48901-7210

William Beaumont Hospital
3601 West 13 Mile Rd.
Royal Oak 48073-6769

MINNESOTA

Mayo School of Health-Related Sciences
200 First St. SW
Rochester 55905

Northwest Technical College, East
Grand Forks
Hwy. 220 N
East Grand Forks 56721

Rochester Community and Technical
College
851 30th Ave. SE
Rochester 55904-4999

MISSISSIPPI

University of Mississippi Medical
Center
2500 North State St.
Jackson 39216

MISSOURI

Research Medical Center School of
Nuclear Medical Technology
2316 East Meyer Blvd.
Kansas City 64132

Saint Louis Community College, Forest
Park
5600 Oakland Ave.
Saint Louis 63110

Saint Luke's College
4426 Wornall Rd.
Kansas City 64111

NEW HAMPSHIRE

New Hampshire Technical Institute
11 Institute Dr.
Concord 03301

NEW JERSEY

Bergen Community College
400 Paramus Rd.
Paramus 07652

Hudson Area School of Radiologic
Technology
29 East 29th St.
Bayonne 07002

Middlesex County College
155 Mill Rd.
Edison 08818-3050

University of Medicine and Dentistry of
New Jersey
30 Bergen St.
Newark 07107

NEW YORK

Bellevue Hospital Center School of
Radiation Technology
First Ave. and 27th St., Rm. D510
New York 10016

Broome Community College
P.O. Box 1017
Binghamton 13902

CUNY New York City Technical College
300 Jay St.
Brooklyn 11201

Hudson Valley Community College
80 Vandenburgh Ave.
Troy 12180

Institute of Allied Medical Professions
405 Park Ave., St. 501
New York 10022

Monroe Community College
1000 East Henrietta Rd.
Rochester 14623

Nassau Community College
One Education Dr.
Garden City 11530

Saint Luke's Memorial Hospital Center
Champlin Rd., P.O. Box 479
Utica 13503-0479

SUNY Health Science Center at
Syracuse
750 East Adams St.
Syracuse 13210

SUNY Westchester Commmunity
College
75 Grasslands Rd.
Valhalla 10595

Trocaire College
360 Choate Ave.
Buffalo 14220

NORTH CAROLINA

Edgecombe Community College
2009 West Wilson St.
Tarboro 27886

Forsyth Technical Community College
2100 Silas Creek Pkwy.
Winston-Salem 27103

Pitt Community College
Hwy. 11 S, P.O. Drawer 7007
Greenville 27835-7007

Southwestern Community College
447 College Dr.
Sylva 28779

OHIO

Cuyahoga Community College District
700 Carnegie Ave.
Cleveland 44115-2878

Kent State University, Salem Regional
Campus
2491 South Rte. 45 S
Salem 44460

Kettering College Medical Arts
3737 Southern Blvd.
Kettering 45429-1299

Lima Technical College
4240 Campus Dr.
Lima 45804

Lorain County Community College
1005 Abbe Rd. N
Elyria 44035

Owens Community College
30335 Oregon Rd.
Toledo 43699-1947

Sinclair Community College
444 West Third St.
Dayton 45402

Tri-Rivers Career Center
2222 Marion Mount Gilead Rd.
Marion 43302

University of Cincinnati, Raymond
Walters College
9555 Plainfield Rd.
Blue Ash 45236

OREGON

Concorde Career Institute
1827 Northeast 44th Ave.
Portland 97213

Oregon Health Science University
3181 Southwest Sam Jackson Park Rd.
Portland 97201

Portland Community College
P.O. Box 19000
Portland 97280-0990

PENNSYLVANIA

Community College of Allegheny
County, Pittsburgh
800 Allegheny Ave.
Pittsburgh 15233-1895

Crozer-Chester Medical Center, Allied
Health Program
One Medical Center Blvd.
Upland 19013

Gannon University
109 West Sixth St.
Erie 16541

Harrisburg Area Community College,
Harrisburg
One Hacc Dr.
Harrisburg 17110

North Hills School of Health
Occupations
1500 Northway Mall
Pittsburgh 15237

Northampton County Area Community
College
3835 Green Pond Rd.
Bethlehem 18020-7599

Ohio Valley Hospital School of Nursing
25 Heckel Rd.
McKees Rocks 15136

RHODE ISLAND

Community College of Rhode Island
400 East Ave.
Warwick 02886-1807

Rhode Island Hospital School of
Nuclear Medicine
593 Eddy St.
Providence 02903

Rhode Island Hospital School of
Radiologic Technology
593 Eddy St.
Providence 02903

SOUTH CAROLINA

Greenville Technical College
P.O. Box 5616, Station B
Greenville 29606-5616

Horry-Georgetown Technical College
P.O. Box 1966
Conway 29526

Trident Technical College
P.O. Box 118067
Charleston 29423-8067

TENNESSEE

Chattanooga State Technical
Community College
4501 Amnicola Hwy.
Chattanooga 37406

East Tennessee State University
P.O. Box 70734
Johnson City 37614-0734

Roane State Community College
276 Patton Ln.
Harriman 37748

Shelby State Community College
P.O. Box 40568
Memphis 38174-0568

TEXAS

Amarillo College
P.O. Box 447
Amarillo 79178

Austin Community College
5930 Middle Fiskville Rd.
Austin 78752

El Centro College
Main and Lamar
Dallas 75202

El Paso Community College
P.O. Box 20500
El Paso 79998

Galveston College
4015 Ave. Q
Galveston 77550

Houston Community College System
22 Waugh Dr.
Houston 77270-7849

Lamar University, Beaumont
P.O. Box 10001, 4400 Mlk
Beaumont 77710

McLennan Community College
1400 College Dr.
Waco 76708

Midwestern State University
3410 Taft Blvd.
Wichita Falls 76308-2099

Saint Philip's College
1801 Martin Luther King Dr.
San Antonio 78203

San Jacinto College, Central Campus
8060 Spencer Hwy.
Pasadena 77505

Ultrasound Diagnostic School
1333 Corporate Dr., Ste. 200
Irving 75038

UTAH

Utah Valley Hospital School of Radiogic
Technology
1034 North Fifth West St.
Provo 84603

VIRGINIA

Tidewater Community College
121 College Pl.
Norfolk 23510

WASHINGTON

Bellevue Community College
3000 Landerholm Circle SE
Bellevue 98007-6484

Tacoma Community College
5900 South 12th St.
Tacoma 98465

Yakima Valley Community College
P.O. Box 1647
Yakima 98907

WEST VIRGINIA

West Virginia University Hospital
School of Radiation Technology
Medical Center Dr., P.O. Box 8062
Morgantown 26506-8062

WISCONSIN

Mercy Medical Center School of
Radiologic Technology
631 Hazel St.
Oshkosh 54902

Milwaukee Area Technical College
700 West State St.
Milwaukee 53233-1443

Saint Joseph's Hospital Histologic
Technician Program
611 Saint Joseph's Ave.
Marshfield 54449

Saint Luke's Medical Center, School of
Diagnostic Medical Sonography
2900 West Oklahoma Ave.
Milwaukee 53215

Registered Nursing

ALABAMA

Bishop State Community College
351 North Broad St.
Mobile 36608

Gadsden State Community College
1001 George Wallace Dr.
Gadsden 35902-0227

George C Wallace State Community
College, Dothan
Rte. 6, Box 62
Dothan 36303-9234

George C Wallace State Community
College, Hanceville
801 Main St. NW
Hanceville 35077-2000

George C Wallace State Community
College, Selma
3000 Earl Goodwin Pkwy.
Selma 36702

Jefferson Davis Community College
220 Alco Dr.
Brewton 36426

Jefferson State Community College
2601 Carson Rd.
Birmingham 35215-3098

John C Calhoun State Community
College
Hwy. 31 N
Decatur 35602

Northeast Alabama State Community
College
Hwy. 35 W
Rainsville 35986

Samford University
800 Lakeshore Dr., Ste. 2240
Birmingham 35229-2240

Shelton State Community College
9500 Old Greensboro Rd.
Tuscaloosa 35405

Southern Union State Community
College
P.O. Box 1000
Wadley 36276

Troy State University, Main Campus
University Ave.
Troy 36082

University of Alabama at Birmingham,
Walker College
1411 Indiana Ave.
Jasper 35501

University of Mobile
P.O. Box 13220
Mobile 36663-0220

University of West Alabama
Station One
Livingston 35470

ALASKA

University of Alaska, Anchorage
3211 Providence Dr.
Anchorage 99508

ARIZONA

Arizona Western College
P.O. Box 929
Yuma 85366

Central Arizona College
8470 North Overfield Rd.
Coolidge 85228-9778

Cochise College
4190 West Hwy. 80
Douglas 85607-9724

Gateway Community College
108 North 40th St.
Phoenix 85034

Glendale Community College
6000 West Olive Ave.
Glendale 85302

Mesa Community College
1833 West Southern Ave.
Mesa 85202

Mohave Community College
1971 Jagerson Ave.
Kingman 86401

Phoenix College
1202 West Thomas Rd.
Phoenix 85013

Pima Community College
2202 West Anklam Rd.
Tucson 85709-0001

Scottsdale Community College
9000 East Chaparral Rd.
Scottsdale 85253

Yavapai College
1100 East Sheldon St.
Prescott 86301

ARKANSAS

Arkansas State University, Main
Campus
P.O. Box 790
State University 72467

Arkansas Valley Technical Institute
P.O. Box 506, Hwy. 23 N
Ozark 72949

Baptist Schools of Nursing and Allied
Health
11900 College Glenn Rd., Ste. 1000
Little Rock 72210-2820

East Arkansas Community College
1700 Newcastle Rd.
Forrest City 72335

Garland County Community College
100 College Dr.
Hot Springs 71913

Jefferson School of Nursing
1515 West 42nd Ave.
Pine Bluff 71603

Mississippi County Community College
P.O. Box 1109
Blytheville 72316-1109

North Arkansas College
1515 Pioneer Dr.
Harrison 72601

Phillips Community College of the
University of Arkansas
Box 785
Helena 72342

Southern Arkansas University, Main
Campus
SAU Box 1288
Magnolia 71753

University of Arkansas at Fayetteville
Administration Bldg. 422
Fayetteville 72701

University of Arkansas at Little Rock
2801 South University Ave.
Little Rock 72204

University of Arkansas at Monticello
P.O. Box 3598
Monticello 71656

Westark College
P.O. Box 3649
Fort Smith 72913

CALIFORNIA

Allan Hancock College
800 South College Dr.
Santa Maria 93454

American River College
4700 College Oak Dr.
Sacramento 95841

Antelope Valley College
3041 West Ave. K
Lancaster 93536

Bakersfield College
1801 Panorama Dr.
Bakersfield 93305-1299

Cabrillo College
6500 Soquel Dr.
Aptos 95003

Cerritos College
11110 Alondra Blvd.
Norwalk 90650

Chabot College
25555 Hesperian Blvd.
Hayward 94545

Chaffey Community College
5885 Haven Ave.
Rancho Cucamonga 91737-3002

City College of San Francisco
50 Phelan Ave.
San Francisco 94112

College of Marin
835 College Ave.
Kentfield 94904

College of San Mateo
1700 West Hillsdale Blvd.
San Mateo 94402

College of the Canyons
26455 Rockwell Canyon Rd.
Santa Clarita 91355

College of the Desert
43-500 Monterey St.
Palm Desert 92260

College of the Redwoods
7351 Tompkins Hill Rd.
Eureka 95501-9302

College of the Sequoias
915 South Mooney Blvd.
Visalia 93277

Compton Community College
1111 East Artesia Blvd.
Compton 90221

Contra Costa College
2600 Mission Bell Dr.
San Pablo 94806

Crafton Hills College
11711 Sand Canyon Rd.
Yucaipa 92399-1799

Cuesta College
P.O. Box 8106
San Luis Obispo 93403-8106

De Anza College
21250 Stevens Creek Blvd.
Cupertino 95014

El Camino College
16007 Crenshaw Blvd.
Torrance 90506

Fresno City College
1101 East University Ave.
Fresno 93741

Gavilan College
5055 Santa Teresa Blvd.
Gilroy 95020

Glendale Community College
1500 North Verdugo Rd.
Glendale 91208-2894

Golden West College
15744 Golden West
Huntington Beach 92647

Grossmont College
8800 Grossmont College Dr.
El Cajon 92020

Hartnell College
156 Homestead Ave.
Salinas 93901

Imperial Valley College
P.O. Box 158
Imperial 92251-0158

Loma Linda University
Loma Linda 92350

Long Beach City College
4901 East Carson St.
Long Beach 90808

Los Angeles County Medical Center
School of Nursing
Muir Hall, Rm. 114
Los Angeles 90033-1084

Los Angeles Harbor College
1111 Figueroa Place
Wilmington 90744

Los Angeles Pierce College
6201 Winnetka Ave.
Woodland Hills 91371

Los Angeles Trade Technical College
400 West Washington Blvd.
Los Angeles 90015-4181

Los Angeles Valley College
5800 Fulton Ave.
Van Nuys 91401

Los Medanos College
2700 East Leland Rd.
Pittsburg 94565

Maric College of Medical Careers
3666 Kearny Villa Rd., Ste. 100
San Diego 92123

Merced College
3600 M St.
Merced 95348-2898

Merritt College
12500 Campus Dr.
Oakland 94619

Mira Costa College
One Barnard Dr.
Oceanside 92056-3899

Modesto Junior College
435 College Ave.
Modesto 95350-5800

Monterey Peninsula College
980 Fremont Blvd.
Monterey 93940-4799

Moorpark College
7075 Campus Rd.
Moorpark 93021

Mount Saint Mary's College
12001 Chalon Rd.
Los Angeles 90049

Mount San Antonio College
1100 North Grand
Walnut 91789

Napa Valley College
2277 Napa Vallejo Hwy.
Napa 94558

Ohlone College
43600 Mission Blvd.
Fremont 94539

Pacific Union College
One Angwin Ave.
Angwin 94508-9707

Palomar College
1140 West Mission
San Marcos 92069-1487

Pasadena City College
1570 East Colorado Blvd.
Pasadena 91106

Rancho Santiago College District
1530 West 17th St.
Santa Ana 92706

Rio Hondo College
3600 Workman Mill Rd.
Whittier 90601-1699

Riverside Community College
4800 Magnolia Ave.
Riverside 92506-1299

Sacramento City College
3835 Freeport Blvd.
Sacramento 95822

San Diego City College
1313 12th Ave.
San Diego 92101

San Joaquin Delta College
5151 Pacific Ave.
Stockton 95207

Santa Barbara City College
721 Cliff Dr.
Santa Barbara 93109-2394

Santa Monica College
1900 Pico Blvd.
Santa Monica 90405-1628

Santa Rosa Junior College
1501 Mendocino Ave.
Santa Rosa 95401-4395

Shasta College
P.O. Box 496006
Redding 96049

Sierra College
5000 Rocklin Rd.
Rocklin 95677

Solano County Community College
District
4000 Suisun Valley Rd.
Suisun 94585-3197

Southwestern College
900 Otay Lakes Rd.
Chula Vista 92010

Ventura College
4667 Telegraph Rd.
Ventura 93003

Victor Valley College
18422 Bear Valley Rd.
Victorville 92392-9699

Yuba College
2088 North Beale Rd.
Marysville 95901

COLORADO

Arapahoe Community College
2500 West College Dr.
Littleton 80160-9002

Community College of Denver
P.O. Box 173363
Denver 80217

Front Range Community College
3645 West 112th Ave.
Westminster 80030

Mesa State College
P.O. Box 2647
Grand Junction 81502

Otero Junior College
1802 Colorado Ave.
La Junta 81050

Pikes Peak Community College
5675 South Academy Blvd.
Colorado Springs 80906-5498

Pueblo College of Business &
Technology
330 Lake Ave.
Pueblo 81004

Pueblo Community College
900 West Orman Ave.
Pueblo 81004

Red Rocks Community College
13300 West Sixth Ave.
Lakewood 80228

Trinidad State Junior College
600 Prospect St.
Trinidad 81082

CONNECTICUT

Bridgeport Hospital School of Nursing
200 Mill Hill Ave.
Bridgeport 06610

Greater Hartford Community College
61 Woodland St.
Hartford 06105-2354

Mattatuck Community College
750 Chase Pkwy.
Waterbury 06708

Mohegan Community College
Mahan Dr., P.O. Box 629
Norwich 06360

Norwalk Community Technical College
188 Richards Ave.
Norwalk 06854

Quinnipiac College
Mount Carmel Ave.
Hamden 06518

St. Vincent's College
2800 Main St.
Bridgeport 06606

Wilcox College of Nursing
28 Crescent St.
Middletown 06457

DELAWARE

Delaware Technical and Community
College, Owens
Box 610
Georgetown 19947

Delaware Technical and Community
College, Stanton, Wilmington
400 Stanton-Christiana Rd.
Newark 19702

FLORIDA

Brevard Community College, Cocoa
Campus
1519 Clearlake Rd.
Cocoa 32922

Broward Community College
225 East Las Olas Blvd.
Fort Lauderdale 33301

Central Florida Community College
3001 Southwest College Rd.
Ocala 34474

Daytona Beach Community College
1200 Volusia Ave.
Daytona Beach 32114

Edison Community College
8099 College Pkwy. SW
Fort Myers 33906-6210

Florida Community College at
Jacksonville
501 West State St.
Jacksonville 32202

Florida Keys Community College
5901 West College Rd.
Key West 33040

Gulf Coast Community College
5230 West Hwy. 98
Panama City 32401

Hillsborough Community College
P.O. Box 31127
Tampa 33631-3127

Indian River Community College
3209 Virginia Ave.
Fort Pierce 34981

Lake City Community College
Rte. 19, Box 1030
Lake City 32025

Lake County Area Vocational-Technical
Center
2001 Kurt St.
Eustis 32726

Lake-Sumter Community College
9501 U.S. Hwy. 441
Leesburg 34788-8751

Manatee Community College
5840 26th St. W
Bradenton 34207

Miami-Dade Community College
300 Northeast Second Ave.
Miami 33132

North Florida Community College
Turner Davis Dr.
Madison 32340

North Technical Education Center
7071 Garden Rd.
Riviera Beach 33404

Palm Beach Community College
4200 Congress Ave.
Lake Worth 33461

Pasco-Hernando Community College
36727 Blanton Rd.
Dade City 33525-7599

Pensacola Junior College
1000 College Blvd.
Pensacola 32504

Pinellas Technical Education Center
901 34th St. S
Saint Petersburg 33711

Polk Community College
999 Ave. H NE
Winter Haven 33881

Saint Petersburg Junior College
8580 66th St. N
Pinellas Park 34665

Santa Fe Community College
3000 Northwest 83rd St.
Gainesville 32606

Seminole Community College
100 Weldon Blvd.
Sanford 32773-6199

Tallahassee Community College
444 Appleyard Dr.
Tallahassee 32304-2895

Valencia Community College
P.O. Box 3028
Orlando 32802

GEORGIA

Abraham Baldwin Agricultural College
ABAC 9, 2802 Moore Hwy.
Tifton 31794-2601

Armstrong Atlantic State College
11935 Abercorn St.
Savannah 31419

Augusta State University
2500 Walton Way
Augusta 30904-2200

Clayton College and State University
5900 North Lee St.
Morrow 30260

Columbus State University
4225 University Ave.
Columbus 31907-5645

Dalton College
213 North College Dr.
Dalton 30720

Darton College
2400 Gillionville Rd.
Albany 31707

Dekalb College
3251 Panthersville Rd.
Decatur 30034

Floyd College
P.O. Box 1864
Rome 30162-1864

Georgia Southwestern State University
800 Wheatley St.
Americus 31709-4693

Gordon College
419 College Dr.
Barnesville 30204

Kennesaw State University
1000 Chastain Rd.
Marietta 30061

Lagrange College
601 Broad St.
La Grange 30240

Macon State College
100 College Station Dr.
Macon 31206

Middle Georgia College
1100 Second St. SE
Cochran 31014-1599

North Georgia College and State
  University
College Ave.
Dahlonega 30597

South Georgia College
100 West College Park Dr.
Douglas 31533

HAWAII

Hawaii Community College
200 West Kawili St.
Hilo 96720-4091

Kapiolani Community College
4303 Diamond Head Rd.
Honolulu 96816

Maui Community College
310 Kaahumanu Ave.
Kahului 96732

University of Hawaii at Manoa
2444 Dole St.
Honolulu 96822

IDAHO

Boise State University
1910 University Dr.
Boise 83725

College of Southern Idaho
P.O. Box 1238
Twin Falls 83301

Lewis-Clark State College
500 Eighth Ave.
Lewiston 83501

North Idaho College
1000 West Garden Ave.
Coeur D'Alene 83814

Ricks College
Rexburg 83460-4107

ILLINOIS

Belleville Area College
2500 Carlyle Rd.
Belleville 62221

Black Hawk College
6600 34th Ave.
Moline 61265

Carl Sandburg College
2232 South Lake Storey Rd.
Galesburg 61401

City Colleges of Chicago, Harry S
  Truman College
1145 Wilson Ave.
Chicago 60640

City Colleges of Chicago, Kennedy-King
  College
6800 South Wentworth Ave.
Chicago 60621

City Colleges of Chicago, Malcolm X
  College
1900 West Van Buren
Chicago 60612

City Colleges of Chicago, Olive-Harvey
  College
10001 South Woodlawn Ave.
Chicago 60628

City Colleges of Chicago, Richard J
  Daley College
7500 South Pulaski Rd.
Chicago 60652

College of Du Page
425 22nd St.
Glen Ellyn 60137-6599

College of Lake County
19351 West Washington St.
Grays Lake 60030-1198

Elgin Community College
1700 Spartan Dr.
Elgin 60123

Highland Community College
2998 West Pearl City Rd.
Freeport 61032-9341

Illinois Central College
One College Dr.
East Peoria 61635-0001

Illinois Eastern Community Colleges,
  Olney Central College
305 North West St.
Olney 62450

Illinois Valley Community College
815 North Orlando Smith Ave.
Oglesby 61348-9692

John A Logan College
700 Logan College Rd.
Carterville 62918

Joliet Junior College
1216 Houbolt Ave.
Joliet 60431

Kankakee Community College
P.O. Box 888
Kankakee 60901

Kaskaskia College
27210 College Rd.
Centralia 62801

Kishwaukee College
21193 Malta Rd.
Malta 60150

Lake Land College
5001 Lake Land Blvd.
Mattoon 61938

Lewis and Clark Community College
5800 Godfrey Rd.
Godfrey 62035

Lincoln Land Community College
Shepherd Rd.
Springfield 62194-9256

Methodist Medical Center of Illinois
  School of Nursing
221 Northeast Glen Oak Ave.
Peoria 61636

Moraine Valley Community College
10900 South 88th Ave.
Palos Hills 60465-0937

Morton College
3801 South Central Ave.
Cicero 60804

Oakton Community College
1600 East Golf Rd.
Des Plaines 60016

Parkland College
2400 West Bradley Ave.
Champaign 61821

Prairie State College
202 Halsted St.
Chicago Heights 60411

Ravenswood Hospital Medical Center
  School of Radiologic Technology
4550 North Winchester Ave.
Chicago 60640-5205

Rend Lake College
468 North Ken Graz Pkwy.
Ina 62846

Rock Valley College
3301 North Mulford Rd.
Rockford 61114

Saint Francis Hospital School of
  Nursing
319 Ridge Ave.
Evanston 60202

Shawnee Community College
8364 Shawnee College Rd.
Ullin 62992

South Suburban College
15800 South State St.
South Holland 60473

Southeastern Illinois College
3575 College Rd.
Harrisburg 62946

Trinity School of Surgical Technology
501 Tenth Ave.
Moline 61265

Triton College
2000 Fifth Ave.
River Grove 60171

Waubonsee Community College
IL Rte. 47 at Harter Rd.
Sugar Grove 60554-0901

William Rainey Harper College
1200 West Algonquin Rd.
Palatine 60067-7398

INDIANA

Ball State University
2000 University Ave.
Muncie 47306

Bethel College
1001 West McKinley Ave.
Mishawaka 46545

Indiana State University
210 North Seventh St.
Terre Haute 47809

Indiana University, East
2325 Chester Blvd.
Richmond 47374

Indiana University, Kokomo
2300 South Washington
Kokomo 46902

Indiana University, Northwest
3400 Broadway
Gary 46408

Indiana University, Purdue University,
  Fort Wayne
2101 Coliseum Blvd. E
Fort Wayne 46805

Indiana University, Purdue University,
  Indianapolis
355 North Lansing
Indianapolis 46202

Indiana University, South Bend
1700 Mishawaka Ave.
South Bend 46615

Ivy Tech State College, North Central
1534 West Sample St.
South Bend 46619

Ivy Tech State College, Southeast
590 Ivy Tech Dr.
Madison 47250

Ivy Tech State College, Southwest
3501 First Ave.
Evansville 47710

Ivy Tech State College, Whitewater
P.O. Box 1145
Richmond 47374

Lutheran College of Health Professions
3024 Fairfield Ave.
Fort Wayne 46807

Marian College
3200 Cold Spring Rd.
Indianapolis 46222-1997

Purdue University, Calumet Campus
2233 171st St.
Hammond 46323

Purdue University, North Central
  Campus
1401 South U.S. Hwy. 421
Westville 46391

Saint Elizabeth School of Nursing
1508 Tippecanoe St.
Lafayette 47904-2198

University of Indianapolis
1400 East Hanna Ave.
Indianapolis 46227

University of Southern Indiana
8600 University Blvd.
Evansville 47712

Vincennes University
1002 North First St.
Vincennes 47591

IOWA

Allen Memorial Hospital, School of
Nursing
1825 Logan Ave.
Waterloo 50703

Des Moines Community College
2006 Ankeny Blvd.
Ankeny 50021

Eastern Iowa Community College
District
306 West River Dr.
Davenport 52801-1221

Hawkeye Community College
1501 East Orange Rd.
Waterloo 50704

Indian Hills Community College
525 Grandview
Ottumwa 52501

Iowa Central Community College
330 Ave. M
Fort Dodge 50501

Iowa Lakes Community College
19 South Seventh St.
Estherville 51334

Iowa Methodist School of Nursing
1117 Pleasant St.
Des Moines 50309

Iowa Valley Community College
District
Box 536
Marshalltown 50158

Iowa Western Community College
2700 College Rd., Box 4C
Council Bluffs 51502

Jennie Edmundson Memorial Hospital
School of Nursing
933 East Pierce St., P.O. Box 2C
Council Bluffs 51502

Kirkwood Community College
P.O. Box 2068
Cedar Rapids 52406

Mercy College of Health Sciences
928 6th Ave.
Des Moines 50309

North Iowa Area Community College
500 College Dr.
Mason City 50401

Northeast Iowa Community College,
Calmar
Box 400, Hwy. 150 S
Calmar 52132-0400

Saint Luke's College of Nursing and
Health Sciences
2720 Stone Park Blvd.
Sioux City 51104-0263

Southeastern Community College
Drawer F, 1015 South Gear Ave.
West Burlington 52655-0605

Southwestern Community College
1501 Townline
Creston 50801

Western Iowa Technical Community
College
4647 Stone Ave., P.O. Box 5199
Sioux City 51102-5199

KANSAS

Baker University College of Arts and
Sciences
8th and Grove
Baldwin City 66006

Barton County Community College
245 Northeast 30th Rd.
Great Bend 67530

Butler County Community College
901 South Haverhill Rd.
El Dorado 67042

Cloud County Community College
2221 Campus Dr., Box 1002
Concordia 66901-1002

Colby Community College
1255 South Range
Colby 67701

Dodge City Community College
2501 North 14th Ave.
Dodge City 67801

Fort Scott Community College
2108 South Horton
Fort Scott 66701

Garden City Community College
801 Campus Dr.
Garden City 67846

Hesston College
Box 3000
Hesston 67062

Hutchinson Community College
1300 North Plum St.
Hutchinson 67501

Johnson County Community College
12345 College Blvd.
Overland Park 66210-1299

Kansas City Area Vocational Technical
School
2220 North 59th St.
Kansas City 66104

Kansas City Kansas Community College
7250 State Ave.
Kansas City 66112

Kansas Newman College
3100 McCormick Ave.
Wichita 67213-2097

Kansas Wesleyan University
100 East Claflin
Salina 67401-6196

Labette Community College
200 South 14th
Parsons 67357

Neosho County Community College
800 West 14th St.
Chanute 66720

Seward County Community College
Box 1137
Liberal 67905-1137

KENTUCKY

Ashland Community College
1400 College Dr.
Ashland 41101

Eastern Kentucky University
Lancaster Ave.
Richmond 40475

Elizabethtown Community College
College Street Rd.
Elizabethtown 42701

Hazard Community College
Hazard 41701

Henderson Community College
2660 South Green St.
Henderson 42420

Hopkinsville Community College
North Dr.
Hopkinsville 42240

Jefferson Community College
109 East Broadway
Louisville 40202

Kentucky State University
East Main St.
Frankfort 40601

Kentucky Wesleyan College
3000 Frederica St.
Owensboro 42302-1039

Lexington Community College
Cooper Dr.
Lexington 40506

Madisonville Community College
University Dr.
Madisonville 42431

Maysville Community College
Maysville 41056

Midway College
512 Stephens St.
Midway 40347-1120

Morehead State University
University Blvd.
Morehead 40351

Northern Kentucky University
University Dr.
Highland Heights 41099

Paducah Community College
P.O. Box 7380
Paducah 42002-7380

Prestonsburg Community College
Bert Combs Dr.
Prestonsburg 41653

Somerset Community College
808 Monticello Rd.
Somerset 42501

Southeast Community College
300 College Rd.
Cumberland 40823

Western Kentucky University
One Big Red Way
Bowling Green 42101-3576

LOUISIANA

Baton Rouge General Medical Center
School of Nursing
3616 North Blvd.
Baton Rouge 70806

Huey P Long Technical Institute
303 South Jones St.
Winnfield 71483

Louisiana State University, Alexandria
8100 Hwy. 71 S
Alexandria 71302-9121

Louisiana State University, Eunice
P.O. Box 1129
Eunice 70535

Louisiana State University Medical
Center
433 Bolivar St.
New Orleans 70112

Louisiana Technical University
P.O. Box 3168, Tech Station
Ruston 71272

Nicholls State University
University Station, LA Hwy. 1
Thibodaux 70310

Northwestern State University of
Louisiana
College Ave.
Natchitoches 71497

Our Lady of the Lake College
5345 Brittany Dr.
Baton Rouge 70808

MAINE

Central Maine Medical Center School of
Nursing
300 Main St.
Lewiston 04240

Kennebec Valley Technical College
92 Western Ave.
Fairfield 04937-1367

Northern Maine Technical College
33 Edgemont Dr.
Presque Isle 04769

Southern Maine Technical College
Fort Rd.
South Portland 04106

University of Maine at Augusta
46 University Dr.
Augusta 04330-9410

MARYLAND

Allegany College of Maryland
12401 Willowbrook Rd. SE
Cumberland 21502

Anne Arundel Community College
101 College Pkwy.
Arnold 21012

Baltimore City Community College
2901 Liberty Heights Ave.
Baltimore 21215

Catonsville Community College
800 South Rolling Rd.
Catonsville 21228

Cecil Community College
1000 North East Rd.
North East 21901-1999

Charles County Community College
8730 Mitchell Rd.
La Plata 20646-0910

Essex Community College
7201 Rossville Blvd.
Baltimore 21237

Frederick Community College
7932 Opossumtown Pike
Frederick 21702

Hagerstown Junior College
11400 Robinwood Dr.
Hagerstown 21742-6590

Harford Community College
401 Thomas Run Rd.
Bel Air 21015

Howard Community College
10901 Little Patuxent Pkwy.
Columbia 21044

Montgomery College of Takoma Park
Takoma Ave. and Fenton St.
Takoma Park 20912

Prince Georges Community College
301 Largo Rd.
Largo 23774-2199

Wor-Wic Community College
32000 Campus Dr.
Salisbury 21801-7131

MASSACHUSETTS

Atlantic Union College
338 Main St.
South Lancaster 01561

Bay State Medical Center School of
Nursing
759 Chestnut St.
Springfield 01199

Berkshire Community College
1350 West St.
Pittsfield 01201-5786

Bristol Community College
777 Elsbree St.
Fall River 02720

Bunker Hill Community College
250 New Rutherford Ave.
Boston 02129

Cape Cod Community College
2240 Iyanough Rd.
West Barnstable 02668-1599

Fisher College
118 Beacon St.
Boston 02116

Framingham Union School of Nursing,
Merrowest Medical Center
85 Lincoln St.
Framingham 01702

Greenfield Community College
One College Dr.
Greenfield 01301-9739

Holyoke Community College
303 Homestead Ave.
Holyoke 01040

Laboure College
2120 Dorchester Ave.
Boston 02124-5698

Massachusetts Bay Community College
50 Oakland St.
Wellesley Hills 02181

Massasoit Community College
One Massasoit Blvd.
Brockton 02402

Middlesex Community College
Springs Rd.
Bedford 01730

Mount Wachusett Community College
444 Green St.
Gardner 01440

North Shore Community College
One Ferncroft Rd.
Danvers 01923

Northern Essex Community College
Elliott Way
Haverhill 01830-2399

Quincy College
34 Coddington St.
Quincy 02169

Quinsigamond Community College
670 West Boylston St.
Worcester 01606

Saint Elizabeth's Hospital School of
Nursing
159 Washington St.
Brighton 02135

Somerville Hospital School of Nursing
125 Lowell St.
Somerville 02143

Springfield Technical Community
College
One Armory Square
Springfield 01105

MICHIGAN

Alpena Community College
666 Johnson St.
Alpena 49707

Bay De Noc Community College
2001 North Lincoln Rd.
Escanaba 49289

Bronson Methodist Hospital
252 East Lovell St.
Kalamazoo 49007

Delta College
University Ctr.
University Center 48710

Ferris State University
901 South State St.
Big Rapids 49307

Grand Rapids Community College
143 Bostwick Ave. NE
Grand Rapids 49503-3295

Great Lakes Junior College of Business,
Saginaw
310 South Washington Ave.
Saginaw 48607

Henry Ford Community College
5101 Evergreen Rd.
Dearborn 48128

Henry Ford Hospital School of
Radiologic Technology
2799 West Grand Blvd.
Detroit 48202

Jackson Community College
2111 Emmons Rd.
Jackson 49201-8399

Kalamazoo Valley Community College
6767 West O Ave.
Kalamazoo 49009

Kellogg Community College
450 North Ave.
Battle Creek 49017

Kirtland Community College
10775 North Saint Helen Rd.
Roscommon 48653

Lake Michigan College
2755 East Napier Ave.
Benton Harbor 49022-8099

Lansing Community College
419 North Capitol Ave.
Lansing 48901-7210

Macomb Community College
14500 Twelve Mile Rd.
Warren 48093-3896

Mid Michigan Community College
1375 South Clare Ave.
Harrison 48625

Monroe County Community College
1555 South Raisinville Rd.
Monroe 48161

Montcalm Community College
2800 College Dr.
Sidney 48885

Mott Community College
1401 East Court St.
Flint 48503

Muskegon Community College
221 South Quarterline Rd.
Muskegon 49442

North Central Michigan College
1515 Howard St.
Petoskey 49770

Northwestern Michigan College
1701 East Front St.
Traverse City 49686

Oakland Community College
2480 Opdyke Rd.
Bloomfield Hills 48304-2266

Saint Clair County Community College
P.O. Box 5015, 323 Erie
Port Huron 48061-5015

Schoolcraft College
18600 Haggerty Rd.
Livonia 48152

Southwestern Michigan College
58900 Cherry Grove Rd.
Dowagiac 49047-9793

Suomi College
601 Quincy St.
Hancock 49930

University of Detroit, Mercy
P.O. Box 19900
Detroit 48219-0900

Washtenaw Community College
P.O. Drawer 1
Ann Arbor 48016-1610

Wayne County Community College
801 West Fort St.
Detroit 48226

West Shore Community College
3000 North Stiles Rd.
Scottville 49454

MINNESOTA

Anoka-Ramsey Community College
11200 Mississippi Blvd.
Coon Rapids 55433-3470

Central Lakes College, Brainerd
501 West College Dr.
Brainerd 56401

Century Community and Technical
College
3300 Century Ave. N
White Bear Lake 55110

College of Saint Catherine, Minneapolis
601 25th Ave. S
Minneapolis 55454

Hibbing Community College, A
Technical and Community College
1515 East 25th St.
Hibbing 55746

Inver Hills Community College
2500 80th St. E
Inver Grove Heights 55076

Minneapolis Community and Technical
College
1501 Hennepin Ave.
Minneapolis 55403

Normandale Community College
9700 France Ave. S
Bloomington 55431

North Hennepin Community College
7411 85th Ave. N
Brooklyn Park 55445

Northland Community and Technical
College
Hwy. 1 E
Thief River Falls 56701

Ridgewater College, A Community and
Technical College, Willmar
P.O. Box 1097
Willmar 56201

Riverland Community College
1900 Eighth Ave. NW
Austin 55912

Rochester Community and Technical
College
851 30th Ave. SE
Rochester 55904-4999

MISSISSIPPI

Alcorn State University
P.O. Box 359
Lorman 39096

Hinds Community College, Raymond
Campus
Raymond 39154

Holmes Community College
Hill St.
Goodman 39079

Itawamba Community College
602 West Hill St.
Fulton 38843

Jones County Junior College
900 South Court St.
Ellisville 39437

Meridian Community College
910 Hwy. 19 N
Meridian 39307

Mississippi Delta Community College
P.O. Box 668
Moorhead 38761

Mississippi Gulf Coast Community
College
Central Office, P.O. Box 67
Perkinston 39573

Mississippi University for Women
P.O. Box W1600
Columbus 39701

Northeast Mississippi Community
College
Cunningham Blvd.
Booneville 38829

Northwest Mississippi Community
College
510 North Panola, Hwy. 51 N
Senatobia 38668

Pearl River Community College
Station A
Poplarville 39470

Southwest Mississippi Community
College
College Dr.
Summit 39666

MISSOURI

Barnes Jewish School of Radiologic
Technology
One Barnes Hospital Plaza
Saint Louis 63110

Central Methodist College
411 Central Methodist Square
Fayette 65248

East Central College
P.O. Box 529
Union 63084

Hannibal-Lagrange College
2800 Palmyra Rd.
Hannibal 63401

Jefferson College
1000 Viking Dr.
Hillsboro 63050

Lincoln University
820 Chestnut
Jefferson City 65102-0029

Lutheran Medical Center School of
Nursing
3547 South Jefferson Ave.
Saint Louis 63118

Mineral Area College
P.O. Box 1000
Park Hills 63601-1000

Missouri Baptist Medical Center School
of Nursing
3015 North Ballas Rd.
Saint Louis 63131

Missouri Southern State College
3950 East Newman Rd.
Joplin 64801-1595

Moberly Area Community Co llege
101 College Ave.
Moberly 65270

North Central Missouri College
1301 Main St.
Trenton 64683

Park College
8700 River Park Dr.
Parkville 64152-3795

Penn Valley Community College
3201 Southwest Trafficway
Kansas City 64111

Saint Charles County Community
College
4601 Mid Rivers Mall Dr.
Saint Peter's 63376

Saint John's School of Nursing
4431 South Fremont
Springfield 65804-2263

Saint Louis Community College, Forest
Park
5600 Oakland Ave.
Saint Louis 63110

Saint Luke's College
4426 Wornall Rd.
Kansas City 64111

Sanford-Brown Business College
12006 Manchester Rd.
Des Peres 63131

Southeast Missouri State University
One University Plaza
Cape Girardeau 63701

Southwest Missouri State University,
West Plains
128 Garfield
West Plains 65775

State Fair Community College
3201 West 16th
Sedalia 65301-2199

Three Rivers Community College
Three Rivers Blvd.
Poplar Bluff 63901

Waynesville Technical Academy
810 Roosevelt
Waynesville 65583

MONTANA

Miles Community College
2715 Dickinson
Miles City 59301

Montana State University, Northern
300 West 11th St.
Havre 59501

Salish Kootenai College
P.O. Box 117
Pablo 59855

NEBRASKA

Bryan Memorial Hospital School of
Nursing
5000 Sumner St.
Lincoln 68506-1398

Central Community College Area
P.O. Box 4903
Grand Island 68802

College of Saint Mary
1901 South 72nd St.
Omaha 68124

Metropolitan Community College Area
5300 North 30th St.
Omaha 68111

Northeast Community College
801 East Benjamin, P.O. Box 469
Norfolk 68702-0469

Southeast Community College Area
1111 O St., Ste. 111
Lincoln 68520

NEVADA

Community College of Southern
Nevada
3200 East Cheyenne Ave.
Las Vegas 89030

Truckee Meadows Community College
7000 Dandini Blvd.
Reno 89512

Western Nevada Community College
2201 West College Pkwy.
Carson City 89703

NEW HAMPSHIRE

New Hampshire Community Technical
College, Berlin/Laco
2020 Riverside Dr.
Berlin 03570

New Hampshire Community Technical
College, Manchester/Stratham
1066 Front St.
Manchester 03102

New Hampshire Technical Institute
11 Institute Dr.
Concord 03301

Rivier College
429 Main St.
Nashua 03060

NEW JERSEY

Ann May School of Nursing, Jersey
Shore Medical Center
1945 Rte. 33
Neptune 07754

Atlantic Community College
5100 Black Horse Pike
Mays Landing 08330-2699

Bergen Community College
400 Paramus Rd.
Paramus 07652

Brookdale Community College
765 Newman Springs Rd.
Lincroft 07738-1599

Burlington County College
Rte. 530
Pemberton 08068

Camden County College
P.O. Box 200
Blackwood 08012

Charles E Gregory School of Nursing
Old Bridge Medical Arts. Bldg. 1
Hospital
Old Bridge 08857

County College of Morris
214 Center Grove Rd.
Randolph 07869

Cumberland County College
P.O. Box 517, College Dr.
Vineland 08360

Englewood Hospital Medical Center
School of Radiology
36 Engle St.
Englewood 07631

Essex County College
303 University Ave.
Newark 07102

Felician College
260 South Main St.
Lodi 07644

Gloucester County College
1400 Tanyard Rd.
Sewell 08080

Helene Fuld School of Nursing
832 Brunswick Ave.
Trenton 08638

Holy Name Hospital School of Nursing
690 Teaneck Rd.
Teaneck 07666

Mercer County Community College
1200 Old Trenton Rd.
Trenton 08690

Mercer Medical Center School of
Nursing
446 Bellevue Ave., Box 1658
Trenton 08607

Mountainside Hospital School of
Nursing
One Bay Ave.
Montclair 07042

Muhlenberg Regional Medical Center,
School of Nursing
Park Ave. and Randolph Rd.
Plainfield 07061

Ocean County College
College Dr.
Toms River 08753

Our Lady of Lourdes School of Nursing
1565 Vesper Blvd.
Camden 08103

Passaic County Community College
One College Blvd.
Paterson 07505-1179

Raritan Valley Community College
P.O. Box 3300, Lamington Rd.
Somerville 08876

Saint Francis Medical Center School of
Nursing
601 Hamilton Ave.
Trenton 08629-1986

Union County College
1033 Springfield Ave.
Cranford 07016

NEW MEXICO

Albuquerque Technical Vocational
Institute
525 Buena Vista SE
Albuquerque 87106

Clovis Community College
417 Schepps Blvd.
Clovis 88101

Eastern New Mexico University, Roswell
Campus
52 University Blvd., Administration Ctr.
Roswell 88202

New Mexico Junior College
5317 Lovington Hwy.
Hobbs 88240

New Mexico State University,
Alamogordo
Box 477, 2400 North Scenic Dr.
Alamogordo 88310

New Mexico State University, Carlsbad
1500 University Dr.
Carlsbad 88220

New Mexico State University, Main
Campus
Box 30001, Department 3Z, Weddell Dr.
Las Cruces 88003

San Juan College
4601 College Blvd.
Farmington 87402

University of New Mexico, Gallup
Campus
200 College Rd.
Gallup 87301

NEW YORK

Adirondack Community College
Bay Rd.
Queensbury 12804

Arnot-Ogden Medical Center School of
Nursing
600 Roe Ave.
Elmira 14905

Broome Community College
P.O. Box 1017
Binghamton 13902

Catholic Medical Center School of
Nursing
175-05 Horace Harding Expy.
Fresh Meadows 11365

Cayuga County Community College
Franklin St.
Auburn 13021

Clinton Community College
136 Clinton Point Dr.
Plattsburgh 12901

Cochran School of Nursing
967 North Broadway, Andrus Pavillion,
Saint John's Riverside Hospital
Yonkers 10701

Columbia-Greene Community College
4400 Rte. 23
Hudson 12534

Corning Community College
Spencer Hill
Corning 14830

Crouse Hospital School of Nursing
736 Irving Ave.
Syracuse 13210

CUNY Borough of Manhattan
Community College
199 Chambers St.
New York 10007

CUNY Bronx Community College
West 181st St. & University Ave.
Bronx 10453

CUNY College of Staten Island
2800 Victory Blvd.
Staten Island 10314

CUNY Kingsborough Community
College
2001 Oriental Blvd.
Brooklyn 11235

CUNY La Guardia Community College
31-10 Thomson Ave.
Long Island City 11101

CUNY New York City Technical College
300 Jay St.
Brooklyn 11201

CUNY Queensborough Community
College
56th Ave. Springfield Blvd.
New York 11364

Dorothea Hopfer School of Nursing,
Mount Vernon Hospital
53 Valentine St.
Mount Vernon 10550

Dutchess Community College
53 Pendell Rd.
Poughkeepsie 12601

Ellis Hospital School of Nursing
1101 Nott St.
Schenectady 12308

Erie Community College, City Campus
121 Ellicott St.
Buffalo 14203

Erie Community College, North
Campus
Main St. and Youngs Rd.
Williamsville 14221

Finger Lakes Community College
4355 Lake Shore Dr.
Canandaigua 14424

Fulton-Montgomery Community
College
2805 State Hwy. 67
Johnstown 12095

Genesee Community College
One College Rd.
Batavia 14020

Helene Fuld School of Nursing
1879 Madison Ave.
New York 10035

Hudson Valley Community College
80 Vandenburgh Ave.
Troy 12180

Iona College
715 North Ave.
New Rochelle 10801

Jamestown Community College
525 Falconer St.
Jamestown 14701

Jefferson Community College
Outer Coffeen St.
Watertown 13601

Long Island College Hospital School of
Nursing
397 Hicks St.
Brooklyn 11201

Maria College of Albany
700 New Scotland Ave.
Albany 12208

Millard Fillmore Hospital School of
Nursing
Three Gates Circle
Buffalo 14209

Mohawk Valley Community College,
Utica Branch
1101 Sherman Dr.
Utica 13501

Monroe Community College
1000 East Henrietta Rd.
Rochester 14623

Nassau Community College
One Education Dr.
Garden City 11530

Niagara County Community College
3111 Saunders Settlement Rd.
Sanborn 14132

North Country Community College
20 Winona Ave., P.O. Box 89
Saranac Lake 12983

Onondaga Community College
4941 Onondaga Rd.
Syracuse 13215

Orange County Community College
115 South St.
Middletown 10940

Pace University, Pleasantville Briarcliff
Bedford Rd.
Pleasantville 10570

Phillips Beth Israel School of Nursing
310 East 22nd St.
New York 10010

Regents College, University of the State
of New York
Seven Columbia Cir.
Albany 12203

Rockland Community College
145 College Rd.
Suffern 10901

Saint Elizabeth College of Nursing
2215 Genessee St.
Utica 13501

Saint Joseph's Hospital Health Center
School of Nursing
206 Prospect Ave.
Syracuse 13203

Samaritan Hospital School of Nursing
2215 Burdett Ave.
Troy 12180

Sisters of Charity Hospital School of
Nursing
2157 Main St.
Buffalo 14214

St. Vincent's Medical Center of
Richmond, School of Nursing
Two Gridley Ave.
Staten Island 10303

Suffolk County Community College,
Ammerman Campus
533 College Rd.
Selden 11784

Suffolk County Community College,
Western Campus
Crooked Hill Rd.
Brentwood 11717

Sullivan County Community College
1000 Le Roy Rd.
Loch Sheldrake 12759-4002

SUNY College of Agriculture &
Technology at Morrisville
Morrisville 13408

SUNY College of Technology at Alfred
Alfred 14802

SUNY College of Technology at Canton
Cornell Dr.
Canton 13617

SUNY College of Technology at Delhi
Delhi 13753

SUNY College of Technology at
Farmingdale
Melville Rd.
Farmingdale 11735-1021

SUNY Ulster County Community
College
Cottekill Rd.
Stone Ridge 12484

SUNY Westchester Commmunity
College
75 Grasslands Rd.
Valhalla 10595

Tompkins-Cortland Community
College
170 North St.
Dryden 13053

Trocaire College
360 Choate Ave.
Buffalo 14220

NORTH CAROLINA

Alamance Community College
P.O. Box 8000
Graham 27253

Asheville Buncombe Technical
Community College
340 Victoria Rd.
Asheville 28801

Beaufort County Community College
Box 1069
Washington 27889

Caldwell Community College and
Technical Institute
Box 600
Lenoir 28645

Cape Fear Community College
411 North Front St.
Wilmington 28401

Catawba Valley Community College
2550 Hwy. 70 SE
Hickory 28602-0699

Central Carolina Community College
1105 Kelly Dr.
Sanford 27330

Central Piedmont Community College
P.O. Box 35009
Charlotte 28235-5009

College of the Albemarle
1208 North Road St.
Elizabeth City 27906-2327

Craven Community College
800 College Ct.
New Bern 28562

Davidson County Community College
297 Davidson Community College Rd.
Lexington 27292

Durham Technical Community College
1637 Lawson St.
Durham 27703

Edgecombe Community College
2009 West Wilson St.
Tarboro 27886

Fayetteville Technical Community
College
2201 Hull Rd.
Fayetteville 28303-0236

Forsyth Technical Community College
2100 Silas Creek Pkwy.
Winston-Salem 27103

Gardner-Webb University
Main St.
Boiling Springs 28017

Gaston College
201 Hwy. 321 S
Dallas 28034

Guilford Technical Community College
Box 309
Jamestown 27282

Halifax Community College
P.O. Drawer 809
Weldon 27890

James Sprunt Community College
P.O. Box 398
Kenansville 28349

Johnston Community College
P.O. Box 2350
Smithfield 27577-2350

Mayland Community College
P.O. Box 547
Spruce Pine 28777

Mercy School of Nursing
1921 Vail Ave.
Charlotte 28207

Mitchell Community College
500 West Broad
Statesville 28677

Nash Community College
P.O. Box 7488
Rocky Mount 27804

Piedmont Community College
P.O. Box 1197
Roxboro 27573

Pitt Community College
Hwy. 11 S, P.O. Drawer 7007
Greenville 27835-7007

Presbyterian Hospital School of
Nursing
1901 East Fifth St.
Charlotte 28204

Randolph Community College
629 Industrial Park Ave.
Asheboro 27204

Robeson Community College
P.O. Box 1420
Lumberton 28359

Rockingham Community College
P.O. Box 38, Hwy. 65W, County Home
Rd.
Wentworth 27375-0038

Rowan-Cabarrus Community College
Box 1595
Salisbury 28145-1595

Sampson Community College
P.O. Box 318
Clinton 28329-0318

Sandhills Community College
2200 Airport Rd.
Pinehurst 28374

Southeastern Community College
4564 Chadburn Hwy.
Whiteville 28472

Stanly Community College
141 College Dr.
Albemarle 28001

Surry Community College
P.O. Box 304
Dobson 27017-0304

Vance-Granville Community College
P.O. Box 917, State Rd. 1126
Henderson 27536

Wake Technical Community College
9101 Fayetteville Rd.
Raleigh 27603-5696

Watts School of Nursing
3643 North Roxboro St.
Durham 27704-2763

Wayne Community College
3000 Wayne Memorial Dr.
Goldsboro 27533-8002

Western Piedmont Community College
1001 Burkemont Ave.
Morganton 28655-9978

Wilson Technical Community College
902 Herring Ave.
Wilson 27893

OHIO

Ashtabula County Joint Vocational
School
1565 State Rte. 167
Jefferson 44047

Aultman Hospital School of Nursing
2600 Sixth St. SW
Canton 44710-1797

Belmont Technical College
120 Fox Shannon Place
Saint Clairsville 43950

Central Ohio Technical College
1179 University Dr.
Newark 43055-1767

Christ Hospital School of Nursing
2139 Auburn Ave.
Cincinnati 45219

Cincinnati State Technical and
Community College
3520 Central Pkwy.
Cincinnati 45223

Clark State Community College
570 East Leffel Ln.
Springfield 45505

Columbus State Community College
550 East Spring St.
Columbus 43216

Community Hospital School of Nursing
330 South Burnett Rd.
Springfield 45505

Cuyahoga Community College District
700 Carnegie Ave.
Cleveland 44115-2878

Edison State Community College
1973 Edison Dr.
Piqua 45356

Fairview General Hospital School of
Nursing
18101 Lorain Ave.
Cleveland 44111

Good Samaritan Hospital School of
Nursing
375 Dixmyth Ave.
Cincinnati 45220

Hocking Technical College
3301 Hocking Pkwy.
Nelsonville 45764

Kent State University, Ashtabula
Regional Campus
3325 West 13th St.
Ashtabula 44004

Kent State University, East Liverpool
Regional Campus
400 East Fourth St.
East Liverpool 43920

Kettering College of Medical Arts
3737 Southern Blvd.
Kettering 45429-1299

Knox County Career Center
306 Martinsburg Rd.
Mount Vernon 43050

Lakeland Community College
7700 Clocktower Dr.
Mentor 44060-5198

Lima Technical College
4240 Campus Dr.
Lima 45804

Lorain County Community College
1005 North Abbe Rd.
Elyria 44035

Mansfield General Hospital School of
Nursing
335 Glessner Ave.
Mansfield 44903-2265

Marion Technical College
1467 Mount Vernon Ave.
Marion 43302-5694

Mercy College of Northwest Ohio
2238 Jefferson Ave.
Toledo 43624-1197

Meridia Huron School of Nursing
13951 Terrace Rd.
Cleveland 44112-4399

Miami University, Oxford
500 High St.
Oxford 45056

North Central Technical College
2441 Kenwood Circle, P.O. Box 698
Mansfield 44901

Northwest State Community College
22-600 South Rte. 34
Archbold 43502-9542

Ohio University, Zanesville Branch
1425 Newark Rd.
Zanesville 43701

Owens Community College
39335 Oregon Rd.
Toledo 43699-1947

Providence Hospital School of Nursing
1912 Hayes Ave.
Sandusky 44870-4788

Queen City Vocational Center
425 Ezzard Charles Dr.
Cincinnati 45203

Saint Elizabeth Health Center School of
Nurse Anesthesiology Inc.
1044 Belmont Ave.
Youngstown 44501-1790

Saint Thomas Medical Center School of
Nursing
41 Arch St.
Akron 44304

Saint Vincent Medical Center School of
Nursing
2201 Cherry St.
Toledo 43608-2603

Shawnee State University
940 Second St.
Portsmouth 45662

Sinclair Community College
444 West Third St.
Dayton 45402

Southern State Community College
100 Hobart Dr.
Hillsboro 45133

University of Cincinnati, Raymond
Walters College
9555 Plainfield Rd.
Blue Ash 45236

University of Rio Grande
North College St.
Rio Grande 45674

University of Toledo
2801 West Bancroft
Toledo 43606

Xavier University
3800 Victory Pkwy.
Cincinnati 45207-1092

OKLAHOMA

Bacone College
2299 Old Bacone Rd.
Muskogee 74403-1597

Cameron University
2800 Gore Blvd.
Lawton 73505

Carl Albert State College
1507 South McKenna
Poteau 74953-5208

Connors State College
Rte. 1, Box 1000
Warner 74469

Eastern Oklahoma State College
1301 West Main St.
Wilburton 74578

Murray State College
One Murray Campus
Tishomingo 73460

Northeastern Oklahoma Agricultural
and Mechanical College
200 I St. NE
Miami 74354

Northern Oklahoma College
Box 310 Tonkawa
Tonkawa 74653

Oklahoma City Community College
7777 South May Ave.
Oklahoma City 73159

Oklahoma State University, Oklahoma
City
900 North Portland
Oklahoma City 73107

Pontotoc Area Vocational Technical
School
601 West 33rd
Ada 74820

Redlands Community College
1300 South Country Club Rd.
El Reno 73036-5304

Rogers University, Claremore
1701 West Will Rogers Blvd.
Claremore 74017

Rose State College
6420 Southeast 15th
Midwest City 73110

Seminole State College
2701 Boren Blvd.
Seminole 74868

Tulsa Community College
6111 East Skelly Dr.
Tulsa 74135

OREGON

Blue Mountain Community College
P.O. Box 100
Pendleton 97801

Central Oregon Community College
2600 Northwest College Way
Bend 97701

Chemeketa Community College
4000 Lancaster Dr. NE
Salem 97305

Clackamas Community College
19600 Molalla Ave.
Oregon City 97045

Clatsop Community College
1653 Jerome St.
Astoria 97103

Lane Community College
4000 East 30th Ave.
Eugene 97405

Linn-Benton Community College
6500 Southwest Pacific Blvd.
Albany 97321

Mount Hood Community College
26000 Southeast Stark St.
Gresham 97030

Portland Community College
P.O. Box 19000
Portland 97280-0990

Rogue Community College
3345 Redwood Hwy.
Grants Pass 97527

Southwestern Oregon Community
College
1988 Newmark Ave.
Coos Bay 97420

Umpqua Community College
P.O. Box 967
Roseburg 97470

PENNSYLVANIA

Abington Memorial Hospital School of
Nursing
2500 Maryland Rd., Ste. 200
Willow Grove 19090-1284

Altoona Hospital School of Medical
Technology
620 Howard Ave.
Altoona 16601-4899

Alvernia College
400 St. Bernardine St.
Reading 19607

Brandywine Hospital School of Nursing
215 Reeceville Rd.
Coatesville 19320-1536

Bucks County Community College
Swamp Rd.
Newtown 18940

Butler County Community College
College Dr. Oak Hills
Butler 16003-1203

Chester County Hospital School of
Nursing
701 East Marshall St.
West Chester 19380

Citizens General Hospital School of
Nursing
651 Fourth Ave.
New Kensington 15068

Clarion University of Pennsylvania
Wood St.
Clarion 16214

Community College of Allegheny
County, Pittsburgh
800 Allegheny Ave.
Pittsburgh 15233-1895

Community College of Beaver County
One Campus Dr.
Monaca 15061

Community College of Philadelphia
1700 Spring Garden St.
Philadelphia 19130

Delaware County Community College
901 South Media Line Rd.
Media 19063-1094

Episcopal Hospital, School of Nursing
100 East Lehigh Ave.
Philadelphia 19125-1098

Gwynedd-Mercy College
Sumneytown Pike
Gwynedd Valley 19437

Harrisburg Area Community College,
Harrisburg
One Hacc Dr.
Harrisburg 17110

Jameson Memorial Hospital
1211 Wilmington Ave.
New Castle 16105-2595

Lancaster General Hospital, Lancaster
Institute for Health Education
143 East Lemon St.
Lancaster 17602

Lehigh Carbon Community College
4525 Education Park Dr.
Schnecksville 18078-2598

Lock Haven University of Pennsylvania
North Fairview St.
Lock Haven 17745-2390

Luzerne County Community College
1333 South Prospect St.
Nanticoke 18634

Mercer County Area Vocational
Technical School
776 Greenville Rd.
Mercer 16137-0152

Montgomery County Community
College
340 Dekalb Pike
Blue Bell 19422

Mount Aloysius College
7373 Admiral Peary Hwy.
Cresson 16630-1999

Northampton County Area Community
College
3835 Green Pond Rd.
Bethlehem 18020-7599

Northeastern Hospital School of
Nursing
2301 East Allegheny Ave. S
Philadelphia 19134

Pennsylvania College of Technology
One College Ave.
Williamsport 17701

Pennsylvania State University, Main
Campus
201 Old Main
University Park 16802

Pottsville Hospital School of Nursing
Washington and Jackson St.
Pottsville 17901

Reading Area Community College
P.O. Box 1706
Reading 19603-1706

Roxborough Memorial Hospital School
of Nursing
5800 Ridge Ave.
Philadelphia 19128

Saint Francis Hospital School of
Nursing
1100 South Mercer St.
New Castle 16101

Saint Luke's Hospital School of Nursing
801 Ostrum
Bethlehem 18015

Saint Vincent Health Center School of
Nursing
P.O. Box 740
Erie 16544

Sewickley Valley Hospital School of
Nursing
720 Blackburn Rd.
Sewickley 15143

Shadyside Hospital School of Nursing
5230 Centre Ave.
Pittsburgh 15232

Sharon Regional Health System School
of Nursing
740 East State St.
Sharon 16146

University of Pittsburgh, Bradford
Campus Dr.
Bradford 16701

Washington Hospital School of Nursing
155 Wilson Ave.
Washington 15301

Western Pennsylvania Hospital School
of Nursing
4900 Friendship Ave.
Pittsburgh 15224

Westmoreland County Community
College
Youngwood 15697-1895

RHODE ISLAND

Community College of Rhode Island
400 East Ave.
Warwick 02886-1807

Saint Joseph Hospital School of Nursing
200 High Service Ave.
North Providence 02904

SOUTH CAROLINA

Florence Darlington Technical College
P.O. Box 100548
Florence 29501-0548

Greenville Technical College
P.O. Box 5616, Station B
Greenville 29606-5616

Midlands Technical College
P.O. Box 2408
Columbia 29202

Orangeburg Calhoun Technical College
3250 Saint Matthew's Rd.
Orangeburg 29118

Piedmont Technical College
P.O. Drawer 1467
Greenwood 29648

Tri-County Technical College
P.O. Box 587
Pendleton 29670

Trident Technical College
P.O. Box 118067
Charleston 29423-8067

University of South Carolina at Aiken
171 University Pkwy.
Aiken 29801

University of South Carolina at
Spartanburg
800 University Way
Spartanburg 29303

SOUTH DAKOTA

Dakota Wesleyan University
1200 West University Ave.
Mitchell 57301-4398

Huron University
333 Ninth St. SW
Huron 57350

Presentation College
1500 North Main
Aberdeen 57401

University of South Dakota
414 East Clark St.
Vermillion 57069-2390

TENNESSEE

Baptist Memorial College of Health
 Sciences
1003 Monroe Ave.
Memphis 38104

Chattanooga State Technical
 Community College
4501 Amnicola Hwy.
Chattanooga 37406

Cleveland State Community College
P.O. Box 3570
Cleveland 37320-3570

Columbia State Community College
P.O. Box 1315
Columbia 38402

Dyersburg State Community College
1510 Lake Rd.
Dyersburg 38024

East Tennessee State University
P.O. Box 70734
Johnson City 37614-0734

Fort Sanders School of Nursing
1915 White Ave.
Knoxville 37916

Jackson State Community College
2046 North Pkwy.
Jackson 38301

Lincoln Memorial University
Cumberland Gap Pkwy.
Harrogate 37752

Methodist Hospital School of Nursing
251 South Claybrook
Memphis 38104

Motlow State Community College
P.O. Box 88100, Ledford Mill Rd.
Tullahoma 37388-8100

Roane State Community College
276 Patton Ln.
Harriman 37748

Saint Joseph Hospital School of Nursing
204 Overton Ave.
Memphis 38105

Shelby State Community College
P.O. Box 40568
Memphis 38174-0568

Southern Adventist University
Box 370, 4881 Taylor Circle
Collegedale 37315-0370

Tennessee State University
3500 John Merritt Blvd.
Nashville 37209-1561

Union University
1050 Union University Dr.
Jackson 38305-9901

Walters State Community College
500 South Davy Crockett Pkwy.
Morristown 37813-6899

TEXAS

Alvin Community College
3110 Mustang Rd.
Alvin 77511

Amarillo College
P.O. Box 447
Amarillo 79178

Angelina College
P.O. Box 1768
Lufkin 75902-1768

Angelo State University
2601 West Ave. N
San Angelo 76909

Austin Community College
5930 Middle Fiskville Rd.
Austin 78752

Baptist Hospital System, Institute of
 Health Education
111 Dallas St.
San Antonio 78205

Blinn College
902 College Ave.
Brenham 77833

Central Texas College
P.O. Box 1800
Killeen 76540-1800

College of the Mainland
1200 Amburn Rd.
Texas City 77591

Collin County Community College,
 Central Park
2200 West University Dr.
McKinney 75070

Del Mar College
101 Baldwin
Corpus Christi 78404-3897

El Centro College
Main and Lamar
Dallas 75202

El Paso Community College
P.O. Box 20500
El Paso 79998

Frank Phillips College
P.O. Box 5118
Borger 79008-5118

Galveston College
4015 Ave. Q
Galveston 77550

Grayson County College
6101 Grayson Dr.
Denison 75020

Houston Baptist University
7502 Fondren Rd.
Houston 77074

Houston Community College System
22 Waugh Dr.
Houston 77270-7849

Howard County Junior College District
1001 Birdwell Ln.
Big Spring 79720

John Peter Smith Healthcare Network
2400 Circle Dr.
Fort Worth 76104

Kilgore College
1100 Broadway
Kilgore 75662-3299

Lamar University, Beaumont
P.O. Box 10001, 4400 Mlk
Beaumont 77710

Lamar University, Orange
410 Front St.
Orange 77630-5899

Laredo Community College
West End Washington St.
Laredo 78040

Lee College
200 Lee Dr.
Baytown 77520-4703

McLennan Community College
1400 College Dr.
Waco 76708

Midland College
3600 North Garfield
Midland 79705

Navarro College
3200 West Seventh
Corsicana 75110

North Harris Montgomery Community
 College District
250 North Sam Houston Pkwy. E, Ste.
 300
Houston 77060

Odessa College
201 West University
Odessa 79764

Paris Junior College
2400 Clarksville St.
Paris 75460

PCI Health Training Center
8101 John Carpenter Fwy.
Dallas 75247

San Antonio College
1300 San Pedro Ave.
San Antonio 78284

San Jacinto College, Central Campus
8060 Spencer Hwy.
Pasadena 77505

South Plains College
1401 College Ave.
Levelland 79336

Southwest Texas Junior College
2401 Garner Field Rd.
Uvalde 78801

Southwestern Adventist College
P.O. Box 567
Keene 76059

Tarrant County Junior College
1500 Houston St.
Fort Worth 76102

Texarkana College
2500 North Robison Rd.
Texarkana 75599

Texas Southmost College
80 Fort Brown
Brownsville 78520

Trinity Valley Community College
500 South Prairieville
Athens 75751

Tyler County Hospital School of
 Nursing
1100 West Bluff
Woodville 75979

Tyler Junior College
1327 South Baxter Ave.
Tyler 75711

The University of Texas, Pan American
1201 West University Dr.
Edinburg 78539-2999

Victoria College
2200 East Red River
Victoria 77901

Wharton County Junior College
911 Boling Hwy.
Wharton 77488

UTAH

Salt Lake Community College
P.O. Box 30808
Salt Lake City 84130

Utah Valley State College
800 West 1200 South
Orem 84058

Weber State University
3750 Harrison Blvd.
Ogden 84408

VERMONT

Norwich University
65 South Main St.
Northfield 05663

University of Vermont and State
 Agricultural College
223 Waterman Building, South Prospect
Burlington 05405-0160

VIRGINIA

Community Hospital of Roanoke Valley
 College of Health Sciences
920 South Jefferson St.
Roanoke 24016

Dabney S Lancaster Community
 College
P.O. Box 1000
Clifton Forge 24422-1000

Danville Community College
1008 South Main St.
Danville 24541

De Paul Medical Center School of
 Nursing
150 Kingsley Ln.
Norfolk 23505

Germanna Community College
2130 Germanna Hwy.
Locust Grove 22508

J Sargeant Reynolds Community
 College
P.O. Box 85622
Richmond 23285-5622

John Tyler Community College
13101 Jefferson Davis Hwy.
Chester 23831-5399

Mountain Empire Community College
Drawer 700
Big Stone Gap 24219

Norfolk State University
2401 Corprew Ave.
Norfolk 23504

Northern Virginia Community College
4001 Wakefield Chapel Rd.
Annandale 22003

Patrick Henry Community College
P.O. Box 5311
Martinsville 24115-5311

Piedmont Virginia Community College
501 College Dr.
Charlottesville 22902

Rappahannock Community College
12745 College Dr.
Glenns 23149

Sentara Norfolk General Hospital
 School of Nursing
600 Gresham Dr., Jenkins Hall
Norfolk 23507

Shenandoah University
1460 University Dr.
Winchester 22601

Southwest Virginia Community College
Box SVCC
Richlands 24641

Thomas Nelson Community College
P.O. Box 9407
Hampton 23670

Tidewater Community College
121 College Pl.
Norfolk 23510

Tidewater Technical
616 Denbigh Blvd.
Newport News 23608

Virginia Highlands Community College
P.O. Box 828
Abingdon 24212-0828

Virginia Western Community College
3095 Colonial Ave.
Roanoke 24015

Wytheville Community College
1000 East Main St.
Wytheville 24382

WASHINGTON

Bellevue Community College
3000 Landerholm Circle SE
Bellevue 98007-6484

Clark College
1800 East McLoughlin Blvd.
Vancouver 98663-3598

Columbia Basin College
2600 North 20th Ave.
Pasco 99301

Everett Community College
801 Wetmore Ave.
Everett 98201

Grays Harbor College
1620 Edward P Smith Dr.
Aberdeen 98520

Highline Community College
P.O. Box 98000
Des Moines 98198-9800

Lower Columbia College
P.O. Box 3010
Longview 98632

Olympic College
1600 Chester Ave.
Bremerton 98310-1699

Seattle Community College, Central
Campus
1701 Broadway
Seattle 98122

Shoreline Community College
16101 Greenwood Ave. N
Seattle 98133

Skagit Valley College
2405 College Way
Mount Vernon 98273

South Puget Sound Community College
2011 Mottman Rd. SW
Olympia 98512

Spokane Community College
North 1810 Greene Ave.
Spokane 99207

Tacoma Community College
5900 South 12th St.
Tacoma 98465

Walla Walla Community College
500 Tausick Way
Walla Walla 99362

Wenatchee Valley College
1300 Fifth St.
Wenatchee 98801

Yakima Valley Community College
P.O. Box 1647
Yakima 98907

WEST VIRGINIA

Bluefield State College
219 Rock St.
Bluefield 24701

Cabell County Vocational Technical
Center
1035 Norway Ave.
Huntington 25705

Davis and Elkins College
100 Campus Dr.
Elkins 26241-3996

Fairmont State College
1201 Locust Ave.
Fairmont 26554

Shepherd College
King St., Ikenberry Hall
Shepherdstown 25443

Southern West Virginia Community
and Technical College
Box 2900
Mt. Gay 25637

University of Charleston
2300 MacCorkle Ave. SE
Charleston 25304

West Virginia Northern Community
College
1704 Market St.
Wheeling 26003

West Virginia University at Parkersburg
300 Campus Dr.
Parkersburg 26101

WISCONSIN

Blackhawk Technical College
P.O. Box 5009
Janesville 53547

Chippewa Valley Technical College
620 West Clairemont Ave.
Eau Claire 54701

Fox Valley Technical College at
Appleton
1825 North Bluemound Dr.
Appleton 54913-2277

Gateway Technical College
3520 30th Ave.
Kenosha 53144-1690

Lakeshore Technical College
1290 North Ave.
Cleveland 53015

Madison Area Technical College
3550 Anderson St.
Madison 53704

Milwaukee Area Technical College
700 West State St.
Milwaukee 53233-1443

Moraine Park Technical College
235 North National Ave.
Fond Du Lac 54936-1940

Nicolet Area Technical College
P.O. Box 518, County Highway G
Rhinelander 54501

Northcentral Technical College
1000 Campus Dr.
Wausau 54401-1899

Northeast Wisconsin Technical College
2740 West Mason St., P.O. Box 19042
Green Bay 54307-9042

Southwest Wisconsin Technical College
1800 Bronson Blvd.
Fennimore 53809

Waukesha County Technical College
800 Main St.
Pewaukee 53072

Western Wisconsin Technical College
304 North Sixth St., P.O. Box 908
La Crosse 54602-0908

Wisconsin Indianhead Technical
College
505 Pine Ridge Dr.
Shell Lake 54871

WYOMING

Casper College
125 College Dr.
Casper 82601

Central Wyoming College
2660 Peck Ave.
Riverton 82501

Laramie County Community College
1400 East College Dr.
Cheyenne 82007

Northwest Community College
231 West Sixth St.
Powell 82435

Sheridan College
3059 Coffeen Ave.
Sheridan 82801

Western Wyoming Community College
2500 College Dr.
Rock Springs 82902

Respiratory Technology

ALABAMA

George C Wallace State Community
College, Hanceville
801 Main St. NW
Hanceville 35077-2000

University of Alabama at Birmingham
Administration Bldg., Ste. 1070-2010
Birmingham 35294-0110

ARIZONA

Apollo College, Phoenix, Inc.
8503 North 27th Ave.
Phoenix 85051

Apollo College, Tri City, Inc.
630 West Southern Ave.
Mesa 85210

Gateway Community College
108 North 40th St.
Phoenix 85034

Long Medical Institute
4126 North Black Canyon Hwy.
Phoenix 85017

Pima Community College
2202 West Anklam Rd.
Tucson 85709-0001

ARKANSAS

Arkansas Valley Technical Institute
P.O. Box 506, Hwy. 23 N
Ozark 72949

Black River Technical College
Box 468, Hwy. 304
Pocahontas 72455

Pulaski Technical College
3000 West Scenic Dr.
North Little Rock 72118

University of Arkansas for Medical
Sciences
4301 West Markham, Slot 601
Little Rock 72205

CALIFORNIA

California College for Health Science
222 West 24th St.
National City 91950

California Paramedical and Technical
College
3745 Long Beach Blvd.
Long Beach 90807

California Paramedical and Technical
College
4550 La Sierra Ave.
Riverside 92505

Concorde Career Institute
12412 Victory Blvd.
North Hollywood 91606

Crafton Hills College
11711 Sand Canyon Rd.
Yucaipa 92399-1799

El Camino College
16007 Crenshaw Blvd.
Torrance 90506

Foothill College
12345 El Monte Rd.
Los Altos Hills 94022

Grossmont-Cuyamaca Community
College District
8800 Grossmont College Dr.
El Cajon 92020

Hacienda La Puente Unified School
District, Adult Education
P.O. Box 60002
City of Industry 91716-0002

Modesto Junior College
435 College Ave.
Modesto 95350-5800

Napa Valley College
2277 Napa Vallejo Hwy.
Napa 94558

San Joaquin Valley College
201 New Stine Rd.
Bakersfield 93309

San Joaquin Valley College
8400 West Mineral King Ave.
Visalia 93291

Simi Valley Adult School
3192 Los Angeles Ave.
Simi Valley 93065

Victor Valley College
18422 Bear Valley Rd.
Victorville 92392-9699

COLORADO

Front Range Community College
3645 West 112th Ave.
Westminster 80030

FLORIDA

ATI Health Education Center
1395 Northwest 167th St.
Miami 33169

Daytona Beach Community College
1200 Volusia Ave.
Daytona Beach 32114

Flagler College
74 Kings St.
St. Augustine 32085-1027

Manatee Community College
5840 26th St. W
Bradenton 34207

Miami-Dade Community College
300 Northeast Second Ave.
Miami 33132

Palm Beach Community College
4200 Congress Ave.
Lake Worth 33461

GEORGIA

Augusta Technical Institute
3116 Deans Bridge Rd.
Augusta 30906

HAWAII

Kapiolani Community College
4303 Diamond Head Rd.
Honolulu 96816

IDAHO

Boise State University
1910 University Dr.
Boise 83725

ILLINOIS

Belleville Area College
2500 Carlyle Rd.
Belleville 62221

College of Du Page
425 22nd St.
Glen Ellyn 60137-6599

Illinois Central College
One College Dr.
East Peoria 61635-0001

Moraine Valley Community College
10900 South 88th Ave.
Palos Hills 60465-0937

Rock Valley College
3301 North Mulford Rd.
Rockford 61114

Saint John's Hospital School of
Respiratory Therapy
800 East Carpenter
Springfield 62769

Triton College
2000 Fifth Ave.
River Grove 60171

INDIANA

Ivy Tech State College, Central Indiana
One West 26th St.
Indianapolis 46206-1763

Ivy Tech State College, Northeast
3800 North Anthony Blvd.
Fort Wayne 46805

KANSAS

Seward County Community College
Box 1137
Liberal 67905-1137

Washburn University of Topeka
1700 College Ave.
Topeka 66621

KENTUCKY

Kentucky Tech, Central Kentucky AVTS
308 Vo Tech Rd.
Lexington 40510-2626

Kentucky Technical, Bowling Green
Regional Technology Center
845 Loop Dr.
Bowling Green 42101-3601

Kentucky Technical, Rowan Regional
Technology Center
609 Viking Dr.
Morehead 40351

LOUISIANA

Bossier Parish Community College
2719 Airline Dr. N
Bossier City 71111

Delgado Community College
615 City Park Ave.
New Orleans 70119

Louisiana Technical College, West
Jefferson Campus
475 Manhattan Blvd.
Harvey 70058

Southeastern Louisiana University
100 West Dakota
Hammond 70402

MICHIGAN

Macomb Community College
14500 Twelve Mile Rd.
Warren 48093-3896

MINNESOTA

Northwest Technical College, East
Grand Forks
Hwy. 220 N
East Grand Forks 56721

MISSISSIPPI

Hinds Community College, Raymond
Campus
Raymond 39154

Mississippi Gulf Coast Community
College
Central Office, P.O. Box 67
Perkinston 39573

University of Mississippi Medical
Center
2500 North State St.
Jackson 39216

MISSOURI

Hannibal Area Vocational Technical
School
4550 McMasters Ave.
Hannibal 63401

MONTANA

Montana State University, College of
Technology, Great Falls
2100 16th Ave. S
Great Falls 59405

NEBRASKA

Metropolitan Community College Area
5300 North 30th St.
Omaha 68111

NEW JERSEY

Gloucester County College
1400 Tanyard Rd.
Sewell 08080

University of Medicine and Dentistry of
New Jersey
30 Bergen St.
Newark 07107

NEW YORK

CUNY Borough of Manhattan
Community College
199 Chambers St.
New York 10007

NYU Medical Center Allied Health
Education
483 First Ave.
New York 10016

Onondaga Community College
4941 Onondaga
Syracuse 13215

NORTH CAROLINA

Carteret Community College
3505 Arendell St.
Morehead City 28557

Durham Technical Community College
1637 Lawson St.
Durham 27703

Edgecombe Community College
2009 West Wilson St.
Tarboro 27886

Stanly Community College
141 College Dr.
Albemarle 28001

OHIO

Columbus State Community College
550 East Spring St.
Columbus 43216

Lima Technical College
4240 Campus Dr.
Lima 45804

University of Toledo
2801 West Bancroft
Toledo 43606

OKLAHOMA

Francis Tuttle Area Vocational-
Technical Center
12777 North Rockwell Ave.
Oklahoma City 73142-2789

OREGON

Apollo College, Portland, Inc.
2600 Southeast 98th Ave.
Portland 97266

PENNSYLVANIA

Lehigh Carbon Community College
4525 Education Park Dr.
Schnecksville 18078-2598

SOUTH CAROLINA

Greenville Technical College
P.O. Box 5616, Station B
Greenville 29606-5616

Midlands Technical College
P.O. Box 2408
Columbia 29202

Spartanburg Technical College
Business I-85
Spartanburg 29305

TENNESSEE

Tennessee Technology Center at
Memphis
550 Alabama Ave.
Memphis 38105-3604

Roane State Community College
276 Patton Ln.
Harriman 37748

TEXAS

Alvin Community College
3110 Mustang Rd.
Alvin 77511

El Centro College
Main and Lamar
Dallas 75202

Houston Community College System
22 Waugh Dr.
Houston 77270-7849

North Harris Montgomery Community
College District
250 North Sam Houston Pkwy. E, Ste.
300
Houston 77060

Saint Philip's College
1801 Martin Luther King Dr.
San Antonio 78203

San Jacinto College, Central Campus
8060 Spencer Hwy.
Pasadena 77505

Southwest Texas State University
601 University Dr.
San Marcos 78666

Temple College
2600 South First St.
Temple 76504-7435

Texas Southmost College
80 Fort Brown
Brownsville 78520

Tyler Junior College
1327 South Baxter Ave.
Tyler 75711

UTAH

Weber State University
3750 Harrison Blvd.
Ogden 84408

VIRGINIA

Northern Virginia Community College
4001 Wakefield Chapel Rd.
Annandale 22003

WASHINGTON

Tacoma Community College
5900 South 12th St.
Tacoma 98465

WEST VIRGINIA

West Virginia Northern Community
College
1704 Market St.
Wheeling 26003

WYOMING

Western Wyoming Community College
2500 College Dr.
Rock Springs 82902

Surgical Technology

ALABAMA

Community College of the Air Force
130 West Maxwell Blvd.
Montgomery 36112-6613

ARIZONA

The Bryman School
4343 North 16th St.
Phoenix 85016

CALIFORNIA

California Paramedical and Technical
College
3745 Long Beach Blvd.
Long Beach 90807

Newbridge College
1840 East 17th St., Ste. 140
Santa Ana 92705

COLORADO

Concorde Career Institute
770 Grant St.
Denver 80203

FLORIDA

Sheridan Vocational Center
5400 Sheridan St.
Hollywood 33021

ILLINOIS

Swedish American Hospital School of
Medical Technology
1400 Charles St.
Rockford 61104-2298

KENTUCKY

Kentucky Tech, Central Kentucky AVTS
308 Vo Tech Rd.
Lexington 40511-2626

Kentucky Technical, Jefferson State
Vocational Technical School
727 West Chestnut
Louisville 40203-2036

LOUISIANA

Delgado Community College
501 City Park Ave.
New Orleans 70119

MASSACHUSETTS

Quincy College
34 Coddington St.
Quincy 02169

MICHIGAN

Lansing Community College
419 North Capitol Ave.
Lansing 48901-7210

MINNESOTA

Northwest Technical College, East
Grand Forks
Hwy. 220 N
East Grand Forks 56721

Saint Cloud Technical College
1540 Northway Dr.
Saint Cloud 56303

MISSISSIPPI

Itawamba Community College
602 West Hill St.
Fulton 38843

PENNSYLVANIA

Delaware County Community College
901 South Media Line Rd.
Media 19063-1094

Mount Aloysius College
7373 Admiral Peary Hwy.
Cresson 16630-1999

Saint Francis Medical Center School of
Nursing
400 45th St.
Pittsburgh 15201

SOUTH CAROLINA

Midlands Technical College
P.O. Box 2408
Columbia 29202

York Technical College
452 South Anderson Rd.
Rock Hill 29730

TENNESSEE

Aquinas College
4210 Harding Rd.
Nashville 37205

Tennessee Technology Center at
Knoxville
1100 Liberty St.
Knoxville 37919

Tennessee Technology Center at
Memphis
550 Alabama Ave.
Memphis 38105-3604

TEXAS

Houston Community College System
22 Waugh Dr.
Houston 77270-7849

San Antonio College of Medical and
Dental Assistants, Central
4205 San Pedro Ave.
San Antonio 78212-1899

South Plains College
1401 College Ave.
Levelland 79336

Temple College
2600 South First St.
Temple 76504-7435

Texas State Technical College,
Harlingen
2424 Boxwood
Harlingen 78550-3697

VIRGINIA

NNPS RRMC School of Surgical
Technology
12420 Warwick Blvd., Ste. 6G
Newport News 23606

WASHINGTON

Seattle Community College, Central
Campus
1701 Broadway
Seattle 98122

WISCONSIN

Northeast Wisconsin Technical College
2740 West Mason St., P.O. Box 19042
Green Bay 54307-9042

Index

All jobs mentioned in this volume are listed and cross-referenced in the index. Entries that appear in all capital letters have occupational profiles. For example, ACUPUNCTURIST, ADMITTING INTERVIEWER, AIDS COUNSELOR and so on are profiles in this volume. Entries that are not capitalized refer to jobs that do not have a separate profile but for which information is given.

Under some capitalized entries there is a section titled "Profile includes." This lists jobs that are mentioned in the profile. For example, in the case of AMBULANCE DRIVER, jobs that are described in the profile are Emergency medical technician and Paramedic.

Some entries are followed by a job title in parentheses after the page number on which it can be found. This job title is the occupational profile in which the entry is discussed. For instance, the Obstetrician/gynecologist entry is followed by the profile title (Physician).